Books by Jan de Hartog

The Hospital

THE
HOSPITAL

JAN DE HARTOG

NEW YORK

ATHENEUM

1964

In accordance with the regulations of the Harris County
Medical Society, Texas, which holds that any form of
publicity concerning members of the medical profession
could be interpreted as an advertisement, the names of
physicians and nursing personnel connected with the Houston
charity hospitals have been changed. All other personages
mentioned in THE HOSPITAL are referred to under
their own names.

The Hospital

IN SEPTEMBER, 1 9 6 2, my wife and I settled in Houston, Texas. I was to teach a course in playwriting at the University of Houston and give a series of public lectures at Texas Southern, its Negro counterpart.

Friends, on hearing where we were going, had been amazed. Why Houston, of all places? Didn't we know that it had the climate of Calcutta, and the highest murder rate in the U.S.? That its surrounding countryside was a burnt-out prairie of unrelenting dreariness, and its atmosphere saturated with industrial fumes? Who, for Pete's sake, would settle in a place like that of his own free will, if he had the woods of Massachusetts, the Blue Ridge Mountains, the beaches of California and the jungle of the Everglades to choose from? It might make sense for young couples, who wanted to get rich fast and get out again as soon as possible; but who in his senses went to live in Houston out of preference for the town?

What had attracted us was what, I suppose, had attracted most others who had come here, and who went on coming by the thousands, with nothing but hope and a willingness to work. I had known Houston as a sailor; Marjorie came to know it when we spent some weeks there in 1957, prior to a long coastal voyage on which she joined me. We had felt an instant welcome there, an immediate personal contact that seemed American in the best sense of the word. Houston still had the atmosphere of a cow town, despite the fact that by now it was a metropolis. Its population of a million and a quarter had doubled over the past ten years; if the prediction of Lloyds of London was to materialize it would, by the turn of the century, be the largest city in the world. The majority of the newcomers were indeed young people, dreaming of individual success: striking an oil well, getting the Nobel Prize, raising a new breed of cattle, landing on the moon. Dreams seemed to be the main import of the city.

Although Marjorie and I were no longer youngsters, we had come back to Houston with a young concern. It was to be my first teaching assignment, an experiment in more senses than one. As I had spent most of my life on the water, I had never really been part of any community larger than a ship. This was to be my first experience as a citizen of a city.

For this purpose, so it seemed, no better city could be found than Houston. It was wide open, anyone was welcome. The moment you arrived in Houston, you were accepted as a Houstonian. There was no breaking-in period, no clannishness; maybe it was this circumstance that gave Houston its unique atmosphere. It was one of the last frontier towns in America.

Within a few days, before we had even found a place to live, a school friend of Marjorie's, married to a doctor who had settled here, arranged a welcoming party for us. In the nature of things, most of those present at the party were of the medical profession. It was there that we first heard the initials "J.D." Our hostess, glass in hand, was telling a strikingly elegant girl, amidst the happy hubbub of the crowd, that she was planning to enroll for a course at the University, now that both her children were in school, just to keep herself occupied.

4

The elegant girl commented, in a peculiarly snooty drawl, "Dear, if I had that much time on my hands, I'd either stay home to loll on a couch, eating bonbons and reading dirty French novels, or I'd go to the Newborn Nursery at J.D. to help feed the babies."

"What babies?"

"It seems they have up to seventy newborn babies in the nursery and not enough staff to cope with them, so they often go hungry."

Marjorie wanted to hear more about this; the *Harper's Bazaar* girl, a doctor's wife called Lucille, told her that the Faculty Wives of Baylor Medical School had been lectured to by the chief of the newborn clinic at J.D., who had urged them to form a group of volunteers to help feed the babies. As many of the Baylor wives had been nurses before they married, they had formed such a group and offered their services to the administration of the hospital, but so far without result.

"You mean your offer was turned down?" Marjorie asked incredulously.

The girl called Lucille laughed. "Oh, no," she said, "nothing as clearcut as that. They did not accept, they did not refuse; they just gave us the old J.D. runaround. You know: never give a straight answer to any question, just procrastinate, if possible indefinitely; then maybe it will go away."

"But why?" Marjorie asked. "What kind of hospital is this?"

We were told that it was the city-county charity hospital, called "Jefferson Davis." It was financed out of taxes, staffed with residents and interns by Baylor University, with nurses by the city and the county. It was overcrowded, understaffed, its accreditation had almost been withdrawn after a staph infection in its maternity ward during which sixteen babies had died; but it was probably no more backward, politics-ridden or neglected than similar institutions of charity all over the country.

"What are you girls talking about?" a jolly peanut eater interrupted.

"J.D.," said Lucille.

"Oh . . ." The jolly face froze.

"You know it?" I asked.

"I should say so, after spending two years there as an intern. Most of us here have."

"What's it like?"

"You a doctor?" he asked, tossing the rest of his peanuts at his tonsils.

"No."

"In that case," he replied, chewing, "let's let the dead bury the dead. Forget about it. It's not your problem."

But we could not forget about it. At least, Marjorie could not. The sound of newborn babies squalling forlornly in the night seemed to haunt her during the drive back to the motel where we stayed.

"I can't believe it," she said. "I'm going to look into this tomorrow."

I knew her well enough, after many years of happy wrangling, not to try to dissuade her. She was a very feminine person, in the sense the Chinese goddess Kwan Yin was feminine, who never succeeded in attaining Nirvana because each time she was about to knock on the gates of heaven she heard a child cry on earth and went back to find out what was the matter. After we had gone to bed and turned off the lights and lay staring at the ceiling in the unfamiliar motel room, restless with the sheet lightning of neon signs, she asked, "Do you think most of those babies are Negro? Could that be the reason why the hospital is so neglected?"

"I don't think so," I said. "I don't know, really. Even if they were mainly Negroes, there is no color problem here in Houston. This is not a Southern town, this is a Western town."

6

"I don't know," she said, thoughtfully. "I've heard the way some of the women here talk about their maids. It's different. They don't talk about them the way we do in Europe, or up North. I think it is a Southern town, pretending to be something else. Don't you?"

I said, "Darling, neither you nor I know anything about it. Let's wait until we have found out."

"I have found out enough," she said, "enough to want to find out more about J.D."

"I know," I said, "I know. Sleep well, *lieverd*."

There was a silence. Then she said, "I wonder what the Meeting is like here. Maybe they could help. Don't you think so?"

I said, "H'm."

"I'd like to go there Sunday," she said, "wouldn't you?"

I did not reply. I was slowly drifting, feet first, into the low fog of sleep, like a ship entering a harbor at nightfall. The pilot would be on the bridge; a late bird would cry forlornly in the darkness. There would be a glow on the horizon, the glow of a city. I fell asleep with a deep nostalgia for the sea, her hand in mine.

2

THE NEXT MORNING, when I went to interview prospective students, Marjorie went to see Lucille. We met again for supper that evening, in an aluminum diner somewhere on Main Street. After we had ordered our cheese omelets, tossed salads and iced tea, she told me, shouting over the thunder of "The Brontosaurus Stomp" from the jukebox, what she had found out about J.D. It was housed in a building out on Allen Parkway, where it had been for thirty years. It was operated by the city and the county and these seemed to be constantly in each other's hair about it. Whenever there was any pressure for economy by the voters, the budget of the charity hospital was cut; for some reason nobody seemed to care about the hospital. She could not understand it. This seemed such a generous town, people were so warm and kind, they were so proud of their growing city, of the museums they were building, their Music Hall, their Medical Center with its seven modern hospitals; it seemed inconceivable that a town like this would tolerate such a backward charity hospital. It didn't make sense. Lucille and she had taken a young doctor who worked there out to lunch; it was very strange: he had been very reticent, almost reluctant to talk about it, as if it were something he was ashamed of. Maybe its employees were sworn to secrecy. In any case, the young doctor had not told them anything new; he had only given them the name of a man who might arrange for them to work as volunteers. Lucille had called that man at the hospital, a very nice man it seemed, with a warm, personable voice and a broad Texan twang, who had been profuse in his thanks for their interest and said that he would inquire at once if they could be placed in Newborn Nursery as they had requested. He had taken down their names and their telephone numbers and promised he would call them back within a week. Lucille had wanted to forge the iron while it was hot and suggested they come to see him that afternoon, but he had parried that. He had told them not to trouble themselves, they would hear from him very soon, and thank you very much, ladies. What did I think?

I must confess that I had not been listening too attentively. I had been looking at her face, her mouth, her kind dark eyes, her hair with its first unobtrusive hints of gray. She was a wonderful girl; I loved her very much. It was perhaps foolish to sit there thinking this, with a jukebox banging away, in the aluminum imitation of a railway carriage on the main street of a prairie town. But for some reason it all came to the surface at that moment. We had gone through many things together, made many voyages, lived through many joys and sorrows; she must be quite a girl, for to be the wife of an artist was bad enough, to be a sailor's wife as well seemed unfair. And there she sat, pretty, elegant, determined, for all the world like a career girl with a dream that she was resolved to realize, and no one was going to stop her. Only her dream concerned hungry Negro babies crying helplessly in the night. I was a lucky man.

"Oh, what's the use!" she said, angrily.

"Pardon?"

"You aren't listening to a word I say! You never listen. All you ever do is stare at me and then your eyes glaze over and I might as well be saying, 'Crocodile, crocodile, where is your hat?' for all you care."

"That's a marvelous poem," I said. "Did you make that up on the spur of the moment?"

"No, seriously. What do you think?"

"About what?"

"There you are!" She sighed. "I am sorry if I have kept you up."

"Darling," I said, with what I realized must be insufferable patience, "I swear to you that I heard every word. But what do you want me to say? So the gentleman with the warm Texas voice is going to call you very soon. That seems to be all there is to it."

I could hear myself that this was a pompous little speech, and I wondered why I did not tell her the truth. Why didn't I say calmly, "Darling, if you want an intelligent answer to what you are saying, you are your own worst enemy. You can't sit there opposite me, looking the way you do, your eyes dark with anger about what a town is doing to its hungry Negro babies, and expect me to listen objectively." My face must have shown some contrition, for she said, "You must have had a pretty hectic day yourself. What was it like?"

I told her. It had been fascinating to meet my students; they had seemed to personify the spirit of this odd, wild town. It was a graduate course, so they were all adults, but they formed a cross-section you would have a hard time finding anywhere else in a class for creative playwriting. There were a Methodist minister, a viola player of the symphony orchestra, a music-hall actress of local repute, an oil drill operator, a Catholic professor from another university, and the son of a millionaire who wanted no part of his father's money and could participate in my class only if I would let him earn his way by giving him secretarial work to do. She was as fascinated as I had been; but she too, at a given moment, sat staring at me with a musing expression. So I said, "Coffee?"

"Pardon?" she asked; then, hastily. "Oh, I don't know. Isn't it rather late?"

I must have smiled, for she suddenly put her hand on mine and said, "I'd love to be in your class. I know you are going to be wonderful, I know it."

It was one of those strange and rare moments which, even as they happen, you know will forever be embedded in your memory. It seemed as if the walls of the diner were fading, and we were sitting, on our plastic seats at our little plastic table, on a vast empty stage underneath the stars. I suddenly realized it was not my students who personified the spirit of this town, but we. She seemed to have spoken for all the wives of all apprehensive husbands, past and present, who ever settled on the American Frontier. "*I know you are going to be wonderful, I know it.*" These must have been the words that launched a nation.

"Got all you want?" a waitress cried, as she seemed to streak past on roller skates.

"Coffee, please," I called after her.

She delivered two cups and the bill on her next orbit, crying, "Hurry back to see us! Coming!" The jukebox gave a deep, male moan, as if a giant had hit his thumb, then it burst into an eardrum-shattering rendition of "Volare." We left.

Outside, the night was hot and humid. Main Street, a shimmering furrow of lights, seemed to fuse with the towering skyline in the distance, in a two-dimensional image. The colored weather ball on one of the skyscrapers seemed to be belching green smoke, as it lit up the low, racing rain clouds. Down that furrow an ambulance came careening, flashing red and white lights. It streaked past us, siren howling, and was followed by another, and yet another. All three of them seemed to be private ones, from different funeral homes. For a few minutes, their sirens drowned all other sounds; there was in their howls nothing human, nothing related to an errand of mercy; they suggested jackals racing toward a prey, scavengers of death.

We drove back to our motel slowly, thoughtfully, looking out the windows at this strange world, distorted by the night, that was to be our home.

3

THE QUAKERS IN HOUSTON, small in number and only recently established, did not have a meeting house; they gathered for worship every Sunday morning in a room in an office building of the Association of Churches. Like most young Meetings on "the growing edge of Quakerism," as it was hopefully called by our headquarters in Philadelphia, its number of actual members was small, the bulk of the congregation being made up by "attenders," the Friendly name for people who like the service, but cannot bring themselves as yet to participate in Quakerly activities in the community.

The Quaker meeting for worship is indeed an attractive service to Protestants unhappy with liturgy, set prayers, sermons and sacraments, consisting as it does of nothing but silence, with only occasionally a member rising from the group to say a few words as the spirit moves him. There are no hymns, no organ music, no ushers, no minister, no collection; just a group of people, anywhere between three and three hundred, sitting quietly in silent prayer or meditation for an hour, at the end of which everyone shakes hands with his neighbor and rises to go home again.

But there is more to Quakerism than the meeting for worship, although it forms the source of all attitudes and activities on the part of the participants during the rest of the week. The Encyclopedia Britannica, whose pride it is to furnish a concise definition for anything under the sun, has found itself foxed at the end of its long essay on "The Religious Society of Friends." It winds up its efforts at defining the elusive movement by saying, "Quakerism is an atmosphere, a manner of life, a method of approaching questions, a habit and an attitude of mind." So, like all efforts to define precisely the essence of Quakerism, it ends up by saying precisely nothing. The best definition I ever heard of the most important aspect of Quakerism is what a bossy German woman cried to a member of a small group of American Friends, who had gone to help feed the children in Germany after the First World War. She observed them at work for a few weeks, then she asked, "Why are you doing this?" When the Friend lacked eloquence in trying to formulate the answer, she cried: "But this is terribly important. You must preach what you practice!" The notion that practice comes before preaching, and that the preaching is optional, seems to me as close a definition of the essence of Quakerism as anyone is likely to arrive at, other than the one an applicant for membership in the nineteenth century provided when he wrote, in answer to the question why he wanted to join the Friends: "Quakers are a God-fearing, money-making sect and I want to be one of them."

Quaker meetings for worship, lacking all outward means with which to create a religious and inspiring atmosphere, rely uniquely on the individual devotion of the participants and therefore can be radiant with a mystical sense of divine presence or as dead and dull as a group of travelers waiting for a bus in speechless, motionless boredom. The best meeting in which Marjorie and I ever participated was, maybe logically enough, the one during which we were married. A Quaker wedding is an alarming and impressive occasion for those involved, more than any other wedding ceremony, I would imagine, as it involves nobody you could eventually blame for the irrevocable act except yourselves. No minister, no third person takes part in the sober ceremony, only the couple who, in effect, marry themselves in front of the Meeting. After the congregation has gathered in silence and "centered down," as the act of settling in the stillness is called in Quaker language, the couple comes in, alone, and sits down among the elders, facing the congregation. After at least twenty minutes of motionless silence, they rise, hand in hand, and the groom says, "Friends, in the presence of God and of this assembly, I now take my Friend Marjorie to be my legal wedded wife, and I promise to be, with divine assistance, a loving and faithful husband to her as long as we both shall live." The bride says the same about her Friend Jan, to whom she promises to be, with divine assistance, a faithful and loving wife. After that, the couple sits down again, and during the ensuing period of silence there may be a few words, spoken by members of the Meeting, or there may just be that silence until finally the elders shake hands and break the meeting, as it is called. In our case, when we entered the meeting gathered in silence, we sensed such radiance, such indescribable, luminous stillness and peace, that it became to us a real, almost physical experience of the presence of God, if He be defined as "An infinite ocean of Light and Love", a formula George Fox, the seventeenth-century founder of the Quaker movement, once used. We both felt, unmistakably, that Presence waiting for us as we came in; members of the Meeting later told us that they had felt the same, but that we had brought it in.

If this had been, without doubt, our most inspired meeting for worship, one of the most dreary we ever sat in on was the one we went to in Houston that Sunday morning. We found a small room, with about half a dozen people scattered over a few rows of folding chairs, all facing a blank wall. The gathering seemed steeped in glumness; but for a few elderly Friends in the front row who welcomed us with a smile, it seemed as if we had wandered inadvertently into a group of mourners. Maybe it was this unpropitious first impression, but during the rest of the meeting I experienced nothing in the sense of an inner tranquillity. Participants came tramping in for half an hour after the meeting had started, with bangs of a screen door, shuffling of feet and scraping of chairs, followed by a gradually subsiding panting. Children, presumably in Sunday school on the floor above, became noisy and unruly as time went by; finally, judging by the sounds, they were playing leapfrog upstairs. The teenagers among us began to heave deep sighs of boredom and to leaf sulkily through books with noisy pages; when at last the meeting ended and everyone got up, one of those books fell at my feet and I saw it was an issue of that well-known devotional magazine *Mad*.

Marjorie, as I found out in the car on our way home, had not been happy either. But after the meeting she had talked to a nice girl called Priscilla Zuck, whose husband was with the Friends Service Committee in town, and who seemed to be interested in the hospital too. They had just moved to Houston, like us; the moment the man from the hospital called back we would get together.

14

4

THE MAN from the hospital did not call back. So Marjorie called him again, a week later, to find out what had happened to their request. She was put through to another male voice, equally cheerful, warm and drawling, who once more took down their names and their telephone numbers and promised they would hear from him within a week. "No, no, ladies, don't trouble yourselves to come out here. I'll forward your request straightaway to the service in question; you'll hear from us momentarily."

Another two weeks elapsed, during which we moved into an old house on a tree-lined lane, near the University; old, that is, by Houston standards: it was built in 1947. As there had been no sign nor sound from the hospital, Marjorie called Priscilla and suggested that her husband could perhaps call the hospital on behalf of the American Friends Service Committee, to show the flag, so to speak. Priscilla did not seem too interested. "If they don't call you back, it probably means the situation is well in hand," she said. "I suggest you let it ride for a while."

Marjorie spoke about her, after putting down the phone, with an embarrassing lack of Quaker tenderness. "If that is typical of the attitude of the Service Committee here," she said, bristling with British indignation, "then there is one body that's not going to leave its mark on this town."

"Maybe there is something to what she said," I ventured. "Maybe things have indeed worked out since that chief of the newborn clinic spoke to the Baylor Wives."

She said, "Pah!" as if she were standing all alone in darkest Africa, pukka mem-sahib complete with topee and veil, and someone had just told her that the pigmies were stampeding in the direction of the Viceroy's palace. "It is obvious," she said, "that I will have to go there myself."

I looked at her, careful not to betray by a hint of a smile

how young and endearing she looked in her British determination. At the same time I wondered what made her so determined; the normal, sensible thing would be for her to wait for the second gentleman to call back; if he did not, she could tell herself that she had done what she could. This, obviously, was what others had told themselves for thirty years. What made her, a girl from Tyneside, England, in her third week in Houston, Texas, zero in on that hospital with such Victorian singlemindedness? I wanted to ask her, but decided to wait until her anger with "those pussy-footing Quakers" had subsided somewhat.

I never got to ask her. The same night, as I sat correcting my first students' papers at the kitchen table in our new home, which was at that time the only table in the house, the new wall telephone rang commandingly in the unfamiliar, echoing hollowness of the empty hall. Marjorie picked up the receiver and said, "Hallo? Oh, hallo." Then she was silent for a while, and I heard her ask, "But—but how on earth did you manage it?" Then there was another silence, and she said, "Oh," and "Oh, I see," and "All right, I'll be there. Nine o'clock. Goodnight." She put back the receiver and looked at the telephone for a moment as if it were a mirror.

"Who was that?" I asked.

"Priscilla." She turned round and looked at me with, I thought, a hint of contrition. "She and I have an appointment with the head of volunteers at Jefferson Davis Hospital, tomorrow morning at nine o'clock."

"That's terrific," I said. "How did she do it?"

"I don't know. She told me that she mentioned the Friends Service Committee."

I said, "Oh."

"Do you know what I think is so strange? She sounded just as bored by the whole thing as she did this morning."

"Maybe that's just the way she talks."

"H'm," she said, dismissing me. "Well, we'll see tomorrow. I wonder if we'll ever actually get in there. But do you know what?" She looked at me with candor. "I don't honestly know whether I want to go in there, now that I can. After all, I don't feel really qualified."

I smiled. The feeling was familiar to me, as it must be to anyone ever promoted at sea, after long and indignant waiting. You always realized that you were not really qualified, the minute you received news of your promotion. "You'll make out," I said. "After all, you don't need any qualifications to feed a baby."

She left early the next morning for her appointment, and I went to the University. When I saw her again at lunchtime, she was the intimidated owner of a yellow uniform, a badge to be sewn on, a cap and a pinafore. She and Priscilla had been enrolled in the volunteer corps at Jefferson Davis Hospital, known as the "Women-in-Yellow." The head of volunteers, a Mrs. Willoughby, had received them kindly enough but turned out to be a rather masterful person. She had brushed aside their request to feed the babies and assigned them to a desk outside the nurseries to type up the charts for the new arrivals. "We need clerical personnel," she had said. "Everybody wants to feed babies, but that's not where the need is." When the girls had expressed the wish to work together as a team, she had said, "Nonsense. I can't have two women behind one typewriter. One of you take Wednesday and the other Monday. Work out between yourselves who takes what."

"Are you going to do it?" I asked.

She shrugged her shoulders. "Why not?" she said. "Let's give it a try. Once we're in there, we may be able to crawl into the nursery through the keyhole."

"What's the hospital like?" I asked.

"I don't really know," she said. "The Maternity Section is the new annex. It seemed rather scruffy, terribly crowded and there were a lot of Negroes around who seemed to have been waiting for hours. But I honestly

17

don't know. Everybody seemed very dedicated. This Mrs. Willoughby, she's been there for twenty-four years, and she seems quite a sensible, no-nonsense type of person. I somehow don't think she would have stuck it there for that length of time if it were really as bad as everybody seems to suggest it is."

"Well, you'll soon find out," I said, opening my folder of essays to be corrected.

"These uniforms are a fright," she said. "Look at this." She held up a yellow mother hubbard that came halfway down her calves. "I don't think you're supposed to," she said, "but I'm going to take up that hem, and never mind what old Willoughby says."

I looked at her over my glasses; J.D. began to sound like a ship to me. I turned back to my corrections. Then I heard her say casually, "If you like, I can make an appointment with her for you."

"To do what?" I asked. "Feed babies?"

"If they could use you, why not? I think someone should have a good look at the hospital. I mean it. She won't dare to put you behind a typewriter."

"Why not? I've done an awful lot of typing in my time. Why should she accept me as a nurse?"

"Because of your experience," she said.

I looked up at her sharply. Man and wife can know a lot about each other without ever putting it into words. It was more than a year ago that my mother died, and still the horror of those months haunted me. I had tried to take up my life where I had left off, but there was no use pretending that nothing had changed. I was a different man; maybe the difference was merely that I had finally become a man. Never before had I so squarely faced the awesome enigma of death, pain and suffering; but when the nightmare was over, I found I could not shake it off. Morbid thoughts of death darkened unexpectedly my sunniest moments, like shadows. Not a day passed in which I was not pursued by unspeakable memories. But I had kept all this to myself, I thought. It now turned out I had not. I suddenly felt self-conscious.

"What good could I possibly do in there?" I asked. "I have no business pretending that I know how to help a sick person. The fact that I have nursed Mother does not entitle me to carry on as if I were an expert, or even a reasonable amateur."

It was silent in the kitchen that still smelled of new paint, in that house that was not yet furnished, in that world that was not yet ours.

I cannot say what prompted me. Maybe it was the realization that I could not forget the enigma, and maybe should not. Suddenly I decided not to run away from it any longer, but to meet it head on. There was no other justification; I knew just about enough of nursing to realize that I knew nothing. But in that silence I said, "All right, if you think so, I'll go and see her."

And then she put her arms around me, and kissed me.

5

A FEW DAYS LATER I set out to visit Mrs. Willoughby in the hospital. It was a sweltering September morning, one of those mornings when, in Houston parking lots, black cars whose owners have forgotten to leave a window open explode in the murderous heat.

There was a great excitement in the air, a joy that I had sensed nowhere quite like this. As I drove through the downtown area with the slow flow of traffic and watched the youthful crowds on the pavement, I sensed their vigor, their optimism, their easy informality. I was caught once more in the spell of this city; it made me feel again that this was a place where a man was still master of his own destiny. Those crowds, scurrying about like human ants underneath the inverted caldron of the hellish sky on boiling pavements quivering with heat, seemed tinged with madness, yet they inspired a feeling of hope and excitement. This was a world in the process of creation, newly built, newly painted, conquered against overwhelming odds. Houston seemed to inspire a fierce loyalty, despite the burnt-out prairie, the poisonous marshes and the industrial fumes. Every man and woman in its torrid streets, while gasping for air, seemed to be full of cheerful self-confidence, myself included, as if the one characteristic common to us all was faith in this city, the blithe faith that here there was no limit to the possibilities for self-realization, for success. Houston's motto that morning seemed to be, "Not knowing it was impossible, we have done it."

When my car left the downtown area and entered the long slow curve of the parkway, I spotted Jefferson Davis Hospital from afar: a huge gray edifice, eleven stories high, lonely tower in a jungle of cheap one-story houses. I had never noticed it before and would not have done so now if Marjorie had not told me to look out for it. It was one of those buildings that are the final outcome of the deliberations of faceless committees: a colossal compromise, so devoid of any individuality that its inconspicuousness amounted to camouflage. Seen from the parkway it might be anything: prison, office building, courthouse; only one thing was unmistakable: it was a public building. Its indefinable dreariness became more depressing as I drew closer. While I stood waiting for the lights to change at the intersection toward its parking lot, I noticed a recent addition that must be the Maternity Annex. This was where Marjorie and Priscilla worked. I wondered where Mrs. Willoughby would place me, if I went through with this. I assumed blissfully that we would just have an exploratory talk to provide me with enough information to make up my mind, in my own good time. This was not something to be gone into lightly.

As I drove into the parking lot, and started looking for a space, I saw a small wooden guardhouse on stilts with, on the platform outside, a pot-bellied policeman slung with guns, chair tilted back, cap on nose, feet on the balustrade, dozing in the sun. He did not move as I drove past, yet I had the uneasy feeling that he was watching me out of the corner of his eye, like the guard at the entrance to a prison. This long-forgotten feeling of being guilty until proven innocent was the first whiff of the once-familiar atmosphere of poverty that I discerned in Houston. It came as a shock to me; I had somehow never considered that in this city of abundance and boundless opportunity anyone could possibly be poor. Even as I drove past the ranks of the parked cars, the thought struck me that although most of them were old and junky they were cars all the same, and that Houston was probably the only city in the world where the poor drove to the charity hospital in their own cars. In the vicinity of the steps that led to the main entrance, was a section marked DOCTORS ONLY, where I saw some low-slung British sports cars of elderly vintage, suggesting young interns precariously meeting monthly payments. I found a spot for my car between an ancient Bentley with a hood twice the length of its seating area, and a dilapidated hearse filled with what looked like at least a dozen Negro children, happily romping in its cavernous insides. One of them flattened his nose against a window framed with the carved drapery of mourning, and squinted at me in man's oldest grimace of playful provocation. I squinted back; the hearse resounded with incongruous whoops and shrieks as I walked away. I could still hear them boo and holler as I opened the outer door to the entrance lobby. Then I opened the second door and entered, for the first time, the reality of J.D.

I had not quite known what to expect; the girls had

come home after their first visits with stories of over-crowding and dirt and chaos, but these had evoked no definite image in my mind; to me, going to Jefferson Davis still meant going to a hospital. I was still preconditioned by the word, evoking images and smells so stereotyped that they amounted to conditioned reflexes: disinfectant, a hushed silence, with only the rustle of starched skirts and the soft "pong-pong" of an intercom gong sounding in long, empty corridors. Another of those words triggering a conditioned reflex is *stockyard:* the stench of blood and excrement, the din of boots on dirt-caked floors, the massive moo of a thousand cattle, mournfully lowing their last. As I entered Jefferson Davis, those two conditioned reflexes short-circuited. My mind commanded "hospital," my senses "stockyard." What surprised me most was the smell.

The smell of poverty cannot be described, although it is the same all over the world. I had smelled it in India, in Paris, in prison camps during the war, but most unforgettably when the first inmates of the Nazi concentration camps came home after their liberation. It brought back to mind images of hordes of people reduced to an animal status, fed by officials doling out food scooped from barrels on the windy platform of a railway station. I had seen freight cars full of human cattle disgorge their crazed contents onto that platform. I had seen well-intentioned humanitarian officers start out by trying to treat them as unfortunate human beings. Before the day was past, they were yelling at them, herding them, pushing their milling, mindless mass around as cowboys push a herd of cattle. I suppose they ended up that way because of the impossibility of identification. It was impossible for normal, civilized men to identify with those stinking, unshaven, dirt-caked, lice- and disease-ridden human wrecks. No one could realistically imagine the conditions these people had been forced to subsist in, which had resulted in their reduction to a panicky herd of cattle, milling aimlessly on the brink of a stampede. I had forgotten their smell; it hit me again, after all those years, as I entered Jefferson Davis Hospital in Houston, Texas.

Behind the desk in the entrance hall sat two young women in yellow uniforms like the one Marjorie wore. They coped with the crowd of visitors waiting to be admitted to the floors in much the same way as the humanitarian officers on that railroad platform in Belgium had dealt with the spokesmen for the clamoring, bleating, booing and whistling herd inside the freight cars about to be unloaded. They were polite enough, but they were talking to another species. Had these ill-clad, cowed people belonged to their own race they might have achieved a degree of identification, but most of them were Negroes. I sensed the moment I entered the hall that this was the crucial issue in the hospital. I had a sudden sense of two different worlds, one in front of the desk and one behind it, the inhabitants of which were utterly unable to see one another as individuals, only as representatives of their race. Five minutes in that entrance hall, waiting for my turn at the desk, convinced me that Marjorie had been right when she suspected that this was a Southern town pretending to belong to the West.

When my turn came, the change in the two young women was marked. I was greeted with the same warmth, friendliness and cheerful recognition that had greeted me everywhere in this town so far, as if we were fellow members of a secret organization, a conspiracy of success. I asked for Mrs. Willoughby and was directed to the second floor, the headquarters of the Women-in-Yellow. I entered the elevator with a group of visitors, all of whom had slips of paper issued to them at the desk, authorizing them to enter the hospital; I was let out on the second floor.

To my left, I saw the frosted glass doors of offices marked ADMINISTRATION; to the right the entrance to a dark corridor. I entered it, and that feeling of the two worlds between which there was no communication came back. The frosted glass-paneled doors to the left seemed to be separated from that corridor by an interplanetary space. On one side authority, order, dignity with a hint of bureaucratic stuffiness, on the other a dark, overcrowded corridor lined with human misery, rows upon rows of dejected humanity, like jetsam on a beach after a gale of destruction. I was to learn later that these were patients waiting for x-rays; all I saw at the time were benches after benches crowded with people in various states of undress, and wheelchairs with human wrecks, sagging, hopeless personifications of utter misery. What separated this world most distinctly from the other one across the landing was the smell, the all-pervading, overpowering stench of poverty, sickness, neglect, unwashed feet, unwashed clothes, foul breath, the stench of vomit and diarrhea. It all went into what, later, I heard referred to as "the J.D. smell." An overwhelming majority of the patients on the benches and in the wheelchairs were Negroes, but all of them seemed to share a concept of time different from that of the rest of the world. It was obvious, from the mere look of them, that they had been waiting there for hours upon weary hours. Those of them who looked up as I passed did so without hope, without desire, without interest, like prisoners in a chain gang, each individual immured in the isolation of mute despair, linked to his neighbor only by the invisible chain of the consecutive numbers of bureaucracy.

Eventually the inevitable was to happen to me too. I was, like all others, to get used to the spectacle of these waiting people, to accept their perpetual, silent presence as an immutable fact of life, like the climate. I set my first step on the road toward that ultimate acceptance during my very first walk down the corridor. I did so by avoiding their glances; I cast down my eyes and noticed how dirty the floor was. Paper cups, refuse, dirty bandages, candy wrappers, cigarette butts; it seemed impossible that all this had been discarded by the people waiting there now; it must be the accumulated filth of several days. With that prim, housewifely thought as a snowplow in front of me, I managed to reach the door of the headquarters of the Women-in-Yellow with unimpaired composure. I knocked, a key was turned on the inside, the door opened and after having identified myself I was admitted into an office by a middle-aged woman in a white coat. When I asked for Mrs. Willoughby, she pointed to a desk at the far end of the room. Behind it sat a small, muscular woman in her middle sixties who, as I approached her, looked me over with a languid, all-seeing glance and nodded me into a chair in front of her desk.

So this was the woman who had been head of volunteers at Jefferson Davis for over twenty years. I could well believe it; she reminded me of the old captains of ocean-going tugboats under whom I had served as a mate's apprentice in my youth, formidable sailors who had towed floating drydocks the size of city blocks to Australia round the Cape of Good Hope with tugboats that would have delighted Walt Disney. As I sat in front of her desk, giving her a curriculum vitae at her request, she listened to me as Captain Bakker of the tugboat *Taurus* had done thirty years earlier, with that same expression of someone listening to a concert. She was obviously not taking in a word I said, but scrutinizing everything about me. In the middle of my monologue she said, irrelevantly, "So you want to feed babies, is that it?"

I said, rather huffily, that I had come to offer my services and would serve in any position where I could be of service. It was one of those impromptu little speeches by a junior officer that never come off, at least not with the absent-minded, faintly nauseated gaze of Captain Bakker

25

of the tugboat *Taurus* resting upon him.

"I see," she said. "You have some nursing experience, I take it?"

I told her about the hospital ship I had commanded, and that I had nursed a patient in the final stages of cancer of the stomach until the end. Her gaze seemed to glaze over, as if the concert she was listening to were by a modern composer. "In that case," she said, "I may have the very spot for you. How about helping out as an orderly in the Emergency Room?"

I managed not to swallow. I became aware that she was watching me with a peculiar interest that I can only describe as appetite.

"If you think I am qualified," I replied.

"That we'll find out soon enough," she said. "If you're still there a week from now, you're qualified."

I managed a hearty little laugh. "Well, when would you like me to start?"

The concert seemed to be over and the applause to have started, for she smiled with satisfaction. "Now," she said, rising. "Let's go and see Miss What's-her-name, the supervisor. She'll show you around. I won't come with you into the Emergency Room itself; I can't stand the sight of blood; I don't see how anybody can." At that, she opened the door for me. Like Captain Bakker, she reached barely to my shoulder.

As we walked back to the elevator through the long dark corridor, past the rows of waiting people, I felt a sudden panic. I had no business going into an Emergency Room; I might have nursed my mother, and made two dutiful daily rounds on board the hospital ship, but that did not mean that I was not terrified of blood, wounds, pus and whatever else went with car accidents or plane wrecks. When I had visualized my working in the hospital, I had thought in terms of putting a cool hand underneath a feverish patient's head to help him sit up and drink, or standing by the side of his bed, patiently listening to his woes to give him a sense of care and companionship. As I walked alongside Mrs. Willoughby through that nightmarish corridor, I felt like an impostor whose bluff had been called, a phony matador on his way to the bull ring. The mere idea of my serving as an orderly in the Emergency Room of this hard-boiled hospital made me want to flee as fast as my feet would carry me.

We went down to the first floor and along another of those endless corridors lined with benches, rows upon rows of them, filled with desolate, waiting people, most of them Negroes; we crossed halls and waiting rooms, untidy jumbles of broken wheelchairs and soiled stretchers and huge old desks, in front of which long queues of people stood waiting. The dejection of those multitudes, looking up at each white-clad form hurrying by with a mute, haunting plea for attention, began to give me a nightmarish sensation, as if I had wandered through a looking glass and now found myself roaming through the chilling, dehumanized world of a novel by Kafka. Mrs. Willoughby turned yet another corner, we crossed yet another waiting room full of benches crowded with suffering humanity, and finally we ended up in front of yet another desk, behind which two elderly women were sitting, writing. Behind us lay another passage full of benches, to the right a small hall with another accumulation of broken-down stretchers and dilapidated wheelchairs, leading to a set of glass doors overlooking a sunlit courtyard that, at that moment, tempted me like a vision of Paradise.

"Could you call out Mrs. Judd?" Mrs. Willoughby asked.

One of the women shot her a long-suffering glance, then wearily murmured something into a microphone.

As we stood waiting, I looked around at the stretchers, the chairs, the floor, the corridor opposite. The stretchers had blue-and-white-striped mattresses on them covered in plastic, all of them soiled with dark, rustlike stains. One was covered with a bloodied sheet, hanging down to the floor. The wheelchairs, as far as I could see, were all broken. Some of them looked as if they had been smashed by a car, with buckled wheels and splintered backs. In one of them sat a Negro girl, her head in her hands; underneath her chair lay what looked like a pool of blood. But then, the whole floor was filthy, covered with the kind of refuse I had noticed all over the hospital: cigarette butts, candy wrappers, paper cups, but here there was also a trail of reddish, smudgy footprints leading from the glass doors to the entrance of the corridor opposite, as if people had to cross a freshly painted floor somewhere outside before entering. The corridor to which the footprints led was so full of stretchers that only a narrow lane remained between them. On all those stretchers bodies were lying, some of them covered with sheets. There was a constant hurried traffic of men in shapeless pajamas, running down the corridor at a trot, or crossing it from door to invisible door; in the distance sounded the muffled screams of a woman, suddenly loud, then muffled again. From the corridor, a trim little white figure came toward us.

She seemed very young to be the supervisor of the Emergency Room; she looked much too gentle and impressionable for what must be one of the toughest jobs in Houston.

"Mrs. Judd," Mrs. Willoughby said with a tugboat captain's charm, "this man is Mr. Hartog, a volunteer who has had some training. If you can use him, he'll work as an orderly in the Emergency Room."

"Use him?" the girl asked, with an enthusiasm that sounded almost gushing. "We could use a dozen of him right now. How long can you stay today?"

"Er—that depends . . ." I began, lamely; but Mrs. Willoughby stood no nonsense. "He'll stay as long as you want him," she said. "Let him call his home, put him in a scrub suit, and put him to work. See you later." Then she looked me up and down, as if she set eyes on me for the first time and was unimpressed by what she saw. "Good luck," she said. "If this is what you want, let me know. In that case I'll get you a yellow band and a name tag." I watched her squat, uncompromising back vanish among the crowd in the waiting room with a feeling of panic. Then the girl by my side said enthusiastically, "I think it's wonderful that you've come to help us! Oh, I can't tell you how we need people like you! Where did you work before this?"

I mumbled something about Holland and the hospital ship and the cancer patient I had nursed, but added that it would be safer to assume that I knew nothing.

"Oh, we'll soon fix that," she said airily. "Let me show you the doctors' locker room. You'll find a scrub suit there to put on. You should not go to work in your street clothes. That would be a pity." She turned to the desk. "Where's the key to the locker room?" she asked.

One of the women sitting behind it answered, "Miss Jennie has it," without looking up.

"Don't you have one here?"

No answer.

"Where *is* Miss Jennie?" the charming young nurse seemed to ask the world in general. As she looked around, she spotted the girl in the wheelchair with the pool of blood beneath her. "Who is that?" she asked.

No answer.

"Who is the patient in that chair, who is hemorrhaging?" There was a sudden note of steel in her voice that sounded incongruous but convincing.

"I wouldn't know," one of the two women said, without looking up. "She hasn't registered."

"Has someone seen her?"

"Not if she hasn't registered."

"Why has she not been registered?" The young girl's patience began to sound alarming.

"Because she hasn't come to the desk," the woman replied, unhurriedly.

I looked at the distance between the desk and the wheelchair and estimated it at three yards.

Mrs. Judd went to the wheelchair, pushed it toward the desk, and asked, "Is this close enough?"

"Yes," the writing woman said, equably.

"In that case, go ahead and register her," the girl said, "while I get the key from Miss Jennie." She smiled at me, added, "I won't be a moment," and walked rapidly into the corridor, looking young and fragile and trim.

The woman, who had been writing all this time, looked up at me and said, "Isn't that a wonderful child? The best we've ever had, you know. She really *cares*, that's why she's not going to last. She'll never get used to it." Then she turned to the Negro girl, who sat looking at her across the counter with the unfocused gaze of those in pain. "All right, honey, what's your name?"

The girl answered in a hoarse whisper, clutching the edge of the counter, trying to suppress a shivering convulsion. The writing woman put a long series of questions, with the impersonal kindness of a telephone operator. Age? Address? Name of parents? Birth dates of parents? Where did she work, what did she earn, had she ever been here before? The girl took a long time answering; again I had that eerie sensation of having blundered into a world with a totally different concept of time. At last the woman asked, "What seems to be the trouble?"

"I'm having a miscarriage," the girl said, quietly.

"How long have you been pregnant?" the woman asked, without betraying any surprise or interest.

"Five months," the girl answered. Her voice broke in the effort of suppressing a convulsion.

The woman looked up, sighed, closed the folder and said, "Then you don't belong here, honey. After four months, you have to go to O.B. This is Emergency."

"How—how do I get there?" the girl asked. She asked it quite calmly, but her voice conveyed with spine-chilling poignancy the sense of nightmare that comes over anyone who finds himself lost in the maze of bureaucracy.

"You go through that waiting room till you get to the hall. Then you turn left and follow the corridor till you get to some double doors. Then you continue down the slope till you get to another desk. That's where you turn right till you get to some elevators. Then you take the elevator down to the basement, that's where you'll find a desk with a lady with whom you'll have to register," the woman said.

"Register . . ." the girl echoed, in her dream.

"Sure, honey, you'll have to register again. You're at the wrong place. This is Emergency. You belong in O.B. Can you get there by yourself?"

"Yes," the girl said.

She started to push the wheels of her wheelchair and managed to detach herself from the counter, but her strength could take her no further. She stopped in the middle of the hall.

"Just put yourself against the wall, honey," the woman behind the counter said. "As soon as there's an orderly free, I'll have him take you down there." Then she looked at me. "You going to work here?"

"I think so," I said.

"Why don't *you* put her against the wall?"

I went toward the girl and pushed her chair toward the wall. She had left a small puddle of blood in front of the desk; prompted by some crazy concept of neatness, I pushed her chair back to where it had been, to cover the large pool she had made before. She covered her face with her hands again; I stood for a moment in helpless indecision, then I patted her shoulder and said, "Take it easy. There'll be someone soon."

She said, politely, "Yes sir."

Mrs. Judd came running back out of the corridor, an outrageous vision of gentleness and youth. "I have the key!" she cried, breathlessly. Then she noticed the girl in the wheelchair, back where she had been. "Did she register?" she asked.

"No, Miss Judd," the writing woman said.

"Why not?"

"She can't be treated here," the woman said. "She is over four months, she belongs in O.B."

"She is hemorrhaging," Mrs. Judd said. "She has to be looked at at once. Have you called O.B.?"

"No, Miss Judd," the woman said. "Not until we have someone to take her there. I don't think she can make it by herself."

Mrs. Judd looked at the two writing women, at two well-fed civilians leaning on the far end of the desk, at a policeman sitting on a bench opposite. All of these looked at her with interested objectivity, as if she were a character on the screen of a television set, acting in a play that was not interesting but the only thing to look at in their unmitigated boredom. I hoped with a fleeting, childish hope that she would say something to make us all wake up out of this dream or spell or whatever it was, that seemed to have trapped us in an insidious cloud of callousness and lassitude.

"What's your name again?" she asked me.

I told her, with the uneasy realization that I was part of the play now. The spectators in the bar were now looking at me.

"All right," she said. "You help me take this patient to O.B., and you, ladies, tell your colleague at the registration desk over there that I am bypassing her. This is an emergency."

I moved toward the chair, but she stopped me. "Here's the key to that locker room over there. Put on a scrub suit; you'll find one on a shelf. Hurry."

I took the key and went to the door she had indicated. As I opened it, a smell of sleep spilled out. I found a small room with two bunks, one above the other; on each of them a man lay sleeping in the position of total exhaustion that I had last seen during the war. I knew I need not worry about waking them as I changed; whoever had to wake them up would have to shake them. The room was in disorder, clothes lay in heaps on chairs and on the floor; on a set of metal shelves against the wall stacks of laundry seemed to have been flung by the armful. A trouser leg dangled from one of the shelves, so I assumed that was where the pants were. I undressed quickly, stuffed my clothes onto the top shelf as that seemed to be the only place available; after I had hastily pulled on the pants I found I had to delve into three untidy heaps before I found a top to go with them.

When I came out I found that the girl in the chair had gone; so had Mrs. Judd. One of the civilians leaning on the desk said, "She went ahead, that-away," and pointed toward the waiting room. I ran after her; as I got to the corridor I looked from right to left and saw her small trim figure disappear at the far end of the long dark hall, pushing a chair. I managed to catch up with her as she was trying to open a heavy double glass door that bore a notice saying, NO VISITORS BEYOND THIS POINT, NO STREET CLOTHES ALLOWED.

"This is the O.B. Annex," she said. "You'll have to help me hold the chair, because we go down a slope here."

I helped her and said, "My wife works here."

"Oh, does she? Where?"

"In the Newborn Nursery."

"What is she? A nurse?"

"No, a volunteer, like me."

"Why?" she asked. "Why are you people doing this?"

I laughed, rather sheepishly. "I don't know that I'll be doing it, Mrs. Judd," I said. "I don't know yet whether I'll be any good at it."

"Don't be silly," she said. "Can't you see how we need you?"

By then, trotting along while restraining the wheelchair, we had reached a nurses' station at the far end of the sloping corridor.

"This is an emergency," Mrs. Judd said. "Did they call you from E.R.?"

A red-haired Negro nurse behind the desk slowly shook her head. "Nobody called us," she said. "She'll have to register first."

Mrs. Judd, without any sign of being exasperated, strode off, opened a door to a ward, seemed to spot someone she knew, called, "John! Come here, will you?"

A young doctor appeared in a green scrub suit. She spoke to him, pointed at the girl. He nodded and took over the wheelchair.

"Thank you," Mrs. Judd said cheerfully, to the nurse behind the desk.

The nurse said, "You're welcome."

We turned round and went back, up the slope, toward the glass doors. "Must be rather frustrating for you at times," I ventured.

"How do you mean?" she asked.

I looked at her and saw that she was genuinely surprised. Her reaction baffled me. "There seems to be quite a lot of red tape around, isn't there?"

"Oh," she said with sincere unconcern, "that's the least of my worries."

"What is your main worry?"

She opened the door before I had a chance to do so. "People," she said. "Not enough of them. But you just have to make the best of it."

That, suddenly, rang a bell. Where had I heard those words before? As we walked back to the Emergency Room, past all those benches jammed with people, through

34

that stench, that filth, that inexpressible misery of neglect and indifference, I remembered where. During the great floods in Holland in 1953, when I had commanded that hospital ship, we had, after the first hectic week, been directed toward one of the worst hit of the villages, that was completely isolated, to remain there as a resident hospital. When we arrived, we found the local doctor and his wife in a makeshift lazaret where I saw the worst scenes I had seen since the war. They lacked everything, even the most primitive nursing aids; but when we arrived they seemed almost resentful, as if the well-equipped hospital ship, suddenly emerging in the middle of their world of destruction and death, interrupted a battle when it was almost won. "We made the best of it," I heard the doctor say to ours, with ill-concealed resentment. "As a matter of fact, we did rather well." Our doctor pointed out to me later that in his marooned colleague making the best of it I had seen a beautiful example of the "disaster syndrome." In the chaotic aftermath of an unimaginable catastrophe, he and his wife had rallied with magnificent courage; but they had been able to do so only after relinquishing all usual standards for the practice of medicine. They achieved a victory over chaos, but after a week of this they had been so conditioned by their distorted values that our intrusion felt like interference. "The disaster syndrome can be diagnosed," our doctor had said, "when normal reactions of protest or outrage in the face of intolerable conditions are absent and the overriding reaction is not to correct those conditions but to accept them as permanent and to circumvent them." At the time, I had remarked that surely this was the only way in which disaster conditions could be coped with and the doctor had replied, "Absolutely, but there comes a point when this emergency approach tends to prolong the conditions that provoked it, and that is the time to make your diagnosis and remove the heroic pioneers from the scene."

It seemed the only explanation for the equanimity with which Mrs. Judd had circumvented the callousness of the two women behind that admission desk, the civilians who had stood leaning on the counter watching her, open-mouthed with sloth, as she alone was moved by compassion to help a girl bleeding to death within their arms' reach. I remembered what the writing woman had said about her, "She's not going to last long, for she'll never get used to it."

"How long have you been here, Mrs. Judd?" I asked her as we turned the corner.

"God," she said, "I don't know. It seems ages, and who cares? Let me show you over Emergency and introduce you to the people."

We never got round to it. The wailing scream of a siren came cart-wheeling out of the world beyond the walls and stopped, a dying groan, outside the swing doors. A stretcher was rushed in by two Negro attendants in business suits. On it a bleeding body lay writhing.

"Gunshot," one of the men cried.

Mrs. Judd was there in the flicker of an eyelid, as if she had taken flight. "Shock room," she said.

The men rushed the stretcher into the corridor of the Emergency Room; she turned round and called, "Come along, Mr. Hartog. This'll show you how it's done!"

I followed her, with trepidation. The stretcher was rushed down the length of the corridor, stopping briefly at a desk where a young man in a scrub suit gave the body a cursory examination and motioned it on. At the far end of the passage, a door was opened and the stretcher pushed inside. People came running from all directions. When I came in, I found a large operating room. The ambulance attendants were transferring the body from their stretcher to an operating table. It was a big fat Negro woman in her thirties, opulently dressed, looking proud and prosperous. The moment she lay on the operating table things happened so fast that I could barely keep track of them. There were at least six people at work on her: two were cutting her clothes, two others preparing bottles and tubes for intravenous infusions at her head and feet, two others taking her blood pressure, checking her eyes, auscultating her. Her jewelry was taken off, her diamond-studded dark glasses; coins fell out of her brassière when it was ripped off; they rolled away across the floor. Within minutes, she was reduced from a proud, swaggering Salome to a frightened child crying, "I want my Mammy! I want my Mammy! Please don't let me die, I want my Mammy!" Amidst all this one of the ambulance drivers was leaning over her. "You have used a twenty-dollar ambulance," I heard him say. "Have you got any money on you?" When the woman did not answer, he produced a bill pad, scribbled on it and said, "Sign here," and when the woman went on moaning, he urged, "Just a cross will do, just put a cross here" and tried to press a pen into her hand. A young man in a scrub suit whom I assumed to be a doctor slapped his hand away and said, "Get the hell out of here! Can't you see I'm trying to get some blood out of her?"

The man retired grudgingly. His place was instantly taken by one of the elderly women from behind the admission desk, who calmly started to put her series of questions to the dying woman, now spreadeagled in distressing nakedness on the blood-dripping table. "What's your name, honey? What's your age? Your address? What's the name and the birth date of your father?"

She somehow managed to get the answers out of the prostrate body while it was rapidly changing into an object bristling with tubes. A small dark hole, slightly swollen, oozed a trickle of blood over her right breast. When a nurse started to push a tube into the body's sex, I turned away and went out into the passage.

I found myself alone, adrift on a sea of suffering. All nursing personnel seemed to be in the Shock Room; when

I appeared, pleading voices quavered all around me, calling, "Doctor!" and "Nurse!" "Please, for God's sake, nurse!" There could not have been more than twenty stretchers in that passage, but as I stood there it seemed to me there must be scores of them, all with patients on them, plaintively calling, bleeding to death, writhing in agony. I was overcome with a sense of horror and panic, yet unable to move. The cries and the wails seemed to increase all around me. By my side, an unconscious man lay shaking on a stretcher in cruel spasms, his twitching body lashed down with leather straps, his wrists tied to the frame of the stretcher with bandages. His eyeballs were rolling, saliva was dripping from his twisting mouth, his groans sounded as if he were obsessed by a demon. Next to him, teetering precariously on his stretcher, a one-eyed old white man, partially draped in a hospital gown that exposed his naked back, croaked, "Pal! Hey, pal! I want to take a leak, pal!"

I said, "Yes sir, all right, sir, I'll be right with you," and I started to move down the passage, hoping to find someone to tell me where the urinals could be found. But I was stopped at the next stretcher by a gentle, delicate elderly lady standing beside it who asked, in a tone of discreet despair, "Could you help us, please? We have been waiting here since six o'clock this morning and Mother is getting worse all the time. Could you please, please, find someone to help us?" She looked on the verge of collapse, steadying herself at the stretcher; on it lay an unconscious old woman looking like a wax statue. "She's never been sick a day in her life," the elderly lady said, her genteel voice now edged with hysteria. "I'm sure she would be all right if only someone would look at her. Can you please get someone to look at her?"

"Have you been standing like this since six o'clock this morning?" I asked.

"Oh, that doesn't matter," she answered gallantly, swaying on her feet. "That doesn't matter. Just find someone to look at Mother, for—for Jesus' sake, I beg you, get someone to look at my mother."

I wanted to make my way to the desk where I had seen the young doctor examine the Shock Room patient, but hands were stretched out to me wherever I went, until it seemed as if I were fleeing down an endless corridor in a nightmare, pursued by waving arms. On every stretcher lay a body; an overweight Negro woman snoring in unconsciousness; an old Negro man shaking violently, his trousers soaked with urine, his bare feet caked with filth and sores; bodies masked in blood-soaked bandages; bodies vomiting, screaming, lying stunned with pain and shock; as I started to run down the passage, trying to make flight look like urgency, my arm was grabbed by an old white man gasping on his back on a stretcher. "Please," he pleaded, "please get me some water. I have to take this, I have to take this tablet, please get me some water, please! I can't stand the pain, I can't stand it!" I looked at his prostrate, swollen body and saw, sticking out from under a sagging sheet, a pair of pitch-black feet covered with sores, like my father's feet a few days before he died. I said, "Yes, sir, I'll be right with you, sir," but as I turned to run on, my way was blocked by an old, white scarecrow on crutches behind whom hovered a sad middle-aged man, looking helpless. "Hey, listen, doc," the old man squeaked with a high, childish voice, "you'll have to do something about me because I'm waterlogged. I've been waiting out there long enough now; I'm waterlogged, and you have to do something. My card number is . . ." and he reeled off a number.

I said, "I'm sorry, I'm not a doctor. I'll get one to see you as soon as I can." I tried to get past him, but he barred my way with one of his crutches and said, "Listen, I've been coming here for forty years. What'd'ye mean, keeping me waiting like this? Look, I'm waterlogged, my card number is . . ."

"Come on, Pa," the middle-aged man behind him said, without conviction. "Let him get past. They'll see to you. Why don't you sit down here? Come on, Pa."

As the old man shrilled, "Shut up!" and threatened him with a crutch, I slipped past, but when I got to the desk where I had seen the young doctor it was empty. Opposite was a small drinking fountain and some paper cups. I stood for a moment still, my eyes closed, fighting the urge to run away, out of this corridor of horrors, back to the sunlight, sanity, life itself. But I could not forget that old man's black, dead feet. I remembered the tenderness and care with which my father had been surrounded during his last illness. So I filled one of the paper cups from the fountain, dedicated it to his memory, went back into the passage and tried to find, amidst the horrors, the old man with his tablet. He saw me coming, and his eyes lit up. "Oh, thank you, God bless you, thank you," he said and tried to sit up; but before I had been able to bring the cup to his lips, my hand was restrained by a black fist. I saw a young Negro in a white scrub suit, who looked at me fiercely and snapped, "What do you mean, giving patients water without asking first? Do you know if this man is allowed liquids?"

I said, "No, I don't."

"Well, ask! Ask the nurse, ask the doctor, ask someone! Don't start giving people water without asking!" and he rushed on. I had no idea who he was. I stood there in helpless indecision with that small paper cup; then I saw a young white man in a scrub suit come down the passage. As he came past I asked, "Doctor, could you tell me please whether this patient is allowed liquids?"

He did not stop, he did not even look; he said, "Not my case. Ask the nurse."

"The hell with them!" the old man cried. "The hell with the whole lot of murderous bastards! Give me that water, for God's sake! I know I'm allowed it! I'm always allowed liquids! For Christ's sake, give me that drink of water! I can't stand this pain any longer, I can't stand it." Then, like a vision of mercy, Mrs. Judd came down the passage.

"Excuse me," I said. "Could you tell me if I'm allowed to give this patient some water?"

She looked at him and said, "Hey, Mr. Hood! How are you? I haven't seen you for a long time. What brings you back to us?"

"Oh, the same old thing, God bless you," the old man said, reclining with a sigh of relief. "It hurts like blazes. I just wanted to take one of these." He opened his fist, in the palm of his deformed hand lay a grimy white tablet.

"What is that?" Mrs. Judd asked.

"Aspirin," he sighed. "Please."

She took the cup from me, put her arm under the old man's head and helped him swallow down the tablet. There was something about the image of her slight white form supporting the swollen body of that lonely, dying man that moved me deeply. For one fleeting moment they seemed to embody something eternal, something I had seen a hundred times in old paintings, hewn in the porches of cathedrals, carved in the dark, gnarled wood of medieval altars. During that one moment their mere presence transformed this hellish corridor into a place of mercy. Then a hand hit my shoulder and a tough voice said, "Listen, be a buddy, will you, and take this old geezer to his car? There is somebody from his nursing home to fetch him."

It was the Negro orderly; he pointed at a wheelchair in which a small shivering form sat huddled. "Make sure you get his gown back," he added, walking away. I started to push the wheelchair toward the exit. It would not ride very well; one of the wheels was twisted and made the chair drive into the stretchers with a malicious will of its own. It was only as I reached the hall that I realized that the shivering form in the chair had only one leg.

In the hall, a swarthy woman in a dirty white coat, cigarette dangling from a corner of her mouth, came toward me and said, "Okay, sport. Take him outside. I'll give you a hand. I'm the nurse." She held the glass doors open as I wheeled out the chair, directed me toward an old car with a leaking radiator standing alongside an ambulance. She opened the back door, got in and said, "Okay, hand him up, sport."

The old man wailed as she lugged him by his arms on to the scurvy back seat. I saw, to my horror, that he was bleeding from his rectum; his body was covered with bedsores. As he lay there, shaking, toothless, completely incoherent, groping about with aimless hands, the woman said, "You want that gown back, I suppose."

I said, "Er—yes . . ."

She pulled it off him until he lay there stark naked, like a hallucination, the way he must have lain on the dressing table as a baby: chortling, waving his arms, groping for his mother, bent over him with sheltering tenderness. The nurse slammed the door shut, got into the front seat, said, "Bye, sport, be seeing you," started the engine and backed out. The car drove off, its exhaust belching smoke.

I stood for a moment in the sunlight with the empty wheelchair, again overcome by the urge to flee. It was the image of that slight white figure, her arm round the shoulders of the dying man, that made me go back. I put the bloodsoaked gown in the broken chair and wheeled it, plopping, back inside.

Mrs. Judd caught sight of me as I appeared at the entrance to the corridor. She beckoned me and when I joined her she said, "Look, this is the next step." She indicated a stretcher that was being wheeled out of the Shock Room. On it lay the inert form of the Negro woman, covered with a sheet. Two IV bottles clanked on portable stands at her head and feet as the stretcher went past; a brown tube had been inserted into her nose, her eyes were closed, her face was a motionless mask, the color of putty.

"She now has to go to X-Ray," Mrs. Judd said. "There they'll take a series of shots of her chest; this will enable the doctors to decide if she has to go up to surgery or if we can treat her here. If it is just a matter of inserting a chest tube to drain her lung, that we can take care of. Let me show you the rest of Emergency."

She opened one of the many doors leading from the corridor. "This is the Bone Room," she said. "This is where we set broken limbs, put on plaster casts . . . Hello, who are you?"

On the table sat an old woman, covered only by a thin hospital gown.

"I'm waiting," the old woman said.

"Has anybody seen you?"

"No, ma'am."

"Who told you to wait?"

"The nurse, ma'am."

"Which nurse?"

"I don't know, ma'am."

"How long have you been waiting?"

"Since half past one last night, ma'am."

"Excuse me." Mrs. Judd brushed past me into the passage. I saw her accost a young doctor. "Do you know about that old lady in the Bone Room?"

The young doctor frowned in concentration. "No," he said. Then he looked in. "Wait a minute! Yes, I know. That's Jim's patient. He was waiting for Dr. Dirksen to see her."

"Dr. Dirksen? Who called him?"

"Well, I don't know. Jim? Someone did, I'm sure. Why? What's wrong?"

"Dr. Dirksen left last night for a week's leave."

"Oh. Did he? I'm sorry, I didn't know that." The young doctor walked away, pulled a folder out of a box over the desk, flicked a switch on an intercom and called. "Annie Jenkins. Annie Jenkins."

"That's one of our problems," Mrs. Judd said, with the unabashed cheerfulness of the disaster syndrome. "Patients are called in from the waiting room by loudspeaker when a doctor pulls their record from that box, then they are told to undress, or put in a room to produce a sample of their urine, and then under the pressure of work they get forgotten. The doctor finds their chart again at a given moment, calls their name, but as they are in a side room they don't hear it. So their charts go back to the desk with the note, 'Left before consultation.' It doesn't happen often, but it happens. Let me get someone to see her." She went away, and I did not expect to see her again for a long time. But she was back almost at once, and continued her guided tour.

In every room there was a patient waiting, sometimes two. Across the hall were the Suture Rooms, small operating rooms with two tables each, all of which were occupied by patients having wounds stitched or burns dressed by young men in scrub suits. "This is where we treat lacerations that don't need Shock Room treatment," Mrs. Judd said. "I'll ask John Rivers, the orderly, to show you how to set up a suture tray. Now here, across the way, is X-Ray. . . ." The door to the X-Ray Department was open; I saw the inert bulk of the Negro Salome lying on the table; by now her voice, again calling for her mother, was hoarse and weak.

Two policemen in riding boots, one of them wearing dark glasses, brought in a small, nattily dressed man; when they saw Mrs. Judd the one with the glasses said, "We'd like a blood test run on this character, nurse."

"Go to the desk over there," Mrs. Judd said. "Mrs. Kowalski will take care of you."

A sad, middle-aged Negro followed them, pushing a wheelchair with, in it, an old woman who seemed to have difficulty breathing. "This is Annie Jenkins," he said. "Her

44

name was called over the radio."

Mrs. Judd pointed. "Go to the desk," she said. "The doctor there will take care of you. Now," she continued, "as I was saying, this is the X-Ray Department, and across the way we have our store room, where you will find portable IV stands, the wooden wedge to put under the mattress on a stretcher when you have a cardiac patient, bottle sets for chest tubes and so on. Now, the most important part of ER is right here." She closed the door of the Utility Room, went past all the stretchers and their pleading voices and outstretched hands to the doctor's desk; beyond it was the entrance to what seemed to be a dark, small ward with beds. Someone called her. She said, "Just a minute," and was gone. At the nurses' station, opposite, a magnificent red-headed nurse of Junoesque stature was drawing blood from the arm of the natty little man brought in for the drunk test. He was protesting in a shrill voice, and sounded angry but completely coherent. It was a scandal, he cried, they would hear more about this, they obviously had no idea whom they were dealing with, the mayor was a personal friend of his; the moment the mayor . . .

The red-headed nurse said regally, "Shut up, mister, or you'll hurt yourself."

The little man obeyed and looked her up and down. What he saw seemed to inspire confidence, for he asked in a stage whisper, "Say, sister, which town is this?"

The red-headed nurse looked at the two policemen and asked, "Do you still want that blood test?"

"The two wards that you see from here," I heard Mrs. Judd's voice say, "are our Observation Wards." I had not noticed her return. "Doctors who want to keep an eye on a patient for up to twenty-four hours put them in here. You will find that here we need you most badly. At the moment we have, I would say, maybe a dozen patients in there, some of whom are critical, and we don't have anyone to look after them properly. We all look after them in a fashion, if we happen to pass through here, but we really need someone who is stationed in Observation and stays there uniquely to look after these patients. Now, when you go in here, you'll find . . ."

The shrill, spiraling wail of an ambulance siren pierced the hubbub of noises in the hall. In the distance a desperate woman's voice cried, "Help! Help, doctor, please help my baby! Please, for God's sake, help!" A stretcher was rushed in, this time by two Latin American attendants; on it lay the small inert form of a baby, its face hidden by an oxygen mask that seemed much too large, hissing loudly. The mother's despair was so harrowing to watch that I turned away and wandered toward the dark Observation Ward.

The moment I entered the short passage that led to it, I stood still, overpowered once more by that urge to turn round and flee. But not, this time, out of squeamishness. This time, I knew, I was facing the real enemy, compared to whom all other challenges were reduced to nothing. I was stopped dead by the impact of the same stench that, a year before, had almost defeated me when I nursed my mother. It was the stench of death, victorious.

I stood still, overwhelmed by the same insurmountable revulsion that had kept me, that night, from opening the door of my mother's hospital room. Then I had ultimately been drawn to open that door because she was my mother; now I stood in the entrance to a ward full of strangers. I just could not face it. I could not. I would do anything they asked me in this Emergency Room. I was sure that eventually I would get used to it all and be able to help. But this I could not face. It did not make me feel guilty; I was not deserting. I just realized that this was where I had to draw the line. Perhaps someone else could, I could not. I was glad in a way that I found this out. It clarified a lot of things.

46

"Will you go and look at bed number nine and see if her IV bottle needs changing?" a voice asked behind me. It was a young doctor at the desk.

"I will, in a minute, doctor," I said shiftily. "Right now they want me in the Shock Room."

Before he was able to question that, I hurried off. I crossed the hall and opened the door to the second Shock Room. Inside were a woman and a Negro girl in a white coat. It was the distraught Mexican mother I had seen come in; the Negro girl was trying to comfort her.

"You must, you must! Oh God, help!" the woman wailed. "Please get him! Please get him! Before it is too late, please get him!"

"Is there anything I can do?" I asked.

The Negro girl shrugged her shoulders. I now remembered I had seen her washing up instruments in the Utility Room. "She wants the priest to come," she said. "Her baby has not been baptized yet. Maybe you'd better tell them in there." She indicated the connecting door between the Shock Rooms, and gave me a wink. "Ask Mrs. Judd or Mrs. Kowalski, they're both in there. Tell them we are going to have a problem on our hands."

The mother, sobbing with despair, tried to rise and follow me as I went to the door.

"Maybe you had better go the other way," the Negro girl said. "Tell Mrs. Kowalski that she will need a shot."

I went out into the passage. A hand grabbed my coat and a voice pleaded, "Pal! Listen, pal! You promised me you'd get me that bottle. I can't keep it any longer, I must take a leak." It was the one-eyed old man on a stretcher. I had completely forgotten him.

"I will," I said, "I will. Just one minute." I opened the door to the other Shock Room and went in.

Three doctors and the two nurses were trying to revive the baby. It looked very small, lying at the head of the operating table. One of the doctors was applying mouth-to-mouth respiration, another was listening on its chest. The nurses stood by with IV's, an oxygen mask and a sort of rubber balloon. The red-headed nurse saw me come in, gave me a withering look from dark, flashing eyes and asked, "What can I do for you?" with icy politeness.

I felt an instant childish antipathy toward her; she made me realize that I was useless. I had no business being here, elbowing myself into the most tragic and private moments of other people's lives. The mere presence of an idle spectator in this place of horrors was an insult.

"I am sorry," I said, "but the young nurse next door thinks the mother may need a shot. She also asked me to inquire whether anyone had called the priest."

"For what?" Mrs. Kowalski asked. "The last rites?"

"No, I think it is for baptism."

"In that case, he had better come right now," one of the doctors said. "The child is on its way out."

"That's going to bring about a crisis," Mrs. Kowalski said. "If she's hysterical already; that'll blow her sky high."

"Well, you do it," the doctor said. "Go ahead, baptize it, but make it snappy."

"I couldn't do that," Mrs. Kowalski said. "I'm Jewish. I don't believe in it."

"Well, what about you, Mrs. Judd?" the doctor said. "Anyone can do it. . . ."

"Hush!" said the one who was listening on the child's chest. There was a silence. He shook his head. His colleague who had been applying the mouth-to-mouth respiration bent over the child once more to continue, but the one who had been listening held him back. "Hadn't you better first investigate what we have here? We are told it choked on its bottle, but for all we know it may be meningitis."

"Oh," the young man said, with an embarrassed little laugh as the remark sank in. "That's a thought, isn't it? Well, let's hope it did indeed choke on its bottle."

48

"Is that what the mother reported?" Mrs. Judd asked.

"Yes," the first doctor said. "She left the child lying on its back, its bottle propped up against a pillow. When she came back the child had choked. They'll never learn."

"Someone had better baptize, right now," said the other doctor, who had been listening again, "or it's Limbo for the poor little bastard," and he folded his stethoscope. A hush fell in the Shock Room, an odd embarrassment in the face of what suddenly seemed a momentous sacrament. The three tough young men, the two young women and I, middle-aged outsider, all of us stood for a moment at a loss round that still little body, staring at the little face with its unformed babyish features, which under our very eyes seemed to acquire the tragic maturity of death.

"What about you, mister?" the red-headed nurse asked me. "You look as if this might be something for you. Do you know how to baptize someone?"

I looked up at her; something in her eyes made me realize that this was not a challenge but a plea. For a fleeting moment they all seemed very young, children playing at doctor and nurse. I realized, with surprise and regret, that they had turned toward me because of my age.

I had often been present at a baptism, but I had never performed one myself, and as a Quaker I was not supposed to believe in it. But it obviously meant a great deal to that mother.

"Have you got some holy water?" I asked.

"We're supposed to have some somewhere," Mrs. Judd said, "but I don't think there's any left, and I wouldn't know where to look for it. Would saline do?" She pointed at the bottle on the IV stand. "It is sterile," she added, tentatively.

"It'll do," I said. With the feeling of being an impostor I held out my right hand. She wetted the tip of my finger with a squirt of saline from the plastic tube. My finger carried the first drop to the baby's forehead and I said, "I

baptize thee, in the Name of the Father . . ." I made a
little sign of the cross and held out my hand once more;
Mrs. Judd wetted my finger again. "The Son . . ." and
again, "and the Holy Ghost. Amen."

There was a silence, and as I stood looking down on the
little child, now dead and still, I thought in our odd
Quaker language, "Farewell, little Friend. God be with
thee."

"Okay," the first young doctor said. "Let's pronounce
it dead, tell the mother and the medical examiner's office.
Will you take care of that, Mrs. Judd? You had better put
the woman somewhere where the priest can see her when
he comes. What about the DOA Room? Is there anyone
who can stay with her until then?"

"Let me give her her shot first," Mrs. Kowalski said,
"then I'll tell her." She turned to me. "How about coming
with me? You can tell her you baptized the child. It'll help
her."

We went through the connecting door and faced the
mother. She gazed at us, her eyes wide with horror, her
mouth covered with her hands. She shook her head, speech-
lessly. "Don't worry," Mrs. Kowalski said by my side.
"This man here baptized your baby. He knew how to do
it. He has the same authority as a priest." Then she muttered to me, "You hang on. I'll get her shot."

The mother, still speechless, stared at me and shook her
head. I did not know what to say. I stood in front of her,
helpless with pity and inexperience. "I'm sorry," I said.
"We did what we could."

She gave a cry, so chilling, so elemental in its age-old
pain and grief, that it sent a shiver down my spine. She fell
on her knees, wailing, rocking to and fro with unbearable
grief. I put my hand on her shoulder, hesitantly; she did
not notice. She moaned, rocking to and fro, and so we remained for what seemed a long time. Then the door
opened and a priest came hurrying in. He was very young

50

and very tired. Mrs. Kowalski followed him, a syringe in her hand.

While she gave the sobbing woman an injection, the priest and I had a strained little conversation, almost surrealistic in its bizarre bureaucracy. He was worried about the procedure used by me. Had I made use of holy water? What were the exact words I had pronounced, and what the exact gestures? Could I please repeat and show what I had done? I did so, realizing that if I had failed to perform or pronounce some part of the magic formula the soul of the child would be condemned to roam forever, homeless, outside Heaven. It seemed, at that moment, unchristian, an insult to the spirit of the Man who had preached the Sermon on the Mount. But then, who was I to judge two thousand years of ecclesiastical evolution? All I had been able to contribute was a quaint little prayer, its language as archaic to others as the priest's magic had been to me. The priest did not seem quite satisfied, his brow was knit in agonized indecision. "It's a pity about the water," he said.

"It was sterile," I ventured. "I don't know, but that may make a difference."

"Yes," he said, "yes." Then he put his hand on the woman's shoulder and started to comfort her in short rhetorical phrases, punctuated by odd, self-conscious little grunts. I left in embarrassment, but obviously he gave the woman comfort.

"Oh, there you are," Mrs. Judd said cheerfully, as she saw me come out of the Shock Room. "Is the priest with her?"

"Yes. I hope I did all the right things. He seems to be worried."

"He always worries," Mrs. Judd said. "He's a very nice man, the only religious person we ever see here."

"You mean you never see a clergyman of any of the other denominations?" I asked, incredulously.

"I should say not," she answered, without rancor. "In the hospitals in the Medical Center you break your neck over them on every floor, but here all we ever see is that little father with the worried face, but he does the work of ten. You'll get to know him, when you've worked here for a while. He's around at all hours, day and night, and he has a regular parish and a school to look after as well. I don't know how he keeps it up; what that man needs is a long leave and a high-calorie diet. It's people like him that keep you going."

She did not give me time to feel ashamed for condemning a man after a few hours in a place where he was wasting away his very life's substance, day and night. "I wonder if you could give me a hand," she said. "The girl with the gunshot has to go up to Surgery, so we'll put her in Observation until they come for her. Could you fetch her from X-Ray, please?"

"Where . . where would you like me to put her?" I asked, in the vain hope that somehow I might wangle out of going in there.

"Oh, anywhere," she said. "Just leave her on the stretcher, and put her in Observation near the elevator, so they'll find her when they come down." Then she walked off toward some sudden, piercing screams that seemed to come from one of the side rooms.

I went to X-Ray and found the Negro Salome on a stretcher outside. Her eyes were closed, her face now looked ashen underneath a transparent dark mask. She no longer called for her mother; she lay there in the strangely formal stillness of unconsciousness, as if she were standing to attention in a dream, heeding the call of a distant trumpet. I tried to push her stretcher gingerly down the passage, but one of its wheels was stuck or twisted; it seemed obsessed by the same mischievous genie that had obsessed the wheelchair with the one-legged old man. I managed to steer it past the doctor's desk into the short corridor, past the drinking fountain. Then the paralyzing stench hit me, unawares.

I could not help it; it stopped me dead once more. It choked me, got through to some hidden center of my will, like snake poison. I looked about me in despair, clutching the cold frame of the stretcher to keep myself from abandoning it in the middle of the floor. I discerned rows of beds in the semi-darkness, each with someone in it. On the one closest to me lay an old tramp, fully dressed, down to his shoes, snoring in open-eyed unconsciousness. His clothes and sheets were soiled with vomit, his trousers soaked. He had obviously been dumped on the bed in a hurry and left there; nobody had found the time to go back and look after him. On the other side of the aisle lay a terrified white girl in her early twenties, covered with a sheet, staring at me in speechless, motionless terror; an IV bottle was hanging, empty, on a stand at the head of her bed; a tube connected it with her arm, taped to a splint. Her gaze was so disconcerting that, rallying all my forces, I pushed the stretcher on. I stopped alongside another bed. On it lay a fat Latin-American woman, uncovered up to the waist, her legs spread wide. An adolescent boy in a scrub suit, too young to be more than a student, was prodding her and peering inside the prostrate body. At the foot of the bed stood two girls, obviously her family; one, plain and tearful, was hiding her face in her hands; the other, pretty and stolid, watched the desecration of the body on the bed with stony detachment. The adolescent looked up from his peering and asked, snidely, "Looking for someone, bud?"

Again I pushed the stretcher on. A whisper called me from the bed beyond. I found myself in a second small ward, darker than the first. In the darkness, a vague shape lay hissing, beckoning. I went toward it and saw it was yet another old man.

"Listen," he said, "I asked you for that bedpan hours

ago. Now I've done it in my bed. I can't help it. I've done it and I've been lying in it ever since."

"I'm sorry," I said. "I'll see what I can do."

"Look!" he cried, pulling aside the top sheet. "Look at this mess! How long am I supposed to lie in this? Boy, if I could use my legs, I would have been out of here this afternoon."

"It is afternoon," I said, idiotically. The stench was stifling.

"Afternoon?" he repeated. "What's the time?"

I looked at my watch and saw, to my astonishment, that I had been here only a little over an hour. Maybe it had stopped. I put it to my ear and listened. "I'm sorry," I said. "It isn't afternoon. It's eleven-twenty."

"At night?"

"No, in the morning."

"You're crazy," the old man said. "I can't have been here twenty-four hours!"

"I . . . I'll find out," I said, and I pushed the stretcher on.

The stench when the old man had uncovered his bed, foul as it was, had for a few moments effaced that other one, the real one. Now it came back, stronger than ever. I looked about me, trying to limit my breathing. Nausea welled up in my throat. I saw, in the darkness beyond, many beds with still forms in them. I heard whispers, idiotic cackling laughter. But what drew my gaze irresistibly was not a bed. It was a stretcher, behind a curtain. I recognized it by the wheels, underneath the curtain. Something told me that this was where the stench came from. As I stood there, staring, feeling the nausea rise, I heard a cry, so quavering, so forlorn, that it froze my heart.

"Help . . ."

A thin voice, like the cry of a child, from behind that curtain.

I knew what was going to happen. I knew that if I did

54

it I would consciously overtax my strength. I knew that
what I would find behind that curtain would make me
turn away and this time really flee. Yet I went slowly toward it, realizing in a detached way, as if I were an observer, that I did this only to confront myself with the
intolerable. If I were to give up before confronting the intolerable, I would forever be beset by the nagging doubt
that I had let myself be chased by my own imagination. I
had to face it, I had to.

As I lifted my hand to open the curtain, I heard a movement inside, a sound like a sigh, and suddenly there was
an overpowering whiff of that stench. I covered my face
with my hands. I could not do it. I could not.

"Hey!" a voice called, behind me. "You aren't going in
there without a mask, are you?"

I looked round and saw a Negro cleaning woman, pushing a little cart with a bucket and mop, rubber gloves on
her hands and a kerchief round her head. "You can't go in
there," she cried, like a schoolmistress at a child across a
yard. "That's TB. Why don't you go and get me some
sheets from the laundry? I'm clean out of them."

"Where is the laundry?" I asked.

"Take the elevator there, down to the basement. As you
come out, turn right, then right again, and you'll see it.
Tell them it's for Emergency. Where's she going?" She
pointed at the stretcher between us.

"Surgery."

"Okay, put her by the elevator." I obeyed her pointing
finger, indicating the elevator with a gesture of command. I was unnerved and at the same time abjectly grateful for her interference.

"Take the empty trolley with you," she called after me.
"It's standing right by the elevator." I heard her little cart
clatter away.

I pressed the button for the elevator. As I stood waiting,
I felt that somehow, in a way I might never discern, I had

missed a crossroads. It had not been a postponement of the moment of truth when I failed to open that curtain; it had been the moment of truth itself. Once I had taken that elevator, I would not be back. I felt, as I stood there, staring at the empty laundry trolley, my hands behind my back turn into fists. I had seen enough to realize that this was an inhuman, scandalous place. This was not a hospital, this was a public utility to keep the dead and the dying off the streets. That this town, with its chauvinistic pride, had the gall to tolerate this chamber of horrors was an outrage.

It was a noble anger. I would have no difficulty at all in casting myself in the role of social reformer, once I was safely out of here. I would substitute words of indignation for acts of compassion under the pretext that it was my function as a writer to do so. But as I stood there, waiting for the elevator, after having turned my back on that feeble cry for help, I knew that no words, no noble indignation, no inspiring sermon could ever efface the fact that I had taken to preaching because I was incapable of practice.

Then I saw it. On the bottom of the empty trolley lay a mask.

The automatic doors of the elevator rumbled open. The empty carriage waited beside me for what seemed a long time; then, with a hiss and a sigh, the doors slid shut. I picked up the mask. As I stood with it in my hand, it occurred to me that it had probably been used.

I went back to the nurses' station, found Mrs. Judd at the far end of the passage, busy with a patient on a stretcher.

"Mrs. Judd, could you tell me where I can find a mask? The TB patient in Observation is calling for help. I think we should go and have a look."

"Who?" she asked, frowning, trying to remember. "Oh, yes, I know. All right. You'll find a mask in the Shock Room, over the sink, in a cardboard box."

I said, trying to make it sound casual, "I wonder if you could give me a hand. I'm not sure that I can cope by myself."

"Why, certainly," she said. "I'll be with you the moment I am through here. It's way back in the second Observation Ward, isn't it?"

I said, "Yes. I'll wait for you."

I went to the Shock Room and opened the door. The dead baby was still lying at the head of the operating table, surrounded by the instruments that had failed to save it. It lay there in utter loneliness, as if everyone had already forgotten about it. A cardboard luggage tag with a name and number on it had been attached to its ankle. In the Utility Room next door I heard laughter and the tinkling of instruments on the sink. On the other side, in the other Shock Room, someone lay calling, hopelessly, like a child in the night.

On a shelf over the sink was a box with a strip of surgical tape pasted on it, saying MASKS in red pencil. I took one and put it on; it smelled faintly chemical. I was ready to go. It would have been a moment for prayer, but no words would form in my mind.

As I opened the door and went back into the hall, my shirt was grabbed and a voice croaked, "Pal! Do you want me to die here? How often must I ask you for that bottle! If I don't get it now, I'll let go!"

It was such an anticlimax that I patted his shoulder and said, "I'm sorry, you're perfectly right. I'll get it for you now." After opening a series of doors, I found a bathroom with a rack stacked with bedpans and urinals. I took a urinal back to him.

"God bless you, pal, God bless you. What's your name?"

"John."

"Okay, John." He rummaged under his sheet. "You're a real pal, man." Then, with a deep sigh, he closed his solitary eye and breathed, "John, brother, what a joy."

"Shall I wait for it, or do you want to take your time?" I asked.

"I'll hang on, hang on," he breathed, voluptuously, as if he were listening to heavenly music. "Come back in half an hour. Maybe I'll be through by then."

I said, "All right," and went to Observation. As I entered the dark ward I passed the white girl with the terrified eyes, lying motionless in her bed. Her fear and her loneliness were so obvious that I stopped and asked, "Anything I can do for you?"

She shook her head.

"Has a doctor looked at you recently?"

She shook her head.

"Why are you here?"

"I'm going to have a baby. . . . It's too early," she said, her voice hoarse after hours of silence.

"Don't worry," I said. "You'll be all right." It was an inane thing to say.

I looked helplessly at the old tramp, lying in his vomit with his shoes on. He was still unconscious, snoring in his sleep. I took off his shoes and covered him with a sheet from an empty bed near him. It was a pointless gesture.

The Latin American woman still lay half-naked on her bed, her legs spread wide, her sheet hanging down. At the foot of the bed stood her two daughters. The young student was gone, but he had left bloody pads of cotton lying on the sheet between the woman's legs. I pulled down her gown, took away the pads, lifted her legs back on the bed and covered her with her sheet. As I went to throw the pads away I noticed two chairs behind a counter near the elevator. I took them to the two girls. The plain one whispered "Thank you . . ." and sat down. The proud one remained standing.

As I entered the second ward a whispering voice called from the darkness, "There you are! I thought you had forgotten about me." It was the old man who had fouled his bed.

I stood by his side, looking down on the mess he was lying in, when suddenly, without any warning, I felt sick. It took me completely by surprise. Mentally, I was prepared to do anything to make him comfortable; but my body revolted. I fled to the counter by the elevator and rested my head on my arms, trying to fight the nausea.

A voice behind me asked, "Are you all right?" It was Mrs. Judd, tying on a mask.

I said, "Yes, yes . . . That's to say, I feel a bit queasy, that's all."

She gave me a searching look, then she said, "What we need is a cup of coffee. Here's the kitchen. Let's stop for a minute."

She pushed open a door behind the counter. I saw a small pantry with a sink, a coffee machine, an icebox and a couple of chairs. I followed her inside. She shut the door behind us.

"This is where we keep our drugs," she said, indicating the icebox. "The key is kept by the supervisor." She ran coffee into paper cups. "Cream or sugar?"

"No, thank you, I'll take it black."

When she gave me the cup, she said, "You know, this is a profession like any other. You can't expect to do everything at once. There are certain things you have to get used to. It takes time."

"Yes," I said. "I realize that. I was prepared to go ahead, but I suddenly packed up."

"What made you pack up?"

"The old man, over there. He needs cleaning up. It seems he's been lying in his own . . . like that for a considerable time."

"Get yourself some peppermints. Whenever you feel nauseated, pop one in your mouth. It helped me, in the beginning. Then there comes the moment that you don't need them any more. You get used to it." She sipped her coffee. "There are some things you should never get used to. But I suppose you realize that."

I looked at her. In the sharp white light of the naked bulb in the ceiling her young and sensitive face seemed prematurely lined, and she had dark rings round her eyes. Maybe it was the unflattering light that made her look so desperately tired. "What, for instance?" I asked.

"The old man lying in his excreta for hours. You may not believe this, but that sort of thing is much easier to get used to than other things. That is the curse of this place, I notice it in myself. There is so much suffering, so much hideous brutality. . . ." Her voice was strained; she gulped her coffee. I realized that underneath her efficient cheerfulness lay a quivering core of outraged gentleness and despair. "We are trying to do too much with too little," she continued. "There's too little of everything: people, equipment, drugs, blankets, pillows, diapers, washcloths, gowns. Some of those things are there, they must be; but they get caught in huge bottlenecks in some basement or attic or chute. It's almost funny, sometimes. You go on asking for, say, pillow slips. You haven't seen pillow slips for a month. Then, suddenly, in comes a trolley from the laundry with nothing but pillow slips. No sheets, no gowns, no drawsheets, no scrub suits; just pillow slips, dozens of them. Those are the times that you feel like just standing still in the middle of the floor and having a good scream." She laughed, and finished her coffee. "And, you know, down here in these wards it's all so temporary. Your patients stay with you for only a few hours. There's no time to get to know them, or for them to get to know you, no time to create an atmosphere of trust. At least, I can't. Maybe you can, for you are lucky. You'll have a chance. You'll be doing the real nursing, as long as you take care to stay at the bottom of the ladder. I'm more a

bookkeeper than a nurse now; even the LVN's spend half
their time making out lists, keeping records, writing out
slips for the lab. It's you orderlies and nurses' aides that do
the nursing here, and that's terribly important. Every one
of us should get, every day, at least a few hours of direct
contact with the patients, doing menial work. Unless we
do, we lose sight of what this is all about. We become obsessed by—by abstractions. Do you understand?"

"I think so," I said.

"There is something about keeping records and the like,"
she continued more to herself than to me, "that, I don't
know how to say it, throws a kind of spell over you. When
I stand at a patient's bedside, helping, and someone calls
me, I say to the patient, 'One minute, honey, I'll be right
back,' and I go, leaving that patient lying there, waiting.
But if I sit writing a record and someone calls me I say,
'Just a minute, let me finish,' and I finish. I don't know, but
to me that seems wrong. That is something we have to
fight, all of us. So whatever you do," she concluded with
a laugh, "don't let yourself be tricked into doing any writing, ever. Be illiterate." She took something out of a pocket
of her uniform and held it out to me. "Here. Suck a peppermint."

I took one and said, "Thank you."

"Now let's have a look at that old man. When we start
working, you stay on the side nearest the passage. I don't
want them to see me from the hall, or I'll be called away
again. Let's go." She opened the door and slipped out, almost furtively.

When we reached his bedside, she said cheerfully,
"Well, sir, here we are at last. I'm Mrs. Judd, this is Mr.
Hartog, the new orderly. We are going to change your
bed for you."

"God bless you," the old man whispered. "You're none
too soon."

"I know," she said. "I'm sorry. This is a busy place.

Now you notice, Mr. Hartog, the first rule: before you start, tell the patient what you are about to do. He is in a strange, frightening world. The first thing to do is to relieve his anxiety about simple things that may seem harmless and natural to you, but that frighten him for the simple reason that, in his condition, everything frightens him."

She pulled down the top sheet and revealed the full heartbreak of his disintegration. His paralyzed body, bruised and swollen, seemed already dead. He lay there, in the semi-darkness, as if he had been taken down from a cross.

I sucked my peppermint manfully, but the nausea welled up in my gullet once more.

"First we'll remove your bottom sheet," Mrs. Judd said to him, "then we'll get some hot water and give you a wash. All right?"

"Oh yes, oh yes," the old man whispered. "Please." Then he added, pathetically, "I'm sorry to give you all this trouble, miss."

"It's no trouble," she said. "I'm glad to do it. Now we're going to turn you on your side, to remove that sheet." She bent over him and took hold of his shoulder. "You raise his hip," she said. "When he's on my side, you push the bottom sheet as far toward the middle of the bed as you can. Here goes."

We heaved the paralyzed body onto its side, and I did as she said.

"All right. Now, sir, we're going to turn you over on your other side. Ready?"

The old man nodded, speechless, his eyes closed.

She gently eased him back, then she said to me, "Now it is your turn to take his shoulder, and I'll raise his hip."

We did so; once the body lay on its other side, she removed the bottom sheet with ease. "You see," she said, "it's simple, but you have to know how. Now we are go-

ing to put you on your back, sir, and the orderly here will
give you a wash."

When the old man lay on his back, eyes closed, exhausted, he whispered, "Sorry. Sorry such trouble."

"Get a basin with warm water, soap and some paper
towels from the bathroom," Mrs. Judd said. "You know
where it is?"

"Yes," I said. I was grateful for the chance to get away.
Despite the good will and the peppermint, I had again
reached the limit of what I could take. I was moving away
when, suddenly, there sounded behind me that thin, feeble cry again.

"Help . . ."

I looked at Mrs. Judd; she was staring at the curtain. She
closed her eyes for a moment, her face a mask of utter
weariness; then she said briskly, "Maybe we had better
give our friend here a little rest, while we have a look at
what's going on in there."

She went to the back of the dark ward and returned
with a sheet and a paper pad. I stood waiting for her with
my back to the curtain. I was sorry, but I had to tell her
that I could not go through with it. Through my mask,
through the smell of the old man's soiled sheet, I had become aware of that other stench again. This was where I
had to give up.

I helped her put the pad under the old man and spread
the sheet over him; he seemed to have fallen asleep, exhausted. She walked round his bed and went toward the
curtain. I heard the sound of rings on a rod as she pulled
it open behind my back. The stench seemed to break over
me like a wave. Then I heard her say behind me, "Good
God . . ."

It made me turn, despite myself. What I saw took my
breath away.

On a stretcher lay a naked body, the body of an old
woman, covered with horrible sores, in a pool of filth and

blood. She stretched out a hand toward me, a clawlike hand, and quavered, "Help . . ."

A wordless sorrow welled up inside me, the same that had overwhelmed me as I stood, helplessly, by my mother's bedside after opening the door. I heard myself say cheerfully, "Hello there! What have we here?" while my eyes filled with tears.

For the woman I found behind that curtain seemed the same woman I had found behind that door.

6

It was dark when I finally left the hospital that night. As I drove my car down the parkway toward the overpass, it was as if I returned to another world after a long absence. I slowed down on the overpass and looked at the city.

The view was magnificent. Houston lay scintillating in the night, a colossal, gold-dusted monument to man's triumph over primeval darkness. Its roads were canyons of light, its towers bejeweled with twinkling windows; beacons and neon signs flashed and cascaded like fountains of fire. Although stars blazed overhead in the cloudless night, a reflection of the luminous city seemed to hover in the upper air like a moonlit shroud. It was unbelievable that this vision of promise and hope harbored the dungeons I had just left behind me. I accelerated and joined the river of red taillights flowing down the long, slow curve of the parkway, toward the shining sea of the town.

When I came home, I found Marjorie waiting for me wearing her black dinner dress, complete with earrings and wedding watch. "We have tickets for the concert tonight, remember?" she said. "I thought I'd better dress, in case you wanted to go. But, believe me, I'll quite understand if you don't."

I said, "I'll be delighted to go. I was just thinking, as I drove home, that I'd like to do something, but I didn't know what. How much time have we?"

"Have you eaten?"

"No, but I don't want anything. I'd like a shower, though. Is there time for that?"

"Of course," she said. "Even if we miss the first part of the program, it doesn't matter." She gave me a look of concern. "What was it like?"

I said, "Terrible."

"I thought so. I sensed it when you telephoned."

"I'll tell you about it in the car," I said. "Now let me go and have that shower. I really need it."

But in the car, on our way to the concert, we were silent. I felt relaxed, yet oddly empty of emotion, a state of tranquillity that would have been pleasant had there not been, underneath it all, a boiling caldron of nightmarish images, waiting to be related to the prosperous, pleasant reality of this car, this town, this elegant girl in her lovely dress.

The Music Hall was teeming with thousands of well-dressed, well-fed, attractive people, a younger audience than anywhere else in the world; the average age of the Houstonian was twenty-seven. We had good seats; we looked down from the first row of the balcony into the vast arena of the hall. It was filled to the last seat with gay young people, uninhibited enough to flaunt their opulence. I was reminded of what an actor of the theatre in the round in town had answered, when I asked him if it was not distracting to perform with an audience all around you. "Not as a rule," he had said, "but here in Houston you are distracted by the flashing of their diamonds."

The icy glitter of the diamonds dimmed as the lights went down; then Sir John Barbirolli came out, modest and minute; after acknowledging the generous applause he raised his baton and the music started.

It had a most unexpected effect on me. The moment the violins and the cellos raised their voices in a swelling chord of beauty, I had to bring out my handkerchief as idiotic tears started to run down my face. Helpless in the heaving sobs of the music, I tried thinking of other things, pinching my hand, cursing myself, but I was unable to stop crying; everything I had seen and heard and felt that day broke over me, a deluge of incoherent sadness.

Finally I managed to get some hold on myself; by the time the next item on the program started, I seemed to have myself well in hand. It was the first symphony by Brahms. When, after the first chords, the melody set sail on a sea of strings, it seemed to conjure up, in the concave gray expanse of the ceiling of the hall, the image of the dead Mexican baby, heartbreakingly alone at the head of the operating table. It seemed as if we had all gathered here to pay tribute to its little soul, now coursing toward God. I saw its face, its small open hands, the luggage tag tied to its ankle; the ocean swell of the majestic music seemed to carry it away into the immensity of the night. I was over-come by the collective memory of all the nights of my life I had stood on the decks of ships, gazing up at the starry sky. Planets, galaxies, nebulae, infinity—into it now rose the Mexican baby, whose name I did not even know. It was as if I watched its motherless little soul set out into space; then, suddenly, out of the corner of my eye, I saw my mother, as I had first seen her when she came home from the Japanese concentration camp in Indonesia, after the war. There she was, small and distant, but unmistakably she, white-haired, on crutches, in a faded cotton dress, a haversack with an Army number dangling from her shoulder. Maybe it had been the word "motherless" that made me think of her at that moment.

I had not thought of her since Mrs. Judd and I discovered the old lady behind the curtain. For one decisive second, it had been she lying there; then the memory had been swept aside. She had lain there so neglected, so dehuman-ized by loneliness and pain that her very individuality seemed to have evaporated under the onslaught of her suf-fering. She had lain there like anybody's mother, every-body's, all dying old mothers of the world personified.

Then, as I gently lifted her swollen arm to help Mrs. Judd take out a needle in her vein that connected her via a thin plastic tube with a bottle, run dry, I noticed on her hand an engagement ring and a wedding band. They sud-denly brought home to me her unique individuality, ob-scured by that mask of suffering and pain. There had never been anyone exactly like her, and there never would be again; she was not just a pathetic patient, but an irreplacea-ble person. The two rings on her hand seemed to convey a welter of images: a young girl waiting behind a window, staring at an empty road; lovers strolling in the darkness of a lane of trees in a summer night; wedding presents, new curtains, a husband teetering on a chair while putting up a rod. I felt it my urgent duty to be aware of all this, to reach out, somehow, to the unique, invaluable person now buried under the debris of her disintegrating body. If the capacity for identification that had made me a writer meant anything at all in this house of pain and death then it was this: to make me aware that each patient, delivered helplessly into my power by the calamity of suffering, was as different from everyone else in the world as I. My most urgent task as an orderly would be to protect that unique, irreplaceable personality from the horror of im-personal charity.

I had not had a chance to articulate all this as I stood beside that stretcher, the dying old hand with the two rings in mine. But in that concert hall I slowly woke up to what had happened to me that day, and I realized that I had set out on a voyage into the unknown, from which there would be no return.

CHAPTER 2

How to describe the rapture of mercy? Like love, it is a state of ecstasy, universal and incommunicable, presenting itself to each individual in an utterly exclusive way. Compassion in action is as deeply emotional and all-transforming as love; it takes over your life, pervades your thoughts, makes your other activities and preoccupations seem secondary to that one overpowering urge: to help the helpless, to dispel darkness.

Even as I write this, I find it acutely embarrassing. I reached intellectual maturity in an age that was obsessed by the compulsion to debunk the sublime. Irrevocably conditioned by the intellectual tradition in which I grew up, I still have an instinctive sensation of truth only when a noble act is unmasked as the effect of ignoble subconscious causes. My life long, the words "charity" and "love" have been suspect, whereas the words "repression" and "libido" inspired confidence. I know, objectively, that a group of present-day analysts explaining the adult activities of Jesus as the outcome of his pre-adolescent predilection for anal eroticism is as grotesque as a group of their colleagues in the Middle Ages trying to determine how many angels could be comfortably seated on a needle's point. Subjectively, because I am part of a generation that must forever mistrust the sublime, I am ready to be convinced by psychoanalysts but never by theologians. So I am prepared to believe an analysis of my compulsion to go back into those little dark wards to mess with the sick and the dying as sublimated lust, and will forever refute the taint of saintliness. At the same time, I am sure that the patients in the Emergency Room did not care whether I helped them on the bedpan or gave them a bedbath out of fecal voyeurism or a thirst for beatification, as long as I did it kindly and expertly. And while I was on the floor I myself could not care less.

From that first day on, the hospital became my prime concern, my life. Even during my work at the University, my lectures, my hours of research and preparation, part of me was preoccupied with patients left behind, tasks to be finished, techniques of nursing to be mastered, bureaucratic obstacles to be circumvented. At first, I went one day a week, then two, finally I took on as many odd hours as I could spare, which amounted to my virtually holding down two jobs, one at the University, one in the hospital.

I began to feel I was getting familiar with the work when I began to sort out all those bewildering initials: IV bottles or Intra Venous feeding, DOA Room for Dead On Arrival, BP for Blood Pressure, EKG for Electrocardiogram, OB for Obstetrics ward, Pedi for Pediatrics, GYN for Gynecological Section, OR for Operating Room, LVN for Licensed Vocational Nurse (a practical nurse with one year's training), and DT'S for Delirium Tremens. The more familiar with the work I became, the more hours I spent at it. The end result was that I spent very little time at home.

It was a lucky circumstance that Marjorie became afflicted by the same compulsion. She and Priscilla had managed, after weeks of dutiful typing behind a desk in OB, to overcome the suspicion of the supervisor of the Newborn Nursery by never failing to turn up at the appointed hour, never complaining, yet making it plain that they sat there in Mrs. Willoughby's mother hubbards only in order to wangle their way into the nursery to help with the babies. Then, one night, the supervisor called on them because one of the nurses had failed to turn up and there were nearly eighty newborn babies to be fed and changed. Once inside the nursery, they stayed there, be it clandestinely. Marjorie became as engrossed in the new arrivals as I in the weary travelers at the other end of the road of life.

A surprising result of my working there was that very soon I no longer stopped to consider whether conditions in the hospital were normal or abnormal, acceptable or unacceptable; to look after the patients in Observation became my sole job and the challenge was so overwhelming that it excluded all abstract considerations. The most critical shortage in the hospital, I discovered, was the lack of staff. This had as a first effect the dissociation of the individual from the team. To ask someone else to do something for you cost more time than to do it yourself, and before you knew it you were a lone wolf. Anything that put itself between you and your objective, whether you were on your way with a bedpan to the hopper or going to the laundry to wheedle blankets out of them or scrounging for pillow slips, of which there was an eternal shortage, your instinctive reaction was to sidestep it and sneak past. This went for obstacles of every kind, but mainly for people. When faced with a shortage of pillow slips you could improvise by using sheets; if you found a drainage set had broken down you took another, and if that one turned out to be broken down too you got a third; but when you got into a conflict with a person, it was going to be time-consuming unless you managed to fade away while the other was bawling you out. And we had some powerful bawlers in Emergency.

There were, first of all, the doctors. Four of them made up the staff for each shift: a surgical resident, a medical resident and two interns. At nighttime and during weekends these were supplemented by more interns and medical students; on Saturday nights there occasionally were as many as a dozen doctors about. Even so, the Emergency Room turned out to be understaffed during those peak periods.

All doctors, even the residents, were young. The chief resident in charge of the Emergency Room, whom we rarely saw, could not be older than in his early thirties. He was an unapproachable young man, called in whenever there was a conflict, never to view a case. He always turned up in either shirtsleeves or a jacket, never in a white coat. I had no idea what kind of man he was, but in his impersonal remoteness he became identified in my mind with the prevailing attitude of the doctors toward their patients. All patients, regardless of age or sex, were addressed by their first name, or failing that by "Buddy" or "Honey." On principle, so it seemed, no one was called "Mister" or "Miss" by the doctors. The entire medical staff of the hospital was furnished by Baylor University, so this was maybe a ruling imposed by the school. But in the practice of the Emergency Room it set a tone of callousness. As most of the doctors were Texans or Southerners, they already had a paternalistic attitude at best toward the Negro patients delivered into their care; under the pressure of their overwhelming numbers, this attitude deteriorated in many cases into contempt.

After my first weekend in Emergency, I could understand why that was so. I saw, to my incredulous astonishment, the place that I had known for two days as a busy clinic, with the occasional interruption of a Shock Room case after a car accident or a shooting, change into a slaughterhouse. I had never seen anything like it, I had not even known that anything like this went on anywhere in the world. Around seven o'clock on Friday night the ambulances started to arrive screaming at the entrance in ever-increasing numbers, disgorging a writhing load of bleeding humanity. Car wrecks, stabbings, shootings, suicides, bottle fights, muggings, abortions, rapings, delirium tremens—within an hour the corridor was choked with stretchers, all the tables in the Suture Rooms were occupied, the rooms themselves jammed with additional stretchers. A dozen doctors tried frantically to keep up with the ever-mounting number of wounds waiting to be sewn up; by ten o'clock there was not a free stretcher left in the whole hospital, all the beds in Observation were occupied with moaning, wailing, cursing or unconscious bodies, most of them ditched there in a hurry, fully dressed, by running orderlies. Additional stretchers were jammed between the beds as the tide of violence and trauma mounted to its peak around two o'clock in the morning.

By then, the place was a chaos. The floors were slippery with blood and vomit, littered with soiled linen, dropped instruments, discarded bottles of Novocaine, torn gloves, paper wrappers of sterile gauze flats and the blood-soaked flats themselves, dropped regardless after the litter baskets had started to overflow. There had been no time to clean the stretchers between patients; blood-soiled mattresses had been flipped over and hastily covered with another sheet, as long as there were sheets. After that they were not even turned over any more; each man lay in the blood of his predecessor. It was a battlefield, monstrous and unimaginable; my overriding emotion was, in the end, an incredulous horror at what human beings could do to one another. Muggings, knifings, mutilations—the night had been a spine-chilling procession of viciousness and cruelty.

As the majority of the victims were Negro, it was asking too much of young Southern white males, already preconditioned by a tradition of racial superiority, to regard the screaming, cursing, vicious creatures whose sprees of bestial brutality ended on the blood-soaked tables in the Emergency Room at dead of night as their brothers, or even as human beings. To remain impervious to the obscene abuse with which some of the raving patients reacted to being strapped down on table or stretcher to have their wounds sewn up became a triumph of mature, humane detachment. To hear oneself accused of criminally assaulting one's own mother while trying to patch up the results of subhuman brutality and not to slap the foul-mouthed bastard in the teeth made the young white physician feel like a paragon of patience, while to deaden the bastard's laceration with an injection of Novocaine before suturing it, so as not to cause him any pain, became an act of unworldly saintliness.

After my first experience of the weekly slaughter I understood why some of the doctors could not bring themselves to define their male Negro patients as "men" but consistently referred to them as "bucks." This word even had a connotation of good-natured indulgence; when the going got really rough, they referred to them as "slobs," "toads" or "spooks." Understaffed, underequipped, taunted by bureaucratic bottlenecks in supplies and housekeeping, their contempt became dignity, their very presence an act of charity.

It was, of course, so they told themselves, a necessary part of their education. The Emergency Room at J.D. was the best school in suturing a man could have in peacetime. Nowhere in the South, with the possible exception of New Orleans, could a young physician expect such a generous and constant supply of stabbed, shot, fractured, lacerated, burnt and otherwise insulted living tissue for his training; and only in that context could he let himself be taunted, defiled and spat upon by the very creatures whose suffering he tried to alleviate. To accord human status to these "toads" and "spooks" was incompatible with any civilized concept of humanity. The only way to accept them was to consider them purely as "cases."

The traumatic nights of those weekends and Christian holidays formed the key to the general attitude of the doctors toward their patients in ER and indeed the whole hospital. The very reasonableness of this communal attitude made a few solitary individuals among the residents and the interns even more impressive in their humanity.

There was, for instance, Dr. Miller, the Medical Resident in ER, a thin, stoop-shouldered, bespectacled young man in his late twenties, so gentle, patient and exhausted that he already had the shuffling gait of an old man. His high-domed forehead under the prematurely receding hair was constantly furrowed with a frown of concern. In a corner of the doctor's desk stood a forgotten cookie tin containing sandwiches, candy bars and an apple, prepared by his wife, whom he must have promised solemnly every morning that he would eat it, between meals, whenever he had a chance. He never did; usually he remembered only at the last moment to take the tin with him when he left at the end of his shift, and distributed its contents among the patients in Observation so as to take it home empty. He was a man of infinite kindness and compassion. As Medical Resident he mainly looked after patients from the Emergency Clinic, but when the usual bloodbath during the weekends became hectic he was there, suturing with the rest. My first Saturday night would have been a night in hell if he had not been there, tranquil and gentle amidst the gore and the obscenities. I was running from room to room, breaking open new suture trays, setting them up, filling the little cups with Mecressin, Creomycin and Novocaine and the irrigation basins with saline. In every room, in the corridor, even in the passage to Observation doctors were calling angrily for 3-o Nylon, 4-o Silk, 3-o Plain, 6-o Dermalon, sterile flats, sterile towels, hemostats; it was a madhouse of disjointed, frenetic activity. In the midst of it all sat Dr. Miller, suturing with infinite care the laceration in the forehead of a woman injured in a car wreck. He worked with such delicate tenderness that his sewing of her wound was gentler than the way her husband threw

74

on her prostrate body the clean dress that he had gone home to fetch. During the week, battered and buffeted by an unending stream of human misery, visibly wilting toward the end of each grueling shift, his patience and concern with each individual patient acquired the stature of saintliness. At the end of my third day I was present in the room where he found himself confronted with an eighty-nine-year-old woman, blind and deaf, who had been delivered early that morning by a Negro orderly from one of the unspeakable private nursing homes that proliferated all over the city. The orderly had left her in the hall without registering her; when he called back to collect her at midnight he refused to wait while she was seen by a doctor; she had stayed in the waiting-room overnight and all next day. It was this harassed old creature, stunned and stulted by inhumanity and neglect, that Dr. Miller found himself faced with that night. Both he and she were utterly exhausted, but undefeated; the result was a weird stage dialogue.

"How old are you, Miss Evans?"

"One fifteen Fraternity Drive."

"HOW OLD?"

"Hattie. Hattie Evans."

"HOW OLD?"

"Don't shout. I can hear. Her name was Fran, Francis Holmes. She has been dead sixty-nine years, what do you want her name for? I have a pain on the top of my head. Why don't you look at it?"

"Where in your head?"

A resigned sigh. "One hundred and fifteen Fraternity Drive. It's a nursing home."

A resigned sigh. "How am I supposed to find out what's ailing an eighty-nine-year-old woman who is both blind and deaf? Let's put her in a bed. I'll have to work her up completely, sometime tonight." As he left, he shyly patted her shoulder, unforgettable gesture of unity in defeat.

During the first days, Dr. Miller did not quite know how to approach me, which bothered me as much as it did him. The unspoken load was finally lifted from our minds when he proffered his lunch tin one day, saying, "Please, Mr. Volunteer, take the candy bar. I couldn't eat another bite."

I accepted it gratefully, realizing what it symbolized, although I couldn't eat another bite either. We had just come out of the Shock Room, where we had been attending, with half a dozen others, to a Negro girl whose leg had been severed by a train. The surgical resident had completed the severance; Mrs. Kowalski had taken a paper bag, written on it in prim nurses' handwriting: FANNY BACKUS, ONE SHOE WITH FOOT, put the foot inside, folded it shut and bidden me take it to the front desk. When I showed the bag to the normally unbending ladies of Reception, they screamed, asked furiously if I had gone crazy, and told me to take it out of there and to the Morgue, where it belonged.

I had never been to the Morgue before, though I had passed its door several times on my way through the basement to the laundry. Occasionally I had seen a stretcher waiting outside, with a still form covered by a sheet. This was the first time I had opened the door, after knocking on it absurdly and waiting for an answer. As I opened it, a strong smell of formaldehyde and a blast of icy cold hit me with unnerving force. In the half light, I saw a cellar-like room with concrete walls and floor. A stretcher with a man-sized steel tray on it stood in the middle of the floor, empty but for a pool of blood. In the corner I saw a heavily insulated door behind which, so I realized, lay the real Morgue, next to it a stack of paper bags, with names written on them. I added my bag to the stack; as I did so I read on one of them, "Hood, Albert" and a number. Where had I heard that name before? Then I saw, in my memory, the old man sitting up on his stretcher in the corridor that first day, his feet black with necrosis, his deformed hand clutching a dirty aspirin; and I heard Mrs. Judd's cheerful voice, "Hey, Mr. Hood! How are you? What brings you to us this time?"

I hastily closed the door and crossed the hall, to lean over the Dutch door of the laundry room and call, "Hello there! Anything for Emergency?" I knew that the women in the white aprons and old-fashioned maids' caps would shake their heads and shout over the noise of machinery, "No, nothing!" for I had collected a full trolley an hour before. I did it only to fill my lungs with the smell of clean linen, and because the head laundress was a jolly, bare-armed person whose grin and bawdy wink never failed to cheer me.

Mrs. Kowalski, the head nurse who had sent me off to the reception desk with that gruesome bag, knowing full well what the result would be, seemed to fit in much better with the prevailing attitude in ER than Mrs. Judd. She was an immensely capable nurse, on her feet without respite for the full eight hours of her shift; but at first sight one would never expect her to do a stroke of work as she had without any doubt the sexiest walk in the building. She never actually walked, let alone ran; she strolled with a sinuous, subtly seductive gait that went well with her flaming red bouffant hair, her striking black eyes and her Junoesque figure. But it went not at all with the broken-down stretchers full of desolate humanity, the benches crowded with wheezing, gasping asthma sufferers, the old, sagging beds with the drunk, the delirious, the dying and the dead in the darkness of the Observation wards. The way she applied tourniquets, put in IV's, took blood pressures or prepped a patient in the Shock Room was impressive in its perfectly controlled, casual craftmanship. But to see her deal with any patients other than those in shock or convulsions was chilling, because of her cold, detached objectivity. She disturbed me deeply when, for the first time, I wit-

77

nessed her reaction to a spine-tingling scream of torment from the darkness of the Observation Ward. There was no reaction whatever; I was sure she had not heard it, or she would not be sitting there like that, it had raised the hair on the nape of my neck.

"Mrs. Kowalski," I ventured. "I believe someone is calling in there. . . ."

She answered, without looking up from the record she was reading, with that mincing drawl of sensual boredom, "Oh, I always ignore their first call, Mr. de Hartog."

One of the doctors, sitting next to her at the desk, said casually, "If you ask me, that was his last."

"All right, Mr. de Hartog," Mrs. Kowalski said, acidly and precisely, closing the record and slipping it back into its box with a somehow provocative gesture. "Why don't you go and have a look at Mr. Borkus and see what he wants this time?" Then she got up and strolled away, riveting the gaze of all males in sight, old and young, sick and healthy, on the fascinating double motion of her magnificent behind.

I had, on one early and embarrassing occasion, come out of Observation and asked her, "Mrs. Kowalski, is the lady in the corner with the broken arm allowed liquids?" She had calmly finished what she was writing, then slowly raised her eyes and fixed me with a gaze so mortifying that I felt like beating a retreat even before she asked, with that veiled seductive voice that carried a mile, "What lady with a broken arm are you referring to, Mr. de Hartog?"

I said, "Well, the lady in the corner. The one with the splint, I mean . . ."

She gazed at me pensively, but the disturbing thing was that she was gazing at my upper lip, as if trying to determine what I would look like with a mustache. Then she said, in the breathless silence she had by then created, "I hear you are a writer, Mr. de Hartog. Is that so?"

I muttered, "Yes, but . . ."

"Well, Mr. de Hartog," she said, charmingly, "one of these days I am going to write a book about *you*. That is not a splint the lady is wearing, that is an IV board." She gave me a small smile, turned back to her writing and added, as an afterthought, "And patients with IV's are, as a rule, not allowed liquids."

It must have been more than forty years ago that I had last blushed; not since my schooldays had I felt such powerless hatred, mixed with equally powerless admiration, for any woman alive. The outrageous circumstance was that I was old enough to be her father, although she inspired me with unfatherly thoughts. After that incident, whenever she spied me in any situation other than carrying a fainted patient or running with a stack of bedpans like a waiter, she would call me with that infuriating inflection of polite condescension of which she had the infernal secret, and ask me to do something that always turned out to be slightly degrading, even for the lowest form of human life in the Emergency Room. "Oh, Mr. de Hartog, the intercom has broken down; would you please stand at the entrance to the corridor and call through the names to the patients in the waiting room as the doctors ask for them?" Or "Mr. de Hartog, Housekeeping has gone to lunch and we have, in Suture Room Number Two, that overweight lady with explosive diarrhea. Could you do something about her, with a sheet perhaps?" I would not have minded either assignment had they been given me by anyone else; but she managed, by her very tone, to make the prospect of my bellowing names between the hall and the waiting room sound entertaining, while the idea of a middle-aged intellectual nervously trying to do something about an overweight lady with explosive diarrhea with a sheet, seemed to promise a *corrida* hilarious enough to attract a crowd.

The difference between Mrs. Judd and Mrs. Kowalski

was typified in the way they administered an injection. Mrs. Judd, victim of compassion and afflicted with a sense of identification, would announce to the patient, as she rubbed the spot on his arm, "Now you're going to feel just a little pinprick, nothing at all." But the very fact of her personal concern made her prediction sound dire; when she gave the shot it would invariably result in a squeal, occasionally some patient with a natural talent for the stage would carry his theatrical reaction to the point of passing out. Mrs. Kowalski always made a point of talking to someone else while she was rubbing her victim's arm for the injection. "Oh, Mr. de Hartog, I hate to bother you with this, but would you mind having a look at the patients' toilet in Observation? I believe there's someone in there who hasn't come out for a number of hours." The mouth of her prey would fall open at this; while he or she stood gaping at me with a growing mental picture of what awaited me when I opened the door of the patients' toilet, Mrs. Kowalski would give the arm a sharp little blow with the side of her hand, like cops on TV who know karate. Her patient would swing round, crying, "Hey, listen! What do you think you are doing?" By then he had received his injection; the only drawback was that people afterward would stubbornly maintain they had *not* had their tetanus shot.

Mrs. Kowalski could perform technical feats of nursing that would have dazzled an audience in the days of vaudeville. She could change the sheets of a bed with a two-hundred-pound unconscious patient in it faster than two male orderlies combined, and she would emerge from this record performance with not a hair out of place, her face unflushed, her lips puckered in that small supercilious pout of boredom that could irritate her subordinates to screaming point, and reduce raving lunatics to performing lambs, producing their specimen cartons of urine submissively, on command. I disliked her heartily, until one day, when I happened to be the only one around, she asked me to help her restrain a deluded white woman who was screaming abuse in the Observation Ward. The moment the woman saw the red-headed pin-up enter her distorted field of vision, she began to screech insults at her. "You little nigger prostitute!" she screamed. "I saw you, you filthy slut! I saw you with those niggers, behind the diner!" Mrs. Kowalski frowned; I expected her to silence the poor soul expertly. To my amazement she stepped quietly back into the shadows, but stayed around to see whether I would need any help. The woman calmed down; when I joined her in the shadows, Mrs. Kowalski said, "This is a sad place, Mr. de Hartog. We have a great responsibility, haven't we?" Then she strolled away languidly, without waiting for my answer.

One of the people I liked best in Emergency was an elderly vocational nurse called Mrs. Birdland. She was an angelic woman, who ministered to the sick and the lonely in Observation with the soothing fussiness of a grandmother. She was probably no great shakes at the finer technical aspects of nursing, but she richly made up for any lack she might have had in that direction by giving each of her patients the feeling of being individually cared for. Mrs. Kowalski, her black eyes flashing Wagnerian lightning, would always manage to bag the scurrying, short-legged form of the fleeing Mrs. Birdland with a thunderbolt, whenever she had done something wrong. "Mrs. Birdland!" she would call, with the carrying power of the Last Trump. "Could you give me the vital signs of the gentleman in bed number nine again, please? According to your treatment-sheet he is dead." The gentleman in No. 9 would, more likely than not, be happily asleep behind his curtain, soothed into slumber at last by Mrs. Birdland's homely ministrations. It seemed a shame to have him waked up from his first sleep by his ministering angel in a high state of fluster, fussing with inflatable cuffs, pressure gauges and stethoscopes in which, so she once confided to me, her eyes round with alarm, she sometimes heard music as she tried to listen to the pulse beat in the crease of a patient's arm. I liked working with Mrs. Birdland, but she was often pulled to other parts of the hospital by the Nursing Office during moments of calm in Emergency. On those occasions I was left alone with Miss Jennie, the Negro cleaning woman.

Miss Jennie had taught me how to fold sheets fresh from the laundry to the proper format before stacking them on the shelves in Observation. She was the only one who folded them that way; during other shifts they were flung onto the shelves by the armful by whoever happened to stop by to grab a few out of the trolley. She made me refold them, regulation fashion, and when it came to making beds she was harder to satisfy than a sergeant major. When I had made a bed on which, mysteriously, the bottom sheet seemed to be longer on one side than it was on the other, she would look at me with incredulous exasperation from under her rabbit-eared scarf, mop in hand, and cry, "How come you are so stupid?" I could never think of a satisfactory answer, so she would command, "Take it off and start all over again! And if again it don't work, go on doing it until I come back. When you think you're through, you can start stacking sheets."

I was not the only one she bossed around; she did the same to the interns in the bunkroom to which she had the key. But she could do no wrong, as far as I was concerned, after I heard her say on my second day in Observation, as I stood helpless between two beds and their gruesome contents, each one of them expiring, "Every time I come through here, I pray for them." It had seemed, at that moment, as if she were the only one in the building who cared about the two poor wretches in that horrible little dark ward. I discovered, as time went on, that she was the only one who could really cope with the worst of the damned, that sometimes lay in the far corner, raving obscenely, spitting in the face of death. I once found, when I arrived, in the back of the second ward, an old naked hallucinating tramp, dying in a tangle of soaked sheets and torn trousers, his wrists and ankles tied to the bed frame, cursing like a madman. When I tried to cover him with a sheet, he cried, "Goddammit, leave me alone! Goddammit, that hurts!" While I stood there, at a loss, he went on cursing and rambling. "I claim the six rings!" he cried. "They were promised to me! Goddammit, those rings are mine!" Then he started to curse again, in an empty litany of obscenity. Suddenly I heard a voice say with quiet indignation, "You should not blaspheme; you should ask God to forgive you." I looked and saw Miss Jennie stand behind me, mop in hand, her glasses shimmering bleakly in the darkness. It seemed a harsh thing to say to a dying man, but suddenly the old tramp cried, "Yes, God, forgive me! . . . God, forgive me, Goddammit, Goddammit . . ." But even as he went on cursing, I had the uncanny feeling that she had done something for him that no one else could have done.

John Rivers, the orderly who had so brusquely stopped me during my first day in Emergency, when I had been about to give Mr. Hood a cup of water for his aspirin, was rarely seen in Observation; his stomping ground was the treatment section. I started out with a feeling of instinctive hostility towards him; in a way he truly integrated me by this feeling: he was the first man I cordially detested despite the fact that he was a Negro. After a few weeks I came to change my opinion of him under the pressure of a growing, reluctant admiration; to see him at work filled me with envy. Also, he knew more about Shakespeare than most of my students, not to mention myself, and the fact that he would, at particularly tense moments in the Shock Room when things hovered on the brink of chaos, calmly and rather pedantically quote the Bard was, so I discovered, part of his mastery of his profession. As time went on, I saw many a medical student saved from embarrassment by his tacit and poker-faced help. When, for instance, a tenderfoot asked with the superciliousness of insecurity for the wrong type of suture to go with the laceration he was about to sew up, John Rivers would say, "Yes, doctor," and drop the right one on his tray. He never committed the error of taste of making this a secret understanding; he managed to help with such aloofness that most students actually believed they had profited from a mistake on his part.

My most vivid memory of him is dated Christmas Eve, 1962, in Emergency. It was, without doubt, the most gruesome night of my life thus far. All through that night he was a tower of strength, impeccably correct, maddeningly unaffected, and seemingly untiring. When, at last, we were ready to hand over the nightmare of Hieronymus Bosch to the seven-to-three shift, we made one more round together to see if all was well. It wasn't; it was like daybreak on a battlefield. But it was the best we could do.

I remember him standing in the doorway to the court-yard, by the admissions desk: the hall filled with stretchers and litters, the air rank with the smell of sickness, the wailing of the damned a haunting litany at this dawn of Christmas Day. For a moment I stood there, overwhelmed by the horrendous notion that all this was hopeless, that it would never change. Then I felt a hand on my shoulder, and I looked up, and that was the first time I saw John Rivers smile.

"Come," he said, opening the door. "Absent thee from felicity awhile."

84

2

WHEN I STARTED work as an orderly in the Emergency Room, I had much to learn. I learned by trial and error, but once I could find my way by myself I started to go about my business with that peculiar feeling of isolation that is the result when too few people are trying to cope with a perpetually chaotic situation in which they feel they can make no more than a dent. Like the rest of the hospital, Emergency was critically understaffed as far as nursing personnel was concerned. On paper, there were not enough of us to start with, but, as the rest of the hospital was cursed with an even worse shortage, the Nursing Office would often call down to Emergency to find out how busy we were and then proceed to pull one of us to another floor. If, soon afterward, the floodgates opened and emergency cases started to pour in, it was impossible to get our colleague back; we had to cope as best we could by ourselves.

So it happened that quite often I found myself entirely alone in the two small Observation Wards in the back toward which I had gravitated. I discovered that I did not care much for the dramatic emergency work in the Shock Rooms and the rest of the treatment section. As a rule, people who came in with severe trauma were looked after expertly and at once; the ER at Jefferson Davis was famous for this; true Shock Room cases always attracted all the staff at hand. They could do without me there; it was in the wards that I felt I really had something to contribute, modest as it might be. It was the most neglected part of Emergency; often, when I arrived in the morning, I would find the patients that had arrived overnight lying on the sagging beds fully dressed, with their shoes still on. IV's, at that time applied to everyone as a matter of routine, were obviously put in in a hurry and forgotten; most of them had run dry by the time I arrived. Beds were rarely made, and cleaned only whenever Miss Jennie could get around to them. Unless someone in there cried out loud enough to attract the attention of a doctor or a nurse at the desk, patients in Observation were rarely looked after, because the person "pulled" most regularly was the LVN assigned there.

It was a grim, tragic place. The mortality, compared to the rest of the hospital, was very high. Patients in Observation were not officially considered admitted to the hospital, so their demise was no threat to the record of cases cured. To every patient brought into Emergency, the bed in one of the little dark wards was the first station after being struck by an accident, attack or sudden illness. The people in Observation were living in a limbo between the past world of their normal daily lives, so dramatically interrupted, and their future world, that of the hospital. Most of them lay in a state of daze, still entangled in the nightmare of what had happened to them: knocked down in an accident, transported in a screaming ambulance to the dreamlike, oblong world of the Emergency corridor ceiling and the sudden glare of the Shock Room lamps; manhandled, lugged about, undressed with frantic urgency, buttons flying, clothes cruelly cut to shreds by scissors; then the dramatic treatment for trauma: the ring of black and white faces in nurses' and operating caps, the searing pain, the terror, the whispering voices, the clatter of instruments, the warm flow of blood, the smell of disinfectant—it was a bad dream, something outrageous, incredible happening in a world removed from reality. And then the slow waking up: alone, cold, forgotten, in the sinister darkness of a little ward, surrounded by moans, feeble cries, and the snoring of a critical patient in the next bed—this part was doubtlessly the worst. I discovered that most cases of extreme agitation, dealt with by restraining the patient with leather straps, armbands and anklets tied to the bedframe, were caused by panic, the waking up with the feeling of being

86

abandoned. Most patients in a state of excitement would calm down the moment it penetrated to them that there was someone around to look after them, who responded to their call. Most of them, however grave their condition, would wake up from the nightmare with the same question, "When can I go home?" That question, I came to realize, stood for: "Am I going to die?" And it was this question that needed to be answered with a cheerful reassurance, at once. Cheerfulness, I found, was the prime requisite for whoever found himself assigned to Observation; cheerfulness and tranquillity. I could only acquire and maintain both if I relinquished all previous standards I might have had as to what a hospital should be like. Not only did I soon find myself to be as consistently and indomitably cheerful as Mrs. Judd, I came to realize that it was the only attitude if you wanted to be of any use at all in this incredible place. To inquire about, criticize or question any aspect or manifestation of the insane world of blood and bureaucracy we were living in was the first sign of cracking up. It was like questioning the sanity of enemy pilots during a bombardment. Nothing was more futile than to clamor for change in a situation that, obviously, would never change.

Politically, the hospital was the responsibility of both the city and the county, who ran it as a combined operation and paid for it from their general fund. Nobody seemed to be able to agree who should shoulder the major part of the cost, the city or the county, and so the two bodies were constantly in each other's hair. Whenever the words "charity hospital" were mentioned, a violent shouting match would ensue and the opponents of city and county vied with one another in threats, accusations and demagogic efforts to burden the other with the sole responsibility. The only responsibility ever discussed was the financial one; no one ever gave a sign of being aware of any responsibility toward the patients. All anyone in public office ever complained of was the cost of operation; the operation itself was the responsibility of the Board of Managers and the administration.

The Chairman of the Board of Managers was a gentleman called Ben Taub, who seemed to be a venerable and influential citizen, but to those who worked inside the hospital he seemed a mythological figure, as mystically remote as the Abominable Snowman of the Himalayas. For to work inside the hospital meant to become involved in the minutiae of daily life, infinitesimal, esoteric conflicts between personalities to whom the Nursing Office was a star chamber and the Administrator an unapproachable and impersonal God.

The bureaucratic hierarchy of the hospital was riddled with personal antagonisms, struggles for power and conspiratory pressure groups, who gave the atmosphere an Oriental quality, reminiscent of descriptions of the Sultan's court in Turkey at the turn of the century. From what I occasionally overheard in the cafeteria, I gathered that the place was full of spies, courtiers, middlemen and small-time politicians, all of whom operated, in an atmosphere of mystery and secrecy, under someone else's protection. Nobody knew who was protected by whom of a higher rank, all the way up to the very top where, in lonely splendor, sat enthroned the legendary Mr. Ben Taub, veiled by the clouds shrouding the top of Mount Olympus.

All this rarely interfered with the work we were doing in Emergency, and my own work in the Observation Wards was so demanding that I did not have the time to be even remotely interested in the harem politics that were purported to rule the destiny of the hospital. Like Mrs. Judd, and anyone else for that matter who was involved with the patients rather than the records, I became adept at getting round any roadblock of bureaucracy or personality that I might find barring my way while trying to fend for my patients. Rather than challenge anyone and risk a conflict, the only way to retain your usefulness as well as your self-respect was to react with the indiscriminate, cheerful meekness of a village idiot.

A good example was the meals for emergency admissions. All meals for the patients in the two wards were collected from the diet kitchen. According to regulations, applications for meals must be made two hours in advance, in writing, stating the name, sex and age of each individual patient to be fed, and adding any information pertinent to his diet like "Low salt" or "Liquid" or "Regular." As the elderly lady in control of the Diet Kitchen was a stickler for protocol, we had to make sure that we got our order in before the stroke of four. If, occasionally, a sudden influx of Shock Room cases made it impossible for the supervisor or the head nurse on duty to write out a list in time, this meant that the patients had to go without food that night, even if we were only five minutes late with our application. The first time this happened, I went to find Mrs. Judd, aggressive with indignation.

"Well, Mrs. Judd!" I said, "You had better go in there swinging. The old woman refused to take our application, saying it was too late; it's only five minutes after four."

"Oh," Mrs. Judd said, cheerfully, "that's all right, let's give them milk," and went about her business.

At the time I thought it was a callous reaction, totally out of character. I realized later that to challenge the lady in the Diet Kitchen was as futile as sticking out your tongue at a passing train; to miss the four o'clock deadline was final, like missing a connection. So we accepted her as an immovable object and circumvented her with the canniness of the weak, eventually learning to turn her bureaucratic idiosyncrasy to the advantage of our patients. During the regulation two hours that had to elapse between the receipt of the order and the issuance of the meals, there would always be new admissions to my two little wards who needed to be fed. These were usually not people who had come in recently from the street; most of them had lain forgotten for hours in a side room or the corridor, to be discovered by accident and found to be in dire need of a meal. To be prepared for these last-minute admissions, we had taken to adding three imaginary names to the list. This was never discovered because the lady, by her very inability to visualize a human being behind a name on a list, accepted unquestioningly the most mischievous additions. John Rivers and I collected meals for William Shakespeare, Lorna Doone, Billy Rasputin, Mark Twain and Gautama Buddha (Ind. male, 53 yrs, veget.)

Apart from the woman in the Diet Kitchen, our only contact with that other world, the world of bureaucracy, was the ladies behind the Emergency admissions desk, and compared to her they seemed humane. As a matter of fact they were, personally, kind and even charming women. Only occasionally would an inhabitant of that other world lose his way and end up among us, for a moment. I remember one instance when I was accosted by a matron in a spotless white coat whom I had never seen before. It was an unusually busy night in the treatment section, all suture tables were occupied, and I had been called in from Observation to help out. That particular night was a cardiac night; I had soon discovered that for some reason certain human afflictions had a tendency to turn up in groups. When two victims of a heart attack followed one another in rapid succession, you could be certain that more were to follow before the end of the shift. Cardiac patients needed to have their heads elevated; as we possessed only one wooden wedge for the purpose the others had to be propped up with pillows. Pillows were in erratic supply, however, as were blankets. You had either to delve through stacks of pillows to find one blanket in the linen trolley, or to operate in a pillowless world with a glut of blankets. In that case you folded blankets to substitute for pillows and I was busy doing this that night when I heard a stern voice say, "I see you are putting blankets under the patients' heads. Don't you know that is not permitted?" I looked up and saw the woman. I had no idea who she was, but, as she was obviously a member of the priesthood of bureaucracy, I had to make my way around her as passively and unobtrusively as I could. So I said, "I am sorry. I do this only because this patient must have his head raised, and there are no pillows."

"There are no blankets either," the woman retorted, with a tone of finality.

"I'm sorry," I answered, "but there are, we received about fifty of them from the laundry tonight."

She snorted. "Nonsense!" she said. "You shall not put blankets under the patients' heads but wait until you receive pillows."

"From whom?" I asked.

"From me," she answered imperiously, and breezed out.

The intriguing point of this incident was that not only had I never seen her before, I never saw her again. Nobody in Emergency had the faintest idea who she was, not even Mrs. Judd, who, as supervisor, functioned as our link with the other world.

This was the toughest part of her job, so it seemed. I once found her hiding in tears in the little kitchen in Observation, her eyes swollen, a crumpled paper handkerchief in her hand. This was not because of real tragedy or sadness; anything to do with our patients she could cope with. It was because the Nursing Office, outpost of bureaucracy in our jungle of human suffering had, because of some petty breach of ritual or regulations, fired our beloved and invaluable Mrs. Birdland. Mrs. Judd, choked with tears of rage and frustration, sat crumpling her handkerchief and said, "I've had it! This time I've had it! I'm five people short as it is, and now they fired one of my best nurses. I've had it. I should never have agreed to work here in the first place. I should have walked straight out, after my first look at this dump, and brought in the newspapers. This is not a hospital, this is a . . . a . . . Well, you are the writer. Maybe *you* have a word for it."

I nodded in vague commiseration, but while Mrs. Judd rushing about the ward was an ally, Mrs. Judd in tears in the kitchen was another obstacle to be circumvented. I said, "Yes, it's a terrible shame, er . . . but the old lady in the far corner has a blood pressure of sixty over forty, and her rectal temperature is ninety-seven point six, so maybe you had better come and have a look."

She seemed reluctant to let go of this moment of self-indulgence which, God knows, must have been rare enough. I added, unfairly, "She is the one that was in a car wreck with her husband. It seems he died in surgery."

"No!" she said. "Who told you that?"

"Mrs. Kowalski said so. It seems someone from OR mentioned it when he came to fetch a patient."

"Oh, my God," she said, getting up. "Poor woman," and off she went, at a trot. I picked up her paper handkerchief and dropped it in the wastebasket.

3

JUST BEFORE CHRISTMAS there came the day when I failed to trick Mrs. Judd out of her anger and frustration. It was a Monday morning, and as usual very busy with clinical patients who always accumulated over the weekend. Dr. Miller's shoulders seemed more stooped and his arches fallen deeper with weariness than ever, as he trudged back and forth from Observation to Bone Room, from Bone Room to Industrial Accident, from Industrial Accident to Shock Room One, from Shock Room One to X-Ray and from X-Ray back to Observation, trying to cope with seven patients simultaneously like a juggler with one plate too many in the air.

"Where the devil are all the nurses?" he asked with uncharacteristic vigor as he came loping past. "I've got three female catheters and one GYN patient waiting, and all I see is men."

"I'll go and have a look, doctor," I said. I thought I had heard voices in the kitchen in Observation.

As I went in there to check, I found Mrs. Judd and a supervisor from another floor sitting there, drinking coffee, showing all the symptoms of virulent gossip.

"Ah, Mr. de Hartog! You are the very man I want," Mrs. Judd cried, when she saw me. "Sit down. I want to talk to you."

"Yes, Mrs. Judd," I said, meekly, "but Dr. Miller just asked where you were because . . ."

"The hell with Dr. Miller!" Mrs. Judd cried, belligerently, making my mouth fall open. "Sit down! This is serious."

I sat down tentatively on the edge of the wastebin, wondering how to could get out of here tactfully. Dr. Miller might have three catheters and a patient in the GYN room, I had two men on bedpans, an old wino with DT's half off his stretcher after worming one hand out of his restraining bandage, and a psycho patient clanking tentatively with a urinal in the toilet. Much as I admired Mrs. Judd, this was not the moment for a kaffee klatsch.

"Why are you doing this, Mr. de Hartog?" Mrs. Judd asked, in a tone as if to open a panel discussion. The thought occurred to me that this must be the nervous breakdown she had been heading for.

"I beg your pardon?"

"I mean, are you doing this work for religious reasons, or merely personal?"

"Mrs. Judd," I started, apologetically, "I'd love to talk, but right now . . ."

"I mean, if your reasons are religious, then there must be

a group of you. I mean, you must know other people who feel the same way you do."

Her colleague, behind her, gravely nodded agreement. As it seemed unlikely that the two of them had come down with a nervous breakdown at the same time, I said, "I—er —I'm a Quaker, but I have that patient they sent down from Ten in the toilet; you know, the one who cut his wrists . . ."

This time it did not work. "Yesterday morning, a patient died on Seven," Mrs. Judd said with an odd calm. "He died of suffocation, because his trach tube was not cleaned on time. It was not cleaned because there was one nurse for sixty patients. That man died of neglect."

I said, "Ah?" It did not shock me. It did not even make an impression on me. I had three people on bedpans, one DT half off his stretcher, and one psycho in the toilet. All I cared about was to get back in there before the ward blew up in my face.

"We all assume that this place cannot be changed," Mrs. Judd said, still with that grim determination, "that we will never get enough people, or equipment, and never get rid of the politicians sitting on the lid."

"Yes," I said, edging toward the door, "it's a pity . . ."

"We have discussed this among ourselves," she continued, "the other supervisors and I. We have come to the conclusion that there is one thing we can do for patients like the one who was killed yesterday morning by neglect. We can get in more people like yourself to help us out on Sunday mornings and maybe during night shifts by doing simple nursing duties like changing water, feeding, making beds, giving bedbaths . . ."

"Mrs. Judd," I said, my hand on the doorknob, "I'd love to talk all this over sometime, but . . ."

"We supervisors know," Mrs. Judd continued, with a crusading fire in her eyes that I had never seen there before, "that of course these volunteers would have to be trained. We cannot bring someone in off the street and put him to work as an orderly without proper schooling. So if you can help us find, say, a dozen mature members of your congregation, then we will train them, ourselves, in our spare time, and supervise them on the floors for five Sunday mornings in succession, until they are ready to work alone."

"But . . . you are working overtime already," I said, taken aback. "How are you going to teach classes and supervise volunteers on the floors as well as what you are already doing?"

"We have all the time in the world!" Mrs. Judd said aggressively. "And even if I have to become a drug addict to do it, I can't stand this any longer. Either I get out, now, or you bring me a dozen people like yourself, and we'll train them, and I'd like to see anyone stop us. We have worn blinkers long enough. As far as I'm concerned, this is it."

I looked from one to the other as it dawned on me how impressive this was. In the face of such generosity and compassion all I could do was to say, "All right, I'll talk to my friends about it," and back out.

The moment I was back in Observation, all other considerations vanished. My psychopathic patient was now hammering ominously in the toilet; the old wino was hopping alongside his stretcher, half tied, trying to pull it sideways between two IV stands with bottles; one of the other patients was off his bedpan and trying to deposit it on the floor, at the point of finding out that his arm was too short to do so with impunity.

Only when my shift was over and I stood drinking a cup of coffee in the crowded small canteen off the general clinic did our conversation come back to mind. It seemed a very good idea, but there obviously was a ruling in the hospital that volunteers were not allowed near patients, at least not in a group, like the Baylor wives. I had better make sure that the hospital administration would accept them before conveying Mrs. Judd's plan to the Meeting. I decided to go and see Mrs. Willoughby.

I had rarely set eyes on her since that first day, when she took me down to Emergency. She never came to the floors, let alone to Observation; and once I had joined the nursing staff she had automatically become a potential adversary, as she was part of the bureaucratic hierarchy that ran the hospital and that everybody in uniform or scrub suit so cordially loathed.

I found her, despite the late hour, sitting at the desk in her office, telephoning. She motioned me into a chair and wound up her conversation. I heard the words "Christmas" and "Pediatrics"; she sounded as if she were talking to a subordinate, but this being her normal tone it might just as well be the Administrator. She slammed the phone back into the cradle, muttered, "Well, let's hope this settles it," and then she gave me a slowly focusing look. When it penetrated to her who I was, her face reassumed that expression of listening to a concert of atonal music. "What can I do for you?" she asked.

I asked her if there was any organized program for the training of volunteer orderlies and nurses' aides within her organization. She frowned and asked me why; I replied that, if so, I might have a suggestion to make.

She stared at me for so long and so intently that I thought her mind must have wandered to other things, but it had not. She had been gathering steam for a withering diatribe against the one single agency in this building that made such a program utterly impossible: the Nursing Office. She spoke about the Nursing Office as Captain Bakker of the tugboat *Taurus* had been in the habit of speaking about the Home Office; the Home Office in turn might have talked about Captain Bakker in the same terms. As long as the Nursing Office refused to cooperate, she said, there could be no such program. It had been tried before and failed. The Nursing Office did not realize what type of ladies were likely to join the Women-in-Yellow. They had no regard for the fact that these were well-educated, highly civilized women who could not be asked to do certain things. I tried to get from her a definition of those things, but she was not listening. "I know my women," she said. "I have worked with them for twenty-five years. These are Southern ladies; the mere fact that they are here to help is a triumph. Believe me, I know, I'm from Mississippi myself. I can get them to sit at the reception desk, to read stories to the children in Pediatrics, to work on the files, even to push people in wheelchairs, but that is as far as I can expect them to go. You cannot ask a Southern woman to carry bedpans for sick niggers. Even if I were ready to do it myself, I cannot ask them to do it. The Nursing Office has to accept that we are in Texas, not in Massachusetts. I am not going to deliver my women into the hands of some inexperienced, high-handed Yankee whippersnapper up on the floors, who would tell them to give enemas to their own maids; I'd find myself without volunteers within a month. So the only condition on which I'll allow such a group to be formed is that they shall be in yellow uniforms, and under my control, not that of the Nursing Office."

There was little I could say to that. But my face must have expressed some reservation, for when I got up to leave, she added, "The fact that you Quakers are prepared to do this work doesn't make you better people. If you yourself had been born and bred here, and then started doing what you're doing now, you might be. As it is, you are a Dutchman or a Hollander or whatever you want me to call you, and it's easy for you to go holy about something you've had no truck with until you came to this town a few months ago. The people I am trying to persuade to help us in this hospital have to overcome a feeling of humbling themselves before they can call a nigger "Mr."

or "Mrs.," as I insist they do at the reception desk. I'm not saying they are right, I'm not saying they are wrong; I'm saying that is the way it is, whether we like it or not. And I'm not going to tell you whether I like it or not, for that's none of your business. Where are you going now? The Nursing Office?"

Like Captain Bakker, she had a direct telephone line connecting her with the secret thoughts of her subordinates. "I thought I might," I answered.

"Remember that you are a Woman-in-Yellow!" she called, when I was at the door. "You are to take orders from nobody but me!"

I gave her a smile which, I hoped, looked innocent and boyish. "I'll remember, Mrs. Willoughby," I said. "Goodby now."

As I left, I saw her pick up the telephone.

I had never met Mrs. Masters, the Director of Nurses; I had never been inside the Nursing Office, for that matter. I was received by the secretary as if I had been a regular and welcome guest. She picked up the telephone, pressed a button and said, "Mrs. Masters, here is Mr. de Hartog; you know, the volunteer orderly from the Emergency Room? He would like to see you. All right, Mrs. Masters, I will. You can go right in," she said. "Mrs. Masters has no one with her right now. That's an exception. This door please."

As I entered I found a high, bare office with a window overlooking the Emergency parking lot and the nurses' building. One wall was entirely covered with a huge chart, full of multicolored thumbtacks. Behind one of two desks, joined front to front, sat a queenly middle-aged woman with rimless glasses that reflected the windows. Her mere presence exuded an immense authority; if Mrs. Willoughby was like the captain of an ocean-going tugboat, Mrs. Masters was the commodore of an ocean liner.

"Glad to meet you, Mr. de Hartog," she said. "I've heard about you. Sit down."

I obeyed, with the conditioned reflex, dormant for thirty years, to put my peaked cap on my knees.

"What can I do for you?" she asked.

I had the uncanny feeling that she knew where I had just been, although I had no idea how she could know. Frankness seemed the best solution. "I've just come from Mrs. Willoughby's office," I said.

"I know," she said. "Mrs. Willoughby just told me. You want to start a corps of volunteer nurses' aides."

So that was what Mrs. Willoughby's telephone call had been. I realized that, much as the two ladies might consider themselves to be antagonists, they both belonged to the same world, that other world. I remembered nurses commenting on the fact that Mrs. Masters was never seen on the floors.

"I must begin by assuring you, Mr. de Hartog," she said, "that what this hospital needs more than anything else is people. If you look at that chart on the wall for a moment, you will see how the numbers of our actual nursing staff compare to the minimum normal standards. That chart is divided into compartments, one compartment for each function: housekeeper, nurses' aide, orderly, LVN, nurse, head nurse, supervisor. The red pins represent the people we have, the black pins the people we need. You see that in all departments, without exception, we are operating with about half the minimum staff required. I need not assure you that a group of people like yourself, ready to be trained as voluntary nurses' aides, would be a godsend."

"Mrs. Judd discussed it with you?" I asked.

"I know all about it," Mrs. Masters said, with a commodore's inflection that somehow disposed of Mrs. Judd.

Loyalty made me say, "I was very impressed that she and her colleagues are willing to train volunteers in their spare time."

Mrs. Masters looked at me pensively, as Mrs. Willoughby had done; neither of them seemed likely to join the Society of Friends of Modern Music. "Mrs. Judd is an idealist," she said, "and we are glad to have her. But even you, who by now I suppose are familiar with the facts of life in this hospital, will realize that Mrs. Judd *has* no spare time. She is already doing the work of two; she is supervisor of the Emergency Room, and works a full shift as head nurse. I can't stop her from doing that, although it is obvious that she will not be able to keep it up indefinitely. As a matter of fact," Mrs. Masters concluded with a frown of impatience, "it isn't even worth discussing. One look at that chart, and you will see that our supervisors have to be Hindu goddesses with three pairs of arms if they want to do their job properly. So, assuming that there is a group of volunteers desirous of being trained as nurses' aides, someone else would have to train them and supervise them. My staff simply does not have the time."

"Well, maybe that could be arranged."

"Maybe," Mrs. Masters said, without conviction. "But there is another point that I might as well bring up now instead of later. Suppose there was a group of volunteer nurses' aides and orderlies available, they would have to be under the authority of the Nursing Office, and no one else's."

"I see," I said.

"I'm sure you do." Mrs. Masters favored me with a wintry smile. "Mrs. Willoughby is a very capable woman. Her volunteers do excellent work. But she would not be where she is now, after more than twenty years, if she were not—how shall I say?—a born leader." Her eyes flashed behind her glasses, and she gave me another smile. I had the sensation of witnessing a battle between pachyderms.

"Mrs. Willoughby will undoubtedly insist that all volunteers admitted to this hospital shall report under her authority," she continued. "I can tell you here and now that I will have no truck with that. I cannot allow her or anyone else to interfere with the running of my department.

As it is, I need the inventiveness of a magician and the wisdom of a Solomon to keep this hospital operating with the means at my disposal. If I had to cope with Mrs. Willoughby as well, I might as well pack up and go home."

"I know that all this is hypothetical," I said, "but suppose there would be a group of trained volunteers available, to serve under your sole authority, would you accept them?"

"Of course," she said, with a hasty show of warmth. "I'd be delighted. But we would need, of course, an okay from the administration, the Board of Managers . . ."

"Would you be able to get that okay?" I asked. "Or, let me put it this way: would you be willing to go for it?"

She weighed that question in her mind. Then she replied, "Quite frankly, Mr. de Hartog, I think that would depend on who they were. This hospital cannot be judged by normal standards. It has survived against odds for thirty years, only because the people in control have had the courage to use any means at their disposal, orthodox or no. You are an intelligent man; you'll understand that the people in control are not going to admit any group of volunteers to the floors unless they are sure that they are not potential troublemakers."

"How could they be?" I asked, with sincere astonishment.

"You'd be surprised, Mr. de Hartog," Mrs. Masters answered calmly, but enigmatically. "So my suggestion is: don't let's rush into anything. Let's give this matter some quiet, constructive thought. Have I made myself clear?"

All I could say was, "I suppose so." We parted with an oddly impersonal handshake. Outside sounded the frantic, undulating wail of an approaching ambulance.

4

WHEN I TOLD Marjorie about Mrs. Judd's suggestion, and the reactions of Mrs. Willoughby and Mrs. Masters, she said, "Of course you must call upon the Meeting! This is what Quakerism is supposed to be about! What good does it do us to sit there every Sunday morning, gazing at that wall, listening to the kids breaking up the second floor? It is time to find out if the gathering we are attending every Sunday morning is a Quaker Meeting or a club."

I could see her point. I only went to meeting for worship because I personally needed the weekly hour of stillness and contemplation, more than ever since I had started work inside the hospital. I had come to care less about the latecomers and the racket overhead because I had achieved a technique of withdrawal. But I sat there often with a secret yearning for the Meeting in Amsterdam.

"I'll call Priscilla," she said. "Maybe we can call an emergency meeting of the membership."

She telephoned Priscilla, who suggested that I write a letter, to be read out at the next meeting for business, that was due to take place in a week. The more formal we made this thing, she hinted, the better it would be, as the old guard would most likely be against it.

Even a small, harmless group like the Houston Meeting of the Religious Society of Friends had two opposing factions within its modest breast. One could be called conservative: it comprised the oldtime, weighty Friends who had been running the Meeting for so long, and were by now so set in their ways that anything suggestive of change seemed to them a threat to its very existence. The other faction, that might be called liberal, was made up of recent arrivals and the younger set, restless with the domination of the Meeting by the conservatives, who to them seemed egocentric and dictatorial.

The night of the monthly meeting for business, I presented to the clerk for inclusion in the agenda a letter, putting the case for our involvement with the charity hospital. There were nineteen members present in the home of the clerk, who was the leader of the conservative faction. Of the nineteen only three could be considered conservative; but, owing to the peculiar way Quakers have run their business for three centuries, those three could block any proposal, if they wanted to, as all decisions had to be made unanimously or postponed to a later meeting for business. There never was a vote; the clerk determined what he considered to be "the sense of the meeting" which, in practice, meant unanimity.

As the meeting proceeded, it began to appear that we would not get unanimity. The clerk, who had read my letter beforehand and had to present it for discussion as chairman of the meeting, tried to evade the issue by postponing it as long as possible. He read out all correspondence received during the past month, lengthily announced and annotated all meetings of other religious bodies to which Quakers were invited; when he started to read out loud a pamphlet that had already been mailed to us all it began to look as if this was a filibuster. One of the younger attenders, who could claim innocence, committed a breach of Quaker practice by butting in and suggesting that the letter about the charity hospital be read before the meeting broke, as it was about to do. Then the conflict came into the open.

Although the three conservatives could not deny that for members to work as nurses' aides in the charity hospital was a legitimate Quaker activity, they balked at the idea that anyone should become involved with this on Sunday mornings, as this posed a threat to our meeting for worship. Here was the chance the younger faction had been waiting for; at last they could state loud and clear what they thought about those meetings for worship. The discussion was heated, and harsh words were spoken. If the old guard thought it more Quakerly to sit staring at a blank wall in holy silence every Sunday than to go and give a drink of water to a patient parched with fever, that was their business; most of the others volunteered to take part in a training course for nurses' aides and orderlies, and to start work in the hospital, as a team, for at least four hours every Sunday morning.

There was a short resistance of reluctance and frustration by the three elderly conservatives; but finally they suggested that, although they were too old to be trained as orderlies or nurses' aides, they could maybe come in and visit patients to read the newspaper to them, or pray, or comb their hair. They suggested this, it turned out, because they had a compromise in mind: they proposed that our meetings for worship would be held in the hospital, instead of in the building of the Association of Churches, so those who worked on Sunday mornings need not forgo the communal period of silence. It was agreed that inquiries would be made as to whether there was a room available to us for that purpose. We agreed only as a gesture of appeasement toward those weighty Friends, so tenaciously clinging to ancient practice; we had no idea as yet how grateful we would be to them.

5

Authorized by the Meeting, I went to see the Administrator of the hospital, to inform him that Jefferson Davis had been made an official concern of the Houston Meeting of the Religious Society of Friends, and that thirteen people offered themselves for training as volunteer nurses' aides or orderlies, six of them men. It was the first time I had sat opposite the Administrator himself. I had occasionally seen him from a distance: a stocky man with glasses, who always seemed in a hurry to get away from something rather than on his way to something. From close quarters and in his own office, there could be no doubt that whatever else he might be he was a man of immense political acumen. He did not commit himself, nor the hospital, to anything. He listened courteously, commended us splendid people for our generous offer, said he would take it up with the Nursing Office and Mrs. Willoughby, and let us know when they had worked out a way to comply with our request. At the end of our amiable encounter, I left with a feeling of satisfaction; it occurred to me only later that, with the smiling casualness of the true expert, he had changed our offer into a request without my even noticing it.

After the Administrator, I went to see Mrs. Willoughby. I wanted to assure her that my going over her head had been a matter of protocol only. For once she listened to me attentively, but noncommittally. When I left her, I had the distinct impression that she did not believe me.

After seeing her, I went to the Nursing Office to inform Mrs. Masters that, much as I would have liked to discuss this with her first, the official nature of my mission had forced me to go directly to the administration. Mrs. Masters sat behind her desk in inscrutable silence, eyeless with the reflection of the window in her glasses. She too, though graciously attentive, gave me the impression that she did not believe me.

Only when I came out of the door of her office was the atmosphere of icy formality and suspicion dispelled, for I was waylaid by Mrs. Judd and her fellow supervisors. There were about half a dozen of them, gathered in an office across the hall, and I was received as if I were the leader of a football team that had just scored a victory for their school. I was completely baffled by their reception, for they could only have heard about this if they had the

Administrator's office wired for sound. The J.D. grapevine had its branches everywhere; they knew everything, including the number of proposed participants in the training course. Their enthusiasm filled me with hope for our success, something that my visits with the *état-major* had failed to do. Mrs. Judd cried triumphantly, "Even if they wanted to stop it now, I don't see how they could. We'll just train you in our own time, somehow, on the floors at dead of night, if necessary. Won't we, girls?"

The girls agreed, but I had the distinct impression that Mrs. Judd was the evangelist and they the congregation. A change had come over her, but it was only a change in intensity. She was the same I had known from the beginning, only more so. She seemed thinner, more tired, but also more serenely out of reach of the daily harassments of the hospital, the petty bureaucratic irritations, the broken equipment, the short-tempered doctors. I had several times in the recent past entered the little kitchen of Observation to find her drinking Metrecal. It had seemed crazy that she, thin enough to crawl through a needle's eye, should be drinking a food substitute, but it turned out she was supplementing her diet with it. She had to gain ten pounds somehow; it was so urgent that, she said with a smile, "I don't even care *where* I gain them." I was convinced that, if need be, she would train us at dead of night, on the floors and in Emergency, when the bureaucrats in the hospital were safely asleep at home. But I hoped it would not be necessary.

6

A FEW DAYS LATER I was called into the Administrator's office. Mrs. Willoughby was there, and so was Mrs. Masters. The Administrator informed me that the hospital was prepared to accept the group of volunteers who had offered themselves to be trained as nurses' aides and orderlies. It would be a sort of pilot program, and the administration had deemed it best, under the circumstances, to limit the first class of trainees to members of our group. He chose the word carefully, avoiding the word "congregation," but it was obvious that someone in the clouds of Mount Olympus had decided that Quakers could be trusted not to be "troublemakers." The Administrator suggested that the training program begin immediately after the first of the New Year; we should not tarry, as the hospital was due to move to its new quarters in the Medical Center during the month of February. It was the first time I had heard a date mentioned for this move; it had been postponed so many times in the past that nobody in the hospital believed in it any more.

As it was patently obvious that the supervisors of the nursing staff did not have the time to train volunteers, the administration had applied to the Red Cross, as the Red Cross had instructors available for just that purpose. One of their instructors would give the theoretical training, but the supervision of the clinical training would be in the hands of the hospital's supervisors. The course consisted of twenty hours theoretical and eighteen clinical, after which the candidates would receive a blue stripe on their caps to distinguish them from the other Women-in-Yellow who had no permission for patient contact. As it was said that the Red Cross would only train a group if it consisted of a minimum of twenty people, Mrs. Willoughby had selected a few reliable women from her own volunteers to supplement the fourteen of our group; fourteen, because Lucille had joined us. When asked what I thought of this, I replied that I was sure that I was speaking on behalf of my friends when I said that we would be delighted to share the course with anyone.

The Administrator rose to his feet. "I think this is an

excellent program," he said. "I have great hopes of its success. It seems to promise better than previous ones." At that, he shook me by the hand, smilingly.

So there had been previous programs. I had suspected this from a word here and there, overheard in the cafeteria and on the floors. I wondered what had happened to those other nurses' aides and orderlies. Where were they now? Why had their programs failed? Maybe we would find out ourselves in the weeks ahead.

After we left the Administrator's office I found, to my surprise, that the news had raced down the grapevine to Emergency already. Mrs. Judd awaited me, radiant, among the stretchers. Flushed with victory, she insisted we drink to our success. As some bumblebee in the bureaucratic hive had ordered the coffee urn removed from the kitchen in Observation, all we had left to drink to the future with was Metrecal.

CHAPTER 3

ON NEW YEAR'S EVE there turned up, in the
bloody ant heap of the Emergency Room, the alien
figure of a press photographer, taking pictures. Not
only was this against the sacrosanct rules of the house,
where no journalists or photographers were normally admitted, it seemed an unnecessarily callous thing to do to a
man mauled in a car wreck, to take a picture of his broken
body as it lay on a stretcher in the corridor. Dr. Miller
normally never threw his weight around, but this time, with
some heat, he asked the gentleman to leave. The photographer then produced a letter from the administration authorizing him to take photographs on all floors at all hours
from December 31 through the first week of January.

Dr. Miller, whose voice rose an octave under the stress
of emotion, cried that he did not care a hoot who wrote
that letter, these were his patients and it was his considered
opinion as their physician that to have their photographs
taken would needlessly aggravate their condition. So would
the gentleman be kind enough to get the—the blazes
out of here? All of us loved Dr. Miller dearly, and this
seemed an unsolicited chance to demonstrate our feelings.
The photographer suddenly found himself surrounded by
nurses, orderlies, a girl from the Utility Room and an X-

Ray technician, all of them eager to bounce him bodily into the street. Muttering an unintelligible protest, he strolled off and was not seen in Emergency again. We heard from the floors, later, that he had been roaming all through the building taking snapshots of the most extraordinary things, like a doctor examining a patient by flashlight, and mothers sleeping on the floor underneath their children's beds in Pediatrics.

A few days later the *Houston Press* started a series of articles that caused a sensation inside the hospital. The first article carried a banner headline across the front page, J.D. PATIENTS ARE DYING NEEDLESSLY BECAUSE THERE IS NOT ENOUGH, SAYS CHIEF OF STAFF. We read to our astonishment that Dr. Olsen, Dean of the School of Medicine of Baylor University, stated openly in the interview that recently a patient had suffocated because his tracheotomy tube had not been cleaned in time, owing to a critical lack of staff, so he had clearly died of neglect. This kind of language had never before been heard about the hospital, certainly not from inside its walls.

The headline would have caused a sensation in any city I knew; I found, to my incredulous amazement, that on the five front-page articles about the charity hospital Houston remained silent, although they were illustrated with photographs that would make anyone's hair stand on end, mentioned scenes of unbelievable neglect, and supplemented all this with statements from unimpeachable authorities that patients were dying needlessly because of the lack of nurses, equipment and money. Nobody cared; it was the most astounding demonstration of public indifference I had ever witnessed.

Everybody in the hospital had his own explanation for the phenomenon, but the only one who seemed to have a realistic point of view was Mrs. Kowalski. "What do you want?" she said with queenly disdain. "We all know that this hospital is a political football. People are just waiting to see what the paper has to say when it winds up its case. Then the cat is bound to come out of the bag." She turned out to be right. The series of emotional articles on the charity hospital, describing it as a place of shame, horror, neglect and indignity, ended with an editorial denouncing the county for not paying its share as compared to the city, which magnanimously carried more than its legally prescribed burden.

To the small group of freshmen volunteers training two nights a week for work in the hospital, all this seemed remote. We congregated in a class room in the nurses' building across the Emergency parking lot, a high cavernous room with schoolbenches and demonstration beds. One of the beds was occupied by a gruesomely realistic, life-sized doll with reversible joints and a detachable trach tube in its plaster throat, whom we learned to refer to by its traditional name of Mr. Chase.

Our instructor, Mrs. Bannerman, Director of Nursing Services with the Harris County chapter of the Red Cross, was a J.D. graduate of long standing and proof of the staunch, undying loyalty this peculiar hospital inspired. I took part in her classes, but as during school hours I also was supposed to be on duty in the Emergency Room I had to run out whenever an ambulance with howling siren came swerving into the parking lot to stop, growling, outside the Emergency entrance. She was a marvelous instructor, tough and thorough, with a dry Texan humor that only emerged as we came to know her better. In the beginning, I often had to shake my head regretfully when she asked, "Do you have this in the hospital?" referring to drawsheets on the beds, individual bedpans for each patient, wastebaskets by the bedside and the like. She frowned, as if she mistrusted my answers. One night she went on a tour of the hospital to see for herself and came back horrified at what she had found. From that moment on, she took a much more personal interest in the class, as if she were a refugee training us for an invasion of her enemy-occupied homeland. We gathered that, years ago, when she was a student nurse in this very hospital, things had been different, but we were not too much interested in the past. We were preoccupied with the future; the freshmen were overcome by apprehension as the day of their entry into the hospital for their clinical training drew near.

We were an odd group, I suppose, if looked at from the outside world. We had among us a professor of physics, a gas station attendant, an executive of an oil company, a schoolteacher, several housewives, a housemaid and a fashion consultant, but social and professional differences faded away the moment we entered the classroom, the girls in their yellow uniforms, the men in their whites. Despite the fact that most of us were Quakers belonging to the same Meeting, the others never felt like outsiders; I had never experienced such a feeling of fellowship since I had left naval college, thirty years before. The first Sunday morning that our group moved into the hospital for the clinical part of our training, Mrs. Judd was there to receive us and distribute us over the wards; we were working in pairs, each pair controlled by a supervisor, or at least that had been the idea. As it turned out, the supervisors, when faced with the pathetic wasteland of uncared-for patients on each floor, seemed to evaporate, for they rolled up their sleeves and went to work themselves.

On the whole, the head nurses on the floors were happy to have the volunteers; there was only one exception, a very young, very dour little nurse in Male Medicine called Miss Lucas. She did not seem to care for the intrusion of the swallowing, nervous amateurs in their badly fitting yellow uniforms; she stated perfunctorily that she did not need them, that she was perfectly capable of coping herself. It was a strange statement, because her floor was one of the worst. As far as I could ascertain, she was alone with one nurse's aide among sixty patients, several of whom were critical.

The reaction of each individual volunteer to the reality of J.D. was different. Some of them blossomed joyfully, started at one end of the ward to give the patients bed-baths, and worked their way toward the other without stopping. They shed around them the sunlight of their jolliness; the effect on the patients was instant and marked. Others among us had a harder time of it. One of our younger attenders, who had just arrived from the North and joined our training group when it was halfway through its theoretical schooling, had lost sight of his supervisor, wandered down a corridor, found an emaciated old man pitifully wailing in a soiled bed and had started to clean him up. He gave him a bedbath, made his bed, fed him milk; after he had worked three quarters of an hour in close proximity to the patient, his supervisor rushed past, spotted him in the little room and cried, "Will you come out of there at once! What do you mean, going in and helping a TB patient?"

"TB?" the young man asked.

"Did nobody tell you? Come out of there at once! It's contagious!" And she was gone.

So, it turned out at the coffee break, was he; without saying anything to anyone, he fled from the building, never to come back. I was sorry to have missed him; had I been able to get hold of him before he left I would have told him that in Emergency, by the time we discovered a man had a contagious disease, it was too late to do anything for those who had been in contact with him. Quite early on, I had asked Dr. Miller what to do about contamination; he had laughed and shrugged his shoulders and said, "Oh, every time one of them coughs at me or breathes in my face, I hope I'll be lucky once more and go and fortify myself with the pork chop and the blackeyed peas in the cafeteria." Mrs. Birdland had another form of psychological self-medication: "We're doing such Christian work down here," she said, "that I'm sure the good Lord has arranged for a special protection for us." What it all boiled down to was that, apart from having a regular check-up and an x-ray, there was nothing you could do.

Between the extremes of the jolly women and our young friend who was never seen again, each of the volunteers had his own personal reaction. We had arranged to meet for worship in the middle of the morning in a lecture room on the second floor, between the Nursing Office and the Operating Rooms. There, surrounded by a blackboard with mathematical formulas and charts of the internal organs of the human body, we put up a circle of chairs and sat down. We arrived singly and in pairs; after about ten minutes, we were all there, including Lucille. I was preoccupied when I sat down in the circle, thinking about our young friend who had fled and others who seemed to be having a hard time; but the moment I closed my eyes something unexpected happened. I was at once gathered in by what obviously was a communal sense of tranquillity, a stillness that I had never before experienced in meeting. It was, I felt sure, shared by all of us. I realized that this was what I had been searching for, hoping for when I had sat in our previous dreary meetings, isolated in glumness. Suddenly a voice among us spoke, softly and hesitatingly but in great anguish. It was one of our women. "I don't think I can go on with this," she said. "It is all so terrible, so ghastly. I am so clumsy at it, so bad. I wish I could go on, but I am afraid that I am totally unsuited for this work. I wish God would give me guidance."

After she had spoken, we sat in silence for a while, with that sense of peace and light growing among us; then another voice spoke, one of our men. "When I want to drive a nail into a wall," he said, "and I can't find a hammer, I use my shoe. I know a shoe is totally unsuited for the work I am trying to make it do, but it is all I have available. Maybe God has the same problem, sometimes. Maybe he uses us to drive in this nail for lack of a hammer. All we can do is trust Him, and hope that He won't hit His thumb."

I had never realized that you could laugh in meeting for worship, and this was the most luminous, the most radiant meeting I had ever attended. We rose with deep gratitude toward the old, weighty Friends who had insisted that we hold our meeting for worship inside the hospital. They had been right. After that meeting, none of us thought of giving up the work.

During the weeks that followed, we went to meeting inside the hospital every Sunday morning in the midst of our work. Every time that radiant, luminous stillness gathered us in. No one spoke any more; all those later meetings were completely silent. To the outsider we were just a circle of people, sitting in silence for half an hour and then getting up and dispersing. But the Houston Meeting, that once had been the dullest we knew, had become the most inspiring. It no longer mattered whether we met in a circle, facing a blank wall or standing in a row. It had nothing to do with seating arrangements or noisy kids upstairs. It had to do with the fact that, for a few moments of stillness, we returned together to the source of our faith in the midst of practice.

2

AT THE END OF OUR training period, the class was called together once more in the schoolroom in the nurses' building where Mrs. Willoughby, for the first time in a yellow uniform herself, handed out the blue stripes for the girls' caps, to distinguish them from the Women-in-Yellow who were not allowed patient contact. We were given our certificates by Mrs. Bannerman, and a speech by Mrs. Masters;

then we went together to the Pancake House next door to celebrate our promotion. We were all in high spirits and reminded each other over the waffles and maple syrup to tune in the next night to the local TV station for the crucial debate between the Mayor and the County Judge on the subject of the hospital.

As it turned out, we could have saved ourselves the trouble. The two gentlemen, solemnly taking turns under the chairmanship of a solemn banker, each proved irrefutably that the other was paying less than his share. At no point during the debate did either of the three men as much as hint at the circumstance that they were dealing with sick, destitute human beings. The debate dealt uniquely in abstractions; the only concrete information we culled from it was that the move to the new building was postponed for another month.

But what had looked remote and sounded abstract on television soon turned out to have been the prelude to something very real that struck at the very existence of J.D. A member of the City Council suggested a cut in the proposed budget of the charity hospital, for the avowed purpose of showing those highwaymen of the County Commissioners' Court that they must not think they were going to gyp the city forever. The cut was to be to the tune of two hundred thousand dollars, reducing the budget of the hospital, already grossly inadequate, to below the level of subsistence.

In the past, the patients had to go without meat on several occasions because the bills had not been paid and the butchers refused to deliver. From now on, the rumor went, the hospital diet would be meatless forever. There were many rumors, one more wild than the other. The new hospital building was already sold. The Federal Government was going to take over. Everybody would be fired and replaced by trusties from the prisons. The Administrator had resigned; Mrs. Masters had resigned; Mr. Taub was on his way to Washington to ask for help from Vice President Johnson. The rumors, by their very wildness, symptomized the wave of demoralization that washed over the hospital at the councilman's suggestion that the budget be cut. Only a few weeks before, the voters had approved a bond issue to finance the building of an air-conditioned stadium, the biggest in the world, to be covered with a plastic cupola of unprecedented daring, to be known as "The Domed Stadium," at an estimated cost of $31 million. As man is forever in need of symbols to express his emotions, the Domed Stadium was often mentioned in the hospital to point up the contrast. Another memorable contrast was that the zoo was air-conditioned, but the charity hospital was not.

I had no idea how deep the feeling of outrage ran among the hospital staff until, a couple of nights later, I came in on extra service to fill in for a member of our group who had been unable to make it that night. I was placed on little Miss Lucas' floor, Male Medicine.

I had not expected her to be there, as her usual shift was seven to three, but there she was, tiny and pugnacious, with the body of a girl and the face of a woman, heavily lined with exhaustion, dark rings of fatigue around her eyes. "Have you changed shifts?" I asked, to be pleasant.

She decided, grudgingly, to at least acknowledge my presence by saying, "No, I'm working sixteen hours today. Okay, you can start taking vital signs. Start over there in the corner—here is the sheet," and she slapped a clipboard in front of me on the desk.

As I started to take temperatures, blood pressures, pulse and respiration rates in the first little ward of four incoherent old men, I discovered Dr. Miller, doing an EKG on one of them.

"Oh, hello," he said. "Isn't it terrible news about the budget? It's a shame, isn't it? A real shame. Would you pass me the left leg, please? The cable with the red tab.

117

That's it. Thank you. How have you been?"

I told him I had been fine and asked how his wife was. He said she was very fine, thank you. Then we both went about our business.

It was sad business; Male Medicine was a sad floor. Most of the patients were old, and their prognosis hopeless. But saddest of all was their neglect; none of them had had any water since that morning; one patient had some left, but only because a cockroach had drowned in his pitcher. The beds were filthy; used bedpans were standing about, uncovered; when I went from one bed to the next, I had to pull my feet off the ground, for my shoes were stuck in a gluelike mixture of urine, spilled food and dextrose from leaking IV's that covered the floor. The stench in those little wards was foul; despair and torpitude hung like a mental smog in the motionless air. Several times when I tried to elevate a patient's head, I found the mechanism had broken down; some beds had their heads propped up with chairs and all of them were in a state of collapse, held together with surgical tape. It was only since the class had started its clinical training that I had come to know the other floors of the hospital well. Compared to them, the Emergency Room was clean and well equipped. Male Medicine seemed to be the worst; it was an unbelievably depressing place of neglect and hopelessness. Only a few of the old men had ever been bathed; unless some student nurses passed that way as part of their training, or unless they had relatives who came in to do it, they never would be. Relatives did most of the nursing on the floors; in that way the hospital reminded me of what I had heard of Dr. Schweitzer's hospital in Lambaréné. Here, too, patients never came alone if they could help it, but brought their families along to look after them. It was one way of solving the nursing problem, but those without relatives were out of luck.

When darkness fell and the lights went on, they made

little difference. Many of the bulbs were broken; the ones that were not were weak; the floor was steeped in gloom; the doctors did their examinations with flashlights. After nightfall, Dr. Miller was joined by a surgical resident whom I had known in Emergency. Someone had brought up some coffee and I was offered a cup by Dr. Miller as I came past the nurses' station. I joined them; of course, they were talking about the budget cut. I was not really listening; I was thinking about a patient I had found lying on a full bedpan. He must have lain on it a long time, and I could have sworn that I saw cockroaches scurry away as I uncovered him. But it probably had been my imagination; the light was very bad. Miss Lucas called me out of my brown study by asking, "And what is our humanist thinking about?"

"Cockroaches," I said.

"Ah!" she replied with mock conversational interest. "A fascinating subject. If you'd care to stay through the night, the cockroaches will become even more fascinating. Or have you already seen them attack the patients?"

"Pardon?"

"Didn't you know?" she asked, with a taut smile. "When the wards get really quiet at dead of night, they come out in search of food. That's when the cursing and the thrashing starts. Patients who can't defend themselves start to scream; the cockroaches try to get underneath their bandages; they go for the blood, you see."

"Come, come, Lucas," the young surgeon said. "You're mixing this place up with the Late Horror Show."

"Don't tell me it isn't true!" Miss Lucas exploded, with sudden, alarming violence. "How dare you sit there and joke about it! How dare you!" and her eyes filled with tears.

"Okay, okay, Lucas," he said, soothingly. "Anything you say, only don't bawl me out, do you hear? I'm sick enough of this place as it is. So don't let's start bawling one another out. Okay?"

But Miss Lucas obviously could no longer control herself; she was like a child rolling down a sand dune, incapable of stopping, gathering speed all the time. The words tumbled from her mouth, shrill, agonized, virulent, choking with despair and anger. It all came out, the whole jumbled, ghastly story of her work in the hospital. First in Pedi, from which she had fled because she could not stand the sight of dying children who needed major surgery to save their lives, which the doctors would not perform because it only made sense if intensive nursing care followed the operation, and there were not enough nurses to give it. She talked with fury and derision about the children's ward that lacked everything: diapers, safety pins, washcloths, gowns, but where a rich local lady had festooned the walls with a fortune in modern paintings as a gift for the children, to teach them beauty. Dr. Miller tried to soothe her by saying, "Well, after all, the woman did a generous thing after her own lights. I mean . . ."

But Miss Lucas would have none of it. She was as fond of Dr. Miller as the rest of us, but this time she tore into him viciously. She went on describing other wards where she had worked, scenes of horror and nightmare that, even taking into account her present overwrought state, conjured up unbelievable images.

"Talk about Sodom and Gomorrah!" she cried. "Here we are, in the richest country in the world, in Houston, its richest city, and look, just look around you! Look! I don't know what is the matter with this town, I don't know what is the matter with everybody, but I'm going to quit! I can't stand it any longer, I can't stand it; I'm going to quit, quit!" She grabbed a basin and a tube and started to go; then she turned, faced us once more, unforgettable little figure of faltering mercy against the backdrop of that black ward. "If there really is a God," she said, "something terrible is going to happen to this town. It must, for no God of love can tolerate this forever. And now they are going to cut the budget, I—I . . ." She looked about her, her face tragic with despair; then, shaking the basin she carried at the ceiling, she cried in a voice choked with tears, "God! If I had to give the earth an enema, I would put the tube in Houston!" Then she ran and vanished in the gloom.

We three men stood for a while in embarrassed silence, then the young surgeon laughed, a little self-consciously, and said, "That Lucas! Full of the old Nick."

"I can quite see her point," Dr. Miller said, in the high voice that I had come to recognize as a sign of tension. "I think, what with the Domed Stadium and all, that this town is not giving a very good impression. In the case of the hospital, I mean."

The surgeon shrugged his shoulders. "I don't know," he said. "I can't see too much wrong with this place. For my line of work it's a good enough training ground."

"Exactly!" Dr. Miller cried, trying to express something he could not find any words for. "Exactly! I mean: exactly."

"Heck, Ben," the other protested, "you have to learn your trade *some*where."

"Exactly!" Dr. Miller repeated. "Exactly, exactly!"

"Gosh, you and Lucas should join a barbershop quartet," the surgeon joked. "You guys in medicine get too involved with your patients, just like these emotional nurses. I don't know about the orderly here," he continued, "but he's probably here to write a book."

"Oh, I wish he would! I wish he would!" Dr. Miller cried with uncharacteristic vehemence. "I wish *somebody* would! I am sure this town is all right, I am sure people would help us out, if only they *knew!* But nobody knows, nobody knows, not even that councilor, or whatever he's called, that man who suggests the budget cut. I'm sure that if only he *knew* he wouldn't do it. He *couldn't* do it. You can't walk through this place and see the faces and suggest giving less money, instead of more. He just can't *know*."

"I'm sorry, Ben, but I don't agree with you there," the surgeon said firmly. "I appreciate that it affects you emotionally, and I'll confess that I'm not all that indifferent either, but let's face the facts. The *Houston Press* published five articles, complete with photographs, giving the full picture, and what was the result? That a guy on the City Council suggests a budget cut. After those articles, nobody could say he did not know."

"But maybe he didn't read them!" Dr. Miller said. "He can't have read them; if he'd read them . . ."

"Look," the surgeon interrupted. "By now, conditions in this joint have become such that nobody believes them any more when they see them described. They think that somebody is writing that kind of exaggerated stuff for political purposes. That's the real trouble with this hospital— you can't mention it anywhere in town, any place, any moment, without people thinking you have a political ax to grind. And there are so many lobbies and pressure groups messing around with this place, behind the scenes, trying to get a finger in the pie, that anything anybody says is contradicted by somebody else. So we might as well stay out of the mess, try to get as good a training as we can, and forget about this slaughterhouse as soon as possible."

"And the patients?" Dr. Miller asked. "Haven't we got a responsibility toward them?"

The resident shook his head. "Wake up, Ben," he said. "You're in Dixie, and this is a nigger hospital. You won't find anybody who's going to emote over them, not in this town," and he walked away.

Dr. Miller took off his glasses to rub his eyes. He looked surprisingly young without glasses; as if he had divined my thoughts, he put them back on. "I always meant to ask you," he said. "Are you indeed here to gather material for a book?"

"No," I answered.

"I didn't want to imply that I am questioning your motives," he added quickly. "I am here to gather material too, to perfect my knowledge of medicine. That does not imply that I am exploiting the suffering of the patients for my own ends; I shall be using it in the future, as a physician, to help others. Can't you use your material for the same purpose?"

"I'm afraid I don't understand."

"I mean—I know about the series in the *Press* and all that, but I mean: an essay in the paper, written by someone from the inside, someone who knows the hospital, might be of great help. You see what I mean?"

Somewhere in the darkness, a plaintive voice was calling, but he did not seem to notice. It was unlike him; I had never known him to ignore a patient's call. "It is obvious," he continued urgently, "that those articles in the *Press* had no effect because the man did not know what he was talking about. He had only been here a couple of nights, he had walked around and taken pictures, but to know what this place is really like you must have worked here, for months. You must have identified yourself completely with the hospital, the patients, the nurses, with us; how many people are there like that?"

"I believe someone is calling."

"Just a minute, just a minute," he said, lifting both hands, "just one more thing. None of us in here, doctor, nurse, nobody can write an article in the paper or a letter to the editor to warn the people that they cannot do this, that they must not cut the budget. We can't do it because we are paid employees. Your professional future would not be endangered by speaking up. Why don't you? For God's sake, why don't you?"

Miss Lucas came back from the darkness with a bedpan. "I hope you gentlemen are enjoying yourselves," she said. "We do our best to make you feel at home."

"I was trying to convince him that he should write about the hospital," Dr. Miller said.

Miss Lucas gave me a short, unloving look. "I'm sure he doesn't need convincing," she said acidly, then she handed me the bedpan. It was full. "Would you mind taking this to the Utility Room?"

As I took it, the feeble voice called again, and Dr. Miller scurried off into the darkness. But he had made me feel, for the first time, that the political shenanigans that determined the fate of the hospital concerned me personally. So far, seen from my lowly position on the nursing staff, the squabble between the city and the county about the budget had seemed remote.

3

LATER THAT EVENING, as I walked down the corridors on my way to OB to fetch Marjorie at the end of our shift, the patients on the benches in the corridors seemed to look up with a different gaze. They had always looked up at my white form passing in front of them with that mute plea for attention, for recognition of their human individuality; this time they sat there in an odd, anxious gloom, as if they were waiting to be vaccinated during an epidemic. There seemed to be an atmosphere of apprehension in the air, a sense of impending disaster. As I rapidly walked down the long straight corridor toward the doors that separated the maternity wing from the rest of the hospital, I sensed the massive fear of those about to be deprived of even the in-adequate impersonal care they were now receiving. For the first time I felt a personal anger toward the councilman who had suggested the budget cut; I felt like taking him on a tour of the hospital. I started to make a list of all the things I would show him, while I rode up in the elevator to the

Newborn Nursery. But when I entered the little waiting hall outside, I forgot about him.

It was baby-showing time; young fathers, their faces pressed against the glass partition as if they were gazing into an aquarium, saw their newborn sons or daughters for the first time. Two gowned and masked figures were hurrying to and fro with small squalling bundles of angry, fist-waving little old men. Most babies had their faces screwed up in miniature anger, eyes tightly closed, and were totally oblivious of the scratchings, drummings and rappings on the glass with which the fathers tried to attract their attention. It probably was a good thing they had their eyes closed; most of the men flattened their noses against the window in their eagerness to see; from the other side they must look like a glass tank full of drunks. Marjorie was one of the figures doing the showing; she came in, a baby in one arm, holding up a card with its name as if it were a prize in a raffle. The winner leaped up and down, banging the window with whoops of joy. I remembered her telling me that this was the nicest part of her work, once she had made the classical mistake of all novices and mixed up two babies called Luther, showing a thunderstruck German father, as his ash-blonde wife's newborn, a pitch-black son.

I had to wait for a quarter of an hour before the parade was over. After the last grinning father had left and the last grandmother had cast a critical look through the glass wall at the nurses, bedding down the babies with the speed and dexterity of professionals, Marjorie came out. "Sorry to have kept you waiting," she said, taking off her scrub gown, "but today they seem to be rushing us in platoons, the little blighters. Seventy-six, if you please, at the latest count. I may have to go back tonight. Do you mind?"

She had put that question so many times by now that she did not even wait for the answer. "What about the budget cut?" she asked. "Isn't it incredible? How can a man be so ignorant? I think it's time somebody told him off, somebody who knows what he is talking about."

There is a peculiar comfort in knowing someone so well that even the slightest effort at dissimulation becomes ludicrous. I took her arm and squeezed it and said, "All right, sweetie, I get the message. You are the second person tonight to tell me that my duty is to write a letter to the paper denouncing the councilman."

It seems to be a female characteristic to be outraged by the obvious. "What on earth do you mean?" she asked. "I didn't even . . ."

"The answer is no," I said. "Let's go and have a pancake, and I'll tell you why."

She replied, indignantly, "I don't want a pancake," and demonstratively pushed open the swing door herself, before I had a chance to do it for her.

When we sat eating our pancakes in the Pancake House, I told her the reasons why I would not write that letter to the newspapers. I wanted to remain part of the body of our group of volunteers, which imposed its own anonymity. Furthermore, the whole business about the budget, the city and the county, the hospital as a public institution, had political ramifications far beyond our grasp; as newcomers to this town we had no business getting mixed up in something we knew nothing about.

When she balked at the last argument, I told her what the young surgeon had said that night in Male Medicine. "This is a nigger hospital, and you are in Dixie. You won't find anybody to emote over them in this town."

"What nonsense!" she cried indignantly. "There are many white patients! And what a brutal, vicious thing to say!"

All I could answer was, "I know. But there you are."

When we had finished our pancakes and were waiting for our coffee, I bought a newspaper from the vending machine. On the back page of the last section we discovered a small item, stating that the move of Jefferson Davis

Hospital to its new quarters in the Medical Center had been indefinitely postponed, because it had been discovered that the architects had omitted to include a jail ward. A committee was to be appointed to find out who was to blame for the omission; after its findings had been made public, and appropriate action taken, a new date for the move would be set.

"Hello there," a flat voice said behind us.

It was Lucille, in uniform, a vision of snooty elegance; she must be the only Woman-in-Yellow who could make Mrs. Willoughby's missionary mother hubbard look like a frolic by Balmain. She sat down at our table and said, "Priscilla is coming; she's making a phone call. Don't look so surprised; we saw your car outside and decided we felt like having a pancake too." She picked up the menu and said casually, "Well, is he going to write that letter to the paper?"

Marjorie said, "Oh, shut up!" but it was too late.

"I see," I said. "I must confess you really had me there for a while. I did not suspect that this was a plot."

"Of course it is," Lucille said. "Aren't you flattered that we go to all this trouble to win you over? Talk about a prima donna." She put down the menu and said, "Well, I might as well put them on and have done with it. Apple pancakes for me. Hi, Priscilla! Come and join the fan club."

"I suppose you've been calling up members of the Meeting to tell them to put the pressure on?" I asked peevishly as Priscilla sat down opposite me. She looked very tired.

"That's right," she said. "You're going to be eldered if you don't get off your knees and wake up this town to whatever may be going on. Are you really going to have apple pancakes?"

"If it's a concern of the Meeting now," I said, "then why doesn't someone else write it, who does not feel the way I do?"

"How does he feel?" Priscilla asked Marjorie.

"Leave him alone," she said. "Let him work it out for himself."

But Priscilla was not listening. She looked at me musingly with her dark eyes; then she said, "I can see how you feel. As a matter of fact, that's what I told them. It's all very well for us to say, 'Let him write it, it's his profession,' but I don't think any of them realize."

"Realize what?" Lucille asked. "That we mustn't be indelicate and elbow ourselves in between him and his Muse? Sorry to talk about you as if you were not there," she added, to me, "but I've just come from Pedi, where I've been alone with one LVN since seven o'clock. When I came on I found a child in a wet gown lying in front of an open window, and all of them who could walk were running wild. There also were again no diapers, no . . . Heck, what am I telling you people for; it's the same old story. It just made me so fighting mad, that right now I feel that anyone who can get hold of a brickbat should throw it at the head of that pompous ass of a councilman in his padded chair. You Quakers go on agonizing over who is going to write what to the papers; I am going to browbeat all my friends, my neighbors, anybody I can get hold of to start a popular movement for the recall of both the City Council and the Commissioner's Court. I am sick of being represented by the Keystone Cops, fighting for their honor with the Three Stooges."

"I don't think they realize," Priscilla continued, laconically, "that you can't just write a letter and leave it at that."

"Why not?" Marjorie asked.

"You can't write a protest without ending up with some suggestion as to how to change the situation. By doing so, whether you like it or not, you put yourself up as a rallying point for people who feel the same way you do. The fact that he has the backing of the Meeting doesn't mean a thing; the moment he writes a letter to the newspapers, he's on his own and has to face the music. For all we know, we may be asking him to let your house be put to the torch, or have a bomb thrown through your window."

"Don't be silly!" Lucille said. "Just because he writes something critical of the hospital? In that case they would have blown the offices of the *Houston Press* sky high, after that series of articles."

"Everybody knew that the *Houston Press* was building up a political case," Priscilla said. "If he should write about the hospital, it would be different; it would be a voice crying for help from inside the ghetto. For make no mistake, that's what it is, Mrs. Willoughby notwithstanding."

I became conscious of Marjorie looking at me quizzically. It was her look that made me conscious of what I felt. She knew me sufficiently to guess my reaction to Priscilla's remark about the bomb. It was a streak in the Dutch national character that had nothing to do with reason, not even with great noble sentiment; but whenever anyone with whom we found ourselves at variance in a discussion of conscience or principle threatened to settle the argument by force, or hinted at such a solution, we immediately dug our heels in and became mulishly intractable. The mere idea that someone might try to shut me up by force, if I were to speak up on behalf of the people in the hospital, made me lose all sight of reason.

"I think we've all made our point by now," Marjorie said lightly. "What about some ice cream? I will, if someone joins me."

We all had ice cream, and the letter to the newspaper was not mentioned again until later that night, when Marjorie and I were home. She was preparing the meal; I sat back to front on a kitchen chair, watching her chop parsley to go on the potatoes, now bubbling on the stove. For some reason we had most of the crucial conversations of our married life in kitchens.

"I've been thinking of what Priscilla said tonight," I started.

"I knew you would," she said. "Frankly, I'm sorry she brought that bomb business up."

"Why? You think she exaggerated?"

"I think it has nothing to do with the issue."

"What *is* the issue? So many people have put their oar in by now that all I feel at the moment is how churlish it would be on my part to play hard to get any longer. Lucille had the right word for it. I feel like a prima donna who wants to be wooed some more before she bursts into song, as everybody knew she would to start with. It's embarrassing."

"I don't know about that," she said, chopping, "but I think the issue is very simple."

"All right: what is it?"

She scraped the parsley together into a little green heap on the board. "All that counts, I would say, is whether or not you think that you have done enough for the patients in Emergency. If you feel you have, that's all that matters. It's nobody's business but your own."

"Sweet of you to say so," I said. "But you know that isn't true. It isn't just *my* business; we're in this together. Priscilla's prediction may be overdramatic, but it is certain that if I should write about the hospital the way I feel I should write, I'll be spoiling for a fight. And you will be in it with me."

"I know," she said.

"And I don't know who the enemy will be, or how long drawn out it will be, or what it will mean to our lives. There is a difference between trying to help people lying in a present-day Black Hole of Calcutta by nursing them, or by challenging the powers who put them there."

"I know," she said.

"I don't have to tell you that I'd much rather stick with nursing. I am happy in my work, certainly since we are in

130

this as a Meeting. I'd hate to lose that sense of . . . I don't know. I don't know what to call it. All I know is that never before have I felt the way I do now, since we've all started working there together. It's very important to me."

"I know," she said. She went to get the potatoes off the stove, and drained them over the sink. As she was arranging them on the serving plate, she asked, "Why should there be a choice? Can't you do both?"

"I'm afraid not. I'm certain that if I were to write to the newspapers about the hospital it would mean the end of my work in the Emergency Room. You know they accepted us in the first place because they thought that, being Quakers, we would not be troublemakers. And you know as well as I do that I couldn't write about the hospital without, in one way or another, making trouble for somebody or other."

She sprinkled the parsley on the potatoes, thoughtfully, with the sense for decorative effect that women must have had since the dawn of time. She seemed at that moment to personify all that was precious to me and must be to every husband in the world: the gentleness, the simplicity, the fragile miracle of a woman making a home for the man she loves. It seemed to bring into focus, for one agonizing moment, all I would put into jeopardy if I were to challenge the unknown, dimly discerned demons in the dark night outside.

"Are you ready for supper?" She put the steaming dish on the table, brought out the others she had prepared from the oven; then we sat down opposite one another and bent our heads to say grace.

Outside, in the jungle of the town, the wail of an ambulance danced in the darkness.

4

LATER THAT NIGHT, in my study, I sat facing my type-writer, with in it the challenge of a blank page.

I had often sat like this, challenged to put into words what until that moment existed only in my mind, as a nebulous cloud of light and darkness, color, music, faces, bits of narrative, snatches of dialogue. I had never faced this challenge: to forgo my Punch and Judy show and rise as a man, to cry out to my fellow citizens in the market place. It would be a cry of anguish and warning, and whatever it might bring about, one thing seemed certain: it would involve me in a political issue, the ramifications of which I could only guess at. Priscilla had been right: I could not just cry out about the hospital and leave it at that; I must suggest a course of action for those who should feel compelled to do something.

What could they do? There were two immediate issues: the proposed budget cut had to be canceled, and the hospital had to move into the new building in the Medical Center as soon as possible. The recent indefinite postponement of the move on the pretext that someone had forgotten to put in a jail ward sounded ominous; the television debate and the suggested budget cut might well have been trial balloons, meant to gauge the extent of public apathy. A suggestion to sell the new facility was certain to find many adherents; the Harris County Medical Society had been against the location of the new hospital from the beginning, the private physicians in town had wanted to keep charity patients out of the Medical Center, and they were opposed to the staffing of the hospital by Baylor Medical School exclusively. Both Baptists and Roman Catholics were eager to acquire a hospital of their own denomination in the Medical Center; unless the citizenry manifested a sudden and dramatic interest in their charity hospital, old

J.D. might well remain the sole representative of the mercy of Houston. The degrading and unhygienic conditions under which patients were treated would deteriorate further; with almost mathematical certainty this would eventually lead to another major catastrophe like the staph infection a few years earlier. The new OB wing had been built in a startled reaction to the nationwide adverse publicity the staph epidemic had brought about; it stood to reason that Houston's reputation would suffer worse than before if the hospital were to burst into the headlines again because of a second calamity resulting from public indifference and neglect.

But how many men before me had tried to arouse the concern of the people of this city and failed? If even those five harrowing articles in the *Houston Press* had failed to arouse any interest, let alone concern, how could I possibly get through to them? What images could I use where the realism of photographs had failed? What opinion could I voice that would be more effective than sober statements by the Chief of Staff? The articles had been written by an obviously highly experienced reporter whose personal concern had been obvious. I had only one advantage over him: I had worked in the thick of it for eight months. Whatever the outcome, I knew that I would never be at peace with myself if I did not at least give it a try.

I put on my glasses, and with the two fingers of the amateur I pecked out a title: "Farewell to Old J.D."

5

When I came out of my study again, I saw it was two o'clock in the morning. I tiptoed to the bedroom; as I was about to open the door, I saw there was still a light on downstairs.

In the living room, I found Marjorie doing her embroidery. A tray with tea and sandwiches stood by her side.

"I heard you stop some time ago, so I made some tea," she said. "I expect it's rather cold by now. Let me make some fresh. Or would you like to read it to me first?"

"Let me read it," I said, "then we can talk it over while you make the tea."

I read the letter to her; she listened quietly, doing her embroidery. Halfway through, she put her embroidery down. When it was over, she looked at me and said, "I think it's one of the best things you've ever done."

I realized that she was deeply moved. I had not been aware of it for, while reading, I had been making mental notes of things I wanted to change.

"Why don't you read it over the phone to Priscilla?" she said. "Maybe I am prejudiced. Let's hear what she says."

"Do you realize what the time is?"

When I told her, she was genuinely surprised.

"What have you been doing all this time?" I asked.

"Nothing, really," she said. "I knew what you were doing when I heard the typewriter; I sat here wishing there was something I could do to help you, and finally I came up with the British answer to everything: I made you a cup of tea. Now I'd better go and make some fresh."

I took the tray from her and carried it to the kitchen and there we sat, waiting for the water to boil, eating sandwiches, talking about J.D. and our future, knowing that from now on the two would be inextricably intertwined.

6

THE NEXT MORNING, I read the letter to Priscilla over the phone. After I finished, she was silent for a while and then she said, with her usual laconic drawl, "Well, that about sums it up, I'd say. Are you going to have it published as is?"

"If they'll take it," I said.

"In that case, why don't you folks come over here and stay with us for the night?" she asked. "I mean, the night after it's in the paper. Mel and I would love to have you."

I laughed and said, "Thank you for the offer, but let's cross that bridge when we get to it. Personally, I think you are just feeling the need for drama."

"Well, what's wrong with that?" she said, affably. "Quakers are not a very exciting lot, although old Walter had a cross burned on his lawn, once. All he had done, dear man, was testify on behalf of the Meeting at a public hearing that Quakers were in favor of school integration."

"Anything you'd like added or changed?" I asked, daring her.

"Good heavens, no," she said. "This'll do fine as far as I'm concerned. I think I'll start bringing out a scratch pad myself. If you ask me, you'll be in need of some backing up, if they print it."

"I see no reason why they shouldn't. It's a public concern that should interest everybody in this town. I hope all three papers will print it."

"I'll be very happy if one paper prints it," Priscilla said. "Do you know anyone on the staff of any of them?"

I told her we knew a reporter on the *Chronicle.*

"Why don't you ask him?" she suggested. "I may be wrong, but I don't think any paper in this town is going to touch it with a barge pole."

"Why shouldn't they, for heaven's sake?"

"Well, you know, they all have some political affiliation or other, and you haven't left much of the Establishment standing in your article. But ask your newspaper friend and see."

It seemed a good idea, so I called my friend Gilles Swinkels at the *Chronicle.* He was a countryman of mine, journalist and photographer, who had been in this country for many years and knew the city intimately, although mainly its seamier side where the garish news was made, filling the newspapers with vivid reminders that, in a sense, this was still the Wild West. We had first met him when he came to interview us on our arrival in Houston, and we had become friends. He looked, at first sight, like a playboy in his thirties; but this appearance was highly deceptive. He was fast, tough, ruthless when it came to catching a scoop, and yet at the same time incorruptible to a point of recklessness. He was a typical answer to the question so often put to the Dutch: "Why, since the beginning of history, have half of the men of Holland left their country to roam all over the globe?" the answer being, "Because of the other half."

When I got him on the phone and told him what it was about, he said he would come at once; ten minutes later, the roar of his sports car came brawling down the quiet street and tires squealed as he swung into the drive.

He had always made a point of appearing unconcerned about anything except catching the competition napping; but after he had read the five pages of manuscript with an occasional snort, he said, "This is too important to run off with as a scoop, as I would like to do. Call the *Press* and the *Post*, tell them what you have here, and that you think it should come out in all the papers, which would be in the Sunday-morning edition. If they agree I can fix it that we do the same. It's the only edition we publish simultaneously. When can I have this typed up?"

"I'll do it now, if you like," Marjorie suggested.

"Fine," he said. "Go ahead. Make as many copies as you can. I'm going to take a couple of them with me if that's all right. In the meantime, you get on the phone to the *Press* and the *Post*." When I hesitated, he continued aggressively, "Listen. Get this into your head: the hospital is a political issue in this town. You make a plea for the human aspect of it, but surely you realize that even so you have a battle on your hands. You can't write stuff calling the City Council and the County Commissioners Court 'maggots' and telling Councilman Mann where to get off, unless you're ready to slug it out. Right? Okay. You know as well as I do that political fights are dirty fights. In this town, they are dirtier than anywhere else. You can get the humanitarian aspect of your appeal across only if you get it published in all three papers simultaneously. If you don't, if you let one paper run away with it, you will have chosen sides. Whatever you may say, however convincingly you may plead your case, you have become a pawn on the political chessboard. See what I mean? So, if you're on the level, if your only concern, really and truly, is for those people lying on those litters in that hellhole on Allen Parkway, then pick up that phone and call the other two."

I did, but the editors of the other two papers did not share Gilles's enthusiasm. The one of the *Press* thought they had flogged the hospital issue sufficiently with their five articles last January; the one of the *Post* advised me politely to send the letter via the usual channels; if it was really as fascinating as its author thought it to be it would undoubtedly arrive on his desk, when he would give it his full and immediate attention. When I told Gilles this, he said something in Dutch that was untranslatable and shook his head. "Pity. That guy is new in town. They brought him in from Austin just a few weeks ago. I doubt he even knows what hospital you were talking about. Well, so much for our concerted civic effort. The boys at the *Chronicle* will be delighted, but I think it's a damned, lousy shame."

When I told him that I thought he was making too much of it he flared like a rocket. "You don't know what the hell you're talking about!" he cried. "You don't know this town! You don't know these people! All you are is a babe in the woods! Now you've lost the *Post* it means that, given the rivalry between our two papers, whether it likes it or not the *Post* will have to pretend it has never heard of you, or of anything that may be going on as a result of this letter. Any reaction you may get to your letter the *Post* will ignore as the outcome of a gimmick by the *Chronicle* to sell more papers."

Marjorie, who had come down with two copies of the letter for him to take with him, overheard the end of this speech. After he had left and the snarl of his sports car's exhausts had roared off, scattering birds and squirrels, she asked, "What was all that about? Another lecture on local politics?"

"Of a sort," I answered. "I'm afraid the *Post* won't take the letter."

"Pity," she said, with equanimity. "What about the *Chronicle?* Does he think they'll want to print it?"

"He said he'd call me as soon as he had any news," I replied. "It's likely to take some time. What's for lunch?"

7

IT WAS PIZZA with mushrooms, and at the first bite the telephone rang. I said the Dutch word of which Gilles had reminded me; it was he. "You've got the chief, the editor of the editorial page and the religious editor all in a huddle," he said. "They haven't come up with anything yet, but I can smell excitement. I thought I'd let you know. I'll call again the moment there is another bulletin."

It was a shame, for I loved Marjorie's pizzas, but this one was wasted on me. By the time it was gone, I couldn't even remember eating it. As if he were watching us via closed-circuit television, the telephone rang again as I was bringing a cup of hot tea to my lips for a first sip; it crashed messily back on its saucer and I grabbed the phone off the hook.

"Yes?" I asked breathlessly.

"Oh, hello, Jan," a girl's voice said, like a model in *Harper's Bazaar* finally deigning to speak. "I heard from Priscilla that you've been marking the spot on your lawn where you want them to put the cross, and I thought . . ."

"One moment," I said. "Here's Marjorie." I handed her the phone. "It's Lucille," I said.

While she was talking, I sat mouthing words at her, and cutting my throat; so she said, "All right, Lucille, thanks very much. It's dear of you to suggest this. I'll let you know, but I'd better hang up now. Jan is waiting for a call from the paper and sits glowering at me, fit to be tied. I'll call you later. Bye."

"I'm sorry," I said. "What did she want?"

"Another invitation to spend the night," Marjorie answered calmly. "It looks as though we'll be able to sleep out on this for weeks."

"Ah, nonsense!" I cried. "All these girls . . ." The telephone rang again.

This time it was Gilles. "Okay," he said, "now hear this. They have come out of their huddle, and they are going to play this for all it is worth. They are cleaning out Sunday's editorial page for it, they are going to run it in full, with picture and editorial comment, but they have one condition—two conditions. First, you may send it to any other paper you like as long as you put a stop on it as follows. . . . Have you got a pencil? Okay. On every copy you send to other papers, you have to write the following: Quote. Embargo, underscore, not to be released until Sunday edition, comma, not, underscored, to be used Saturday. Unquote. And you sign it. Got that? Good. The other condition is that you agree to delete the words 'sadist' and 'sadism' on page two, paragraph one. They think you make your point sufficiently without accusing anybody of a sexual aberration. They also want to delete the words 'of a concentration camp' in the paragraph after that. Okay?"

"Yes, that's okay," I said.

"Roger. Now listen: this is going to be a real big splash and you never know in this town, some diehards may get riled up about it. As they will be printing your full name and address at the bottom in accordance with common practice, I think you had better be prepared for some fireworks on Saturday night. You know that the Sunday papers in this town hit the sidewalk around four on Saturday afternoon. If you like, I can fix you up with police protection."

"Don't be silly," I said, Little Boy on the Burning Deck. "We'll take care of it."

"Don't be a damned stubborn Dutchman," he said. "With your guts blown out, you wouldn't be any good to man or beast. Why risk it? You carry fire insurance too, don't you?"

I said, "No, I don't."

He said, "The hell with you," and hung up, before I had had a chance to explain to him that, as this was a rented house, we did not need fire insurance. Even so, he had given me food for thought.

When I mentioned it to Marjorie, ready to turn it into a terse commando briefing, full of stiff upper lips and understatements toneless with heroism, she said, "Let's see how things are when the time comes. Drink your tea while it's hot."

Glumly, I obeyed. She had reduced the whole thing to boys and Band-aids. She was a girl in a million. I should be ashamed of myself.

Ashamed . . . As I slowly sipped my tea, I sat musing about flaming crosses, bomb explosions, burning houses from which I would emerge disheveled and blackened by smoke, the blood of a flesh wound trickling down my shirt front, carrying the unconscious body of my child wife out onto the lawn with the magnolias. Cameras would be whirring; I could see the headlines, and the picture on the front page.

"Why does everybody assume that people are going to throw bombs?" Marjorie asked, interrupting the trailer for *Gone with the Wind*. "After I had read that letter, I felt like giving you a big hug and something warm for those children in Pediatrics. I think it's unfair to expect that kind of reaction from this city; so far, everybody I have met here has been decent and kind."

"What about J.D.?" I asked. "Would you call that decent and kind too?"

"The people in there, certainly," she answered. "They are not to blame for the chronic shortage of money. All it takes is for some sensible citizens to say, 'Let's forget about arguing who is to blame. Let's sit down together and work out what we are going to do about it.' Or just: Let's sit down together."

"With a cup of tea?" I suggested, ungallantly.

"That might not be a bad idea," she said. "Better than this stupid talk about people throwing bombs. A moment ago you sat there as if you were thinking about what to throw back."

"What on earth gave you that disgusting idea?" I asked, angrily.

"If I were a woman, living in this town, who did not know you and saw you sitting there like this after reading that letter, I—I would be disappointed."

Mortified, I protested, "But, sweetheart, you aren't just a woman in this town. You . . ."

"But I am!" she cried, with sudden exasperation. "That is just what I am! Or I wouldn't *be* here!"

Leaving me to work out that feminine argument, she poured me another cup of tea.

CHAPTER 4

THAT NEXT SATURDAY AFTERNOON was
hot and muggy. Short, fierce squalls lashed across
the city, gusts of wind whirled down the tree-lined
streets, driving in front of them spinning dervishes of dust,
litter and azalea petals.

I sat waiting in my car in the parking lot of Palm Center,
a new shopping plaza close to our old quarter with the
tree-lined streets, the nearest place to buy a paper. Gilles
had said the Sunday editions came out Saturday afternoon
at four, but when I got to the corner where the newsboys
would be I found I was too early. I sat in my car for half an
hour; then, just as a rain squall came sweeping across the
four-lane highway and the parking lot, a truck marked
HOUSTON CHRONICLE drew up at the corner, and a bundle of
papers was thrown onto the sidewalk. I got out of my car,
oblivious of the rain, and hurried toward it; it was tightly
tied with baling wire. I had to untwist that before I could
detach a copy; I put the money on top of the rest and ran
back through the rain.

Inside the car, the paper open on the steering wheel, I
hastily leafed my way through the huge Sunday edition until I got to the editorial page; then I gasped at what I saw: a
five-by-seven picture of a leering pixie, wrinkled like an

old apple; a dramatic headline *"What Is Mercy?"* followed by the announcement: *"This distinguished Dutch play-wright, currently teaching at the University of Houston, is a Quaker. For eight months, he has worked as a volunteer orderly in the Emergency Room of Jefferson Davis Hospital. Here is his moving letter, a plea to strip politics from the hospital."* The editorial column contained a paragraph headed, "A Human Cry," in which the editor urged the reader not to miss the letter opposite. It seemed unlikely that anyone could miss the Human Cry, to say nothing of the Crier, ogling them, pineapple size, from the corner. It took me a while to recover from the splash; then I began to feel distinctly uncomfortable. I realized that Gilles might well be right. I felt like a pawn in some vast political game. I felt as if a patrol of soldiers, armed to the teeth, was trying to cross the same bridge as I, behind my back. I began to read my letter with trepidation.

Not many will mourn the demise of Jefferson Davis Hospital, but it is a matter of conjecture among the staff how long it will take for the new hospital in the Medical Center to turn into the same pigsty filled with medieval horrors as Old J.D.

Guesses vary from three months to six; nobody believes that, under the present budget, it will take longer than six months for the cockroaches, the bugs and the filth to over-power the new building. And now Councilman Frank Mann has suggested that the budget be cut some more.

It seems that in this town, as in a convex mirror, are caught all the qualities and all the evils that went into the making of the frontier. Courage, initiative, informality, optimism and an immense vitality are, at first sight, the characteristics of Houston.

What does not meet the eye, what is hidden behind the new buildings, the prosperity, the pride, the politicians and their speeches, is the gimlet eye of greed, the selfishness of the gambler, the merciless drive of the prospector.

In no other town in the civilized world would two bodies of government dare to toy and dally with human suffering for quite so long and with quite such a callous lack of concern as the officials of the City of Houston and of Harris County have been allowed to do. For months, these elected representatives of the people of Greater Houston have been carrying on a feud as puerile as a pillow fight and as inhuman as a battle of snarling hyenas.

They even showed themselves on television "to put their case in front of the public"; but it became a spine-chilling demonstration of callousness, for not one of the participating politicians mentioned THE SICK. *They each had their own case to put in front of the public; none of them pleaded the case for humanity. It might have been a discussion about street lighting, or the water system, or . . . no, not the Domed Stadium.*

Now Councilman Mann suggests, blithely, that the budget of the charity hospital, already shamefully low, be cut again. And why? To show the county commissioners, that's why. We, the City Council, will no longer let ourselves be gyped and swindled by the county commissioners, and we will show 'em by cutting the budget of the charity hospital. If anyone cries "Shame!" we will point at the county commissioners; and then the commissioners will do what they have done all along: they will point back and stick out their tongues. And all this will be called: Government, Houston, 1963.

I would like to invite Councilman Mann to come with me for a tour of Jefferson Davis Hospital, before we say farewell to that monument of misery. I would like to show him the Middle Ages in his back yard, the pest house underneath the stunning dome of the stadium.

I would like to show him the Emergency Room, where I have worked as a volunteer orderly for eight months now: the hall with the stretchers that are never empty, the two dark wards in the back, where, because of the lack of staff, the sick, the drunk, the desperate and the dying are often ditched into the old sagging beds fully dressed, trousers soaked with urine.

I would like to show him the treatment rooms, where the wounds and lacerations of car wrecks, fights and abortive suicides are sutured and dressed, twenty-four hours a day, and where, on weekends and Christian holidays, the floors are slippery with blood and vomit and the doctors jostle each other, suturing, three to a room.

I would like to show him the rest of the hospital, lead him to the bedside of some of the patients; beds that can no longer be elevated because the mechanism has broken down, so they are propped up with chairs under the mattress and held together with surgical tape. I might have some difficulty guiding him to the next bed, as his feet might be stuck in the unspeakable goo of spilled food and filth that covers the floor; the housekeeping department is pitifully understaffed too.

I would show him the children's floor, where a fabulous extravagance in modern paintings (donated by a child-loving millionairess) is balanced by a lack of nurses, diapers, safety pins, the most elementary graces of civilized life. I would show him the truth about J.D., and make the word "charity" forever stick in his throat.

Houston, 1963, is a remnant of the Middle Ages as far as its charity hospital is concerned; and now yet another cut in its budget is proposed I can no longer remain silent, although, for obvious reasons, I would have preferred to continue my work there in appropriate anonymity.

If the cut goes into effect, Houston will soon boast the most expensive stadium and the most backward charity hospital in the civilized world. Then the new building, with all its gadgets, will be exactly what hospitals were in the Dark Ages: a place where the poor are dumped to die.

I, for one, would be ashamed to admit that I lived in

145

Houston, for this is no longer permissible in twentieth-century America. This is a desecration of everything this country stands for. This is to govern a modern metropolis with the mentality of a colony of maggots, feeding on the suppurating wounds of the illiterate, the damned.

The circumstance that this monument of misery has not turned into a chamber of horrors is due to a handful of doctors and nurses, who dispel the infernal darkness of J.D. with the light of their compassion. I have seen two successive lots of new interns arrive in Emergency at the beginning of their three months' stint of duty. All of them start as young, capable, civilized young men, ready to help and learn. None of them remain that way. They cannot, nobody can.

Under the onslaught of the huge, brute suffering of the poor, and faced with a scandalous lack of equipment, no man can remain blandly young, capable, civilized. It strips him of his veneer, and shows his true mettle, his quality as a human being.

Some of them, moved by mercy, acquire a quality of character that I can only describe as gruff and unsentimental saintliness. Others retract from the horrors they are confronted with and the indignities they are forced to commit into a carapace of noncommitment, and turn into medical mechanics, trying to repair the pieces of human machinery allotted to them with the shabby and inadequate tools at their disposal as best they can, in tight-lipped disregard for the individual humanity of the patients.

A minority, unaware of the seed of evil that slumbers in the same furrow of our souls as the miracle of mercy, turn into bullies, without ever becoming aware of the depth of their damnation. The curse of callousness that rests on old J.D., filtered down from the politicians who determine its fate, has as a result that a man is as free to acquire saintliness in its stinking catacombs as he is free to practice the reverse.

In J.D. there is no other authority governing behavior toward the helpless than each man's and each woman's personal maturity. In consequence, some of the staff would have graced that monument to human compassion: the Hôtel de Dieu in Paris, France's oldest public hospital, of which the entire nursing staff was wiped out five times in succession during the Great Plague of the thirteenth century; others would have felt more at home in the guards' barracks that surrounded it.

There is a Jewish legend about Thirty-six Just Men in each generation, who by their righteousness save the rest of mankind from the wrath of God. The crucial part of this legend is that none of them knows he—or she—is one of the thirty-six. In this generation, here in Houston, it may be you, it may be me, it may be Councilman Mann.

Maybe we should be grateful that he has had the courage to become the voice of the intolerable. For this can no longer be tolerated; the city and county officials must no longer be permitted to indulge in their game of pass-the-buck with the charity hospital for a pawn, and in doing so abuse, obscenely, the huge, prostrate body of the indigent sick of Houston.

Let us, before moving into the new building, say farewell to old J.D. and all it stands for. Let us wake up to the fact that we are a metropolis now, and that not only the eyes of Texas are upon us, or those of the United States, or even the world, but the eyes of God. They gaze at us from every litter carried into the dungeon that is our charity hospital.

The Director of Nurses said, a few months ago, with rueful resignation: "And to think that it would take so little to make this the finest hospital of its kind in the world. . . ." What she meant was not just money. It was mercy—the only hope for man's survival. You, who have now read this, are no longer innocent: You KNOW. And those who know, and turn away as if they did not notice, are guilty under the Highway Code, or any other code that ever made a society of men different from that of maggots. The charity hospital is YOUR *hospital—every insult to humanity, perpetrated or proposed within its walls, will from now on be committed in* YOUR *name.*

So first let us put a stop to Councilman Mann's shameless suggestion by letting the city and the county officials know, individually and by the voice of the social committees, civic groups, clubs and organizations of charity in this community, that the limit has been reached to which elected representatives of the people can go and still call themselves representative.

Next, let a committee of prominent citizens be formed, above political and religious distinctions, to explore the possibilities for a prompt and permanent removal of the charity hospital from the political arena. For I cannot believe that it is the will of the citizens of Houston that our growing Medical Center, rightly becoming famous all over the world, shall be allowed to harbor the cancerous sore of man's inhumanity to man.

This would irrevocably happen if the same politicians would be allowed to continue the same cynical game with the new hospital. It would turn the entire Medical Center, planned as Houston's glory, into Houston's shame.

Well, there it was—address, house number and all. It was out of my hands now, for better or for worse. I folded the paper slowly, and wiped the inside of the windshield and the windows that had steamed over as I sat reading in the rain. I realized that it was probably naïve to assume that a letter of this nature could be slipped in unnoticed, but this dramatic display seemed unnecessarily taunting. I reflected that, had a foreigner published this letter in Holland, meddling in local politics in these terms, I could think of several people who would have found that ample justification to grab him by the scruff of his neck and kick him

148

out of the country.

I drove slowly back home among the stream of traffic on the four-lane highway, branched off at the park, crossed the bayou and turned the corner of the tree-lined street where we lived. I saw Gilles's red sports car standing in our drive, an unexpectedly welcome sight. Until that moment, I had not realized that I was afraid.

I found him in the living room with Marjorie. They were drinking tea. It was too late in the day for tea; I realized that she was afraid too. Gilles had brought a stack of papers; she obviously had seen the page.

"Quite a display, isn't it?" I said.

"Rather," she replied.

Gilles said, "I told you they were going to play it for all it was worth. Those boys don't do anything by halves. All we can do now is lean back and enjoy it."

"You aren't by any chance referring to the Chinese proverb, are you, old man?" I asked, sounding for some reason like a Polish air ace I had known during the war who had talked in such terms as "wizard show."

"I still think you are nuts not to go away for the weekend," Gilles said. "Why take risks if it isn't necessary?"

I took a breath for one of those little speeches you know you are going to regret even before you start, but that somehow seem to have a life of their own, like stomach rumbles, when Marjorie, complete with teacup and saucer as if she were visiting the headmistress of her old school at Bishopshalt, said calmly, "It seems to me that, once one has gone in for this kind of performance, the least one can do is to stay on the stage and wait for either the boos or the applause. To run off into the wings at this point does not seem quite the ticket."

Gilles looked from her to me with perplexity. "Do you people talk that way when you're alone?" he asked.

"I think this is ridiculous!" Marjorie continued with beautifully mannered belligerence. "First everybody carries on at him to stand up and shout; the moment he does, you get into a flap and want to drag us into hiding. What do you take us for? Agitators, or something?"

"Listen, honey, I never . . ." Gilles started, but she did not notice.

"I am convinced that this town is full of people who will feel exactly the way he does, when they read that letter. I think that to go away now and leave the house dark would be an insult to those people, to every decent person in this town. I can't understand how you can even suggest that we would think of running for shelter. Shelter from what? Our own bad conscience?"

"Sweetie, you're talking to the wrong person," Gilles said appeasingly. "All I suggested . . ."

"And if there should be ruffians in this town who feel the urge to throw something at my husband, then I want to meet them and find out who they are. To run away from them before they have even shown their noses would be to admit that they have a power I respect."

Gilles got up, and I could not blame him. He was not in love with this girl; all he could see was a preposterously British young woman, straight from the *Tatler*, haranguing him as if he were a crowd and she herself chained to the gates of Parliament, a latter-day Mrs. Pankhurst.

"Why don't you write all this on the back of a piece of wallpaper and nail it to the tree out there?" he suggested. "Then they would at least know *why* you are sitting here, ready to bat their bomb with a teacup."

"Oh, piffle!" she cried and he left, laughing.

I saw him to his car; he started the engine and said, over the muffled grumble of the exhausts, "What's the matter with her? Why won't she see reason?"

I said, "You mustn't mind. She just feels strongly that we should—well—stick around. To her it is more important, at the moment, than reason. You know women."

He grunted. Then he said, "Look, I talked this over with

a guy at the paper who knows this town, really knows it. He was born here, and his beat is local politics. He says you'll have against you the River Oaks rich, and the ultra right-wingers; but they won't take to violence. It is the poor whites that may. You know: the T-shirt-and-side-burns-set in the old jalopies, who do the shooting and the bombing all over the South. To them, J.D. is a place they love, a place they can look down on, for that's where the poor niggers go: their niggers. Their reasoning is that what they want to do with their niggers is their business; any foreigner—if he comes from the North or from over-seas makes no difference—who messes with 'their' niggers is going to be taught a lesson. There has been so much vio-lence lately in the South that they are beginning to feel left out of it. So they may jump at this chance to have some fun of their own. This is what the man told me, and I felt you should know it. Okay?" He slipped the clutch into gear. "Okay. So: why don't you take her out to dinner to-night? And after that the movies, and maybe a night club? Seems she needs some diversion."

I said insincerely, "That's a good idea. Thanks." He backed out, blasted off, roared down the street and was gone.

As I came in, Marjorie was reading the paper. I poured myself some tea, gazed at the expanse of newsprint behind which she was hiding and said, "I never heard you say 'piffle' before."

She muttered something behind the paper.

"Pardon?"

She lowered the paper. "I said you should have heard what I did *not* say." She retired behind the paper again.

I felt restless and found myself gazing at the window un-intentionally at frequent intervals, so I said, "I think I'll rake those leaves off the lawn. This seems a good occasion."

Without lowering the paper she said, still in that tone of a girl announcer in London's Paddington Station, "If you

151

feel in need of exercise, why don't you go and put up the laundry line in the back yard that you promised to put up three months ago?"

"You don't mean that, under the circumstances, you'd rather I worked in the back yard than on the front lawn, do you?"

"Huh?" She lowered the paper and looked at me with a frown, as if I kept her from reading. She looked so unconvincing that I grinned at her and she quickly lifted the paper again.

"You do whatever you like, dear," she said behind it.

Normally, I would have dived straight through the paper and let the devil take the hindmost, but I was beginning to feel the symptoms of claustrophobia. I felt irresistibly drawn toward that front lawn, so I went out to the garage, got an unsuitable rake and started to make ritual movements with it on the front lawn. The dead leaves, hard and brittle after a long winter, jumped away from it like tiddlywinks; all it did was pull out tufts of grass that were making a gallant effort to grow. I saw, with a sense of relief, several of my neighbors, mostly University professors like me, busy with various horticultural projects on their front lawns. Some were digging with brand-new spades that still seemed to have Christmas wishes taped to their handles; others were snipping away at mangy hedges with vicious-sounding shears. Across the road, a colleague with whom I had a waving acquaintance was planting what looked like a trussed dwarf magnolia; he had already dug a hole to put it in and was now concocting a mixture in a wheelbarrow from a bag of peat moss and another bag with the legend REAL DEODORIZED COW MANURE which I had noticed on sale in a gas station at the entrance to the stockyards nearby.

The squalls obviously had blown over; it promised to be a perfect evening, fragrant and warm. I felt like one waking up from a bizarre and slightly idiotic dream. To think of any violence in reaction to my letter in the paper in this setting suddenly seemed ludicrous. I decided to stop depilating the lawn and to cross the road for a neighborly chat. Maybe I could help him mix his moss with the right quantities of deodorized cow manure; the way he agonized over spoonfuls seemed to indicate that it was a critical mixture. I was just about to step off the lawn into the street when I saw an old, dull gray Chevrolet with a divided windshield drive past at a crawl. I waited for it to pass; as I looked up I noticed the driver peering at the house numbers on our side of the street. He was a youngish man with long sideburns, wearing a torn T-shirt. In the back, I discerned a hatchet-faced old woman. When he spotted our number, the driver turned round and said something at which the old woman wound down her window. They peered at me intently as they drove by. There was something about that old car that gave me gooseflesh. I knew it was nonsense and I cursed myself for it, but I picked up my rake, put it back in the garage, entered the house through the kitchen, went up to my study, and there I stood, peering through the curtains, watching the road.

Sure enough: shortly afterward there it was again, the same dull gray Chevrolet with the man with the sideburns at the wheel and the old harridan in the back. Again they were peering intently at the house. He was talking over his shoulder. I decided that if I saw them a third time I would go down and get Marjorie out of that sitting room with its big windows overlooking the lawn. It was all very well to sit it out, but we could just as well sit it out in the back of the house. Even so, something inside me knew it was not true, knew it was all nonsense, that I was exaggerating shamelessly, that I had let myself be influenced by panic mongers. This was not Birmingham, Alabama; it was not even New Orleans, Louisiana; this was Houston, Texas, capital of the Space Age. Even without the Space Age, it somehow did not tie in with the character of the town as I had gauged it during the months that I had lived here. It might be a wild town, it might be brazen, it might be a haven for all sorts of hate groups referred to as the lunatic fringe; it was not a town where red-necked ruffians threw bombs at Negro churches. People here shot one another for the flimsiest of reasons; in the Emergency Room, I had seen victims hit by bird shot, slugs from pistols, .22 rifles, even antique muskets for reasons varying from throwing dirt onto their neighbors' lawn, coveting his wife or saying things that in other towns would have caused nothing more violent than a raised eyebrow. In one month more murders were committed in Houston than in the whole of Holland during one year; yet, for reasons that I could not define, this was not a town where people threw bombs at political . . . Then I saw the car come crawling round the corner once more.

I ran downstairs; Marjorie was just taking the tea tray to the kitchen.

"What's the matter with you?" she asked as she saw me come stumbling down the stairs.

"There's a car passing in front of the house for the third time," I said. "Look! There it is!"

Our front door was glass-paneled; I took her by the arm and guided her to look. We peered through the door, just as the car drew level with our lawn. I saw the driver, I saw the back window and noticed it was open; then, suddenly, I saw a bare arm jut out and something wrapped in brown paper twirled through the air as it was hurled at the house. Luckily I had her by the arm; I yanked her aside, we hit the floor together just as the deafening crash exploded in our ears.

I don't know how long we lay there, motionless; then her calm voice said, "Well, that settles it. Now we must have the carpet shampooed."

She looked at the tea tray, which had spilled its contents all over the hall; the pot had emptied on the carpet, mak-

154

ing a large, dark patch. The front door, which I had expected to be hanging loose on its hinges, jagged and splintered, had nothing wrong with it. Sitting up, I peered through one of the glass panels and saw the brown parcel lying on the lawn. It obviously had not exploded. The deafening explosion had been the tea tray hitting the floor.

Somewhat sheepishly, I helped her collect the pieces and dropped them, tinkling, on the tray. Then, as she went to get some paper toweling to try to do something about the tea stain, I opened the door and went to have a look at the parcel.

Despite the fact that it looked like all brown paper parcels containing bombs that I had ever seen on television and in the movies, I felt acutely ashamed of myself until I noticed something strange. At first I could not define what it was; but as I looked round, I suddenly realized that the street was deserted. There was nobody left on any of the lawns; the wheelbarrow with the moss and the cow manure stood idly across the road, by the side of the hole with the leaning tree in it, still trussed into a bundle. Maybe they had all gone in for tea; even so, their sudden absence gave me a shiver of an insidious, creepy fear.

I realized that to stand on a lawn, six feet away from a brown paper parcel and gazing anxiously about me, was not a position I cared to maintain indefinitely. I went to the parcel, saw my name and address written on it in an unscholarly hand; after a short hesitation I picked it up, carried it up the drive and into the back garden.

"What is it?" Marjorie called from the kitchen window.

"I don't know," I answered. "I'll open it in a minute. I need some scissors." I went into the house, got the fire tongs and a poker from the hearth, and went out again into the garden through the glass doors of the den.

Standing at a safe distance from the parcel with my tongs and poker, I suddenly felt angry. It was that mulish Dutch anger again, that had never in my life done me any good. I threw the ludicrous tools of the coward down in the grass with that Dutch expletive, then I went to open the parcel.

"Wait!" Marjorie called from the kitchen with a voice that suddenly had lost all Britishness. "I'm coming . . . !"

It was a moving gesture; as she came running out I realized that she did not want me to know why, for she brought something from the kitchen drawer to cut the string with. The only trouble was that what she had brought was a pizza cutter, a handle with a little serrated wheel. That took care of my anger. I did not know what to say, took the pizza cutter and tried to cut the twine. It took some doing; then it snapped. She put her arm through mine as I opened the paper.

Inside was a box, a soft cardboard box, taped shut with the type of brown paper tape found on store counters. The pizza cutter worked fine on that. I opened the lid; the first thing we saw was a carton with twelve safety pins. They were peculiar pins with plastic heads. Underneath I found a package in cellophane with the legend BABY'S DELIGHT, TWELVE HI-QUALITY HI-ABSORBENT ALL COTTON DIAPERS, STERILIZED FOR YOUR HEIR'S PROTECTION. As I lifted the package out of the box, I found at the bottom a small stack of children's T-shirts with the prices still attached, and a note that said, in printed handwriting, "*Hope you can use this for those sick kids. There is more where this came from. I will talk to my neighbors and I am sure. God bless you and keep it up.*" There was no signature. The T-shirts, as I took them out one by one, turned out to be very small, with animals on them. The last one had Mickey Mouse on it and the legend HERE COMES THE MIGHTY MOUSE. I turned it round and found, printed on the back, HERE GOES THE MIGHTY MOUSE.

Then Marjorie burst into tears. She cried so uncontrollably that she had to rest her head on my shoulder. As I stood there, my arms around her, gently stroking her hair, I felt very grateful that she had suddenly gone feminine and helpless. For, had I not stood there with her sobbing on my shoulder, I would have looked very, very silly.

2

EVEN SO, we had a restless night. Each of us woke up many times thinking we heard steps in the garden, laughter, surreptitious scrapings, the clanking of metal. Dogs started to bark wildly at odd hours all through the night; only when toward daybreak gray light filtered through the Venetian blinds did we sleep solidly for a few hours.

The morning was sunny and tranquil. The Sunday papers lay on our lawn; we read them at breakfast, studiously avoiding the editorial page of the *Houston Chronicle*. At half past ten we went to meeting for worship.

Since the completion of the training program, the Quakers no longer congregated inside the hospital; most of us now served on other days. We had gone back to the room in the building of the Association of Churches, but the spirit of those Sunday mornings in the hospital had followed us back into the old quarters, which had once seemed so depressing.

As we came in, a small number of people were already there, sitting quietly; as the room filled up during the next ten minutes, we noticed many uniforms, despite the fact that officially only four of us now worked on Sunday mornings. The others must be putting in extra hours.

It was a quiet meeting. Of late, we had had more vocal ministry than before; it seemed as if the concern about the hospital stimulated others. People had got up in meeting to talk about visiting prisoners in jail, about collecting blankets for refugees in Algeria. We had suddenly realized that we were surrounded by a host of pressing claims, in our new awareness of our neighbors in this world. But that

Sunday nobody spoke. There was a hesitancy in the air, a silence that was not tranquillity. Maybe it was just us, but I could not center down, neither could Marjorie, as I found out afterward.

When the meeting broke, it turned out that only a few people had read the letter in the paper; most of them had either come from the hospital or got out of bed late and hurried to meeting. Those who had, said they thought it was a fine letter; but there was a distinct lack of enthusiasm, almost reticence. I thought I understood why; if I had still been working merely as an orderly in the Emergency Room, all my attention, all my concern would be concentrated on the patients in my care, and I would have resented that letter for its dramatic, jarring alarm. The disaster syndrome seeped into the subconscious unnoticed, like water; the new nurses' aides and orderlies, irresistibly drawn toward the hospital at all times, going there for extra service every hour they could spare, felt threatened by this sudden publicity that, whether they liked it or not, put the spotlight on all of us.

When we arrived home, the telephone was ringing as we came in. I hurried to pick it up; it was Western Union, reading out a telegram. It was a long telegram endorsing my letter to the paper, offering support, asking what the next step would be; it was signed by a prominent local lawyer. I scribbled it down as the operator read it out; I was just reading it back to Marjorie when we heard a sound that triggered an instant alarm.

Outside, a car had stopped with squealing tires. We ran to the window, saw an old automobile crazily parked in front of the house, its door open; across the lawn the figure of a man staggered toward us, both hands on his head, obviously in blind panic. He looked as if someone had hit him over the head with a bottle; I recognized him as an actor taking part in a show my students and I were putting on at the University of Houston. He did not belong to the University, but had generously contributed his time and talent to act a part for which we had no student actor and for which he was indeed ideal.

We hurriedly opened the door and he came staggering in, his huge comic's eyes bulging with fright, his face a mask of terror.

"Bill! What happened?" I cried.

"I read . . . I read you . . . you people work in the hospital . . . in the Emergency Room. . . ."

"Yes, yes!" I cried. "What's the matter?"

"Thank God," he sighed, and it looked as if he were about to faint. "Help me, I'm wounded on the head. . . ."

I took his hands away and Marjorie inspected his scalp. There was nothing to be seen.

"Who did it?" we asked.

He looked at us as in a dream, and whispered, "A bird."

Marjorie gave me a calm level look, "I'll get some anti-septic," she said, and went upstairs.

When she came back we dabbed our actor's scalp with Listerine and he related, incoherent with emotion, what had happened. He had understood there was to be a re-hearsal this morning, so he had gone to the campus theatre, found nobody, felt angry at having been made to get up at such an ungodly hour for nothing, and shouted, "Hello there . . . ! Where is everybody?" or something. The an-swer had been a small squeak from the shrubs.

He had called again, and again heard that squeak. He had gone to look and found a small bird that could not fly, a woodpecker or something, and as he bent over it a mon-ster had suddenly come swooping down from the sky and pecked him on the top of his head. It must have been the beast's mother or, in any case, a close relation. Because he had read in this morning's *Chronicle* that I worked in the Emergency Room, he had stumbled to his car, one hand on his head, driving with the other, and rushed to our house. Now what was going to happen to him? Was it true that birds' beaks were poisonous? Would it have to be cauterized, or something? We reassured him that, as the skin was not broken, there was no risk of infection.

In the midst of this, Lucille arrived on her way to the hospital, where she was due to work that afternoon on the children's floor; she had come to collect the parcel with the diapers. Finding himself surrounded by three nurses, our friend's apprehension gradually subsided, and he left relieved, with a new lease on life.

"Well," Lucille said, after the patient had driven off, his head doused with disinfectant, "it seems this episode is running true to form, isn't it?"

"What do you mean?" I asked. "What form?"

She smiled superciliously. "Anything to do with local politics in this town instantly turns into slapstick comedy. It looks as if the gods refuse to take Houston seriously. We all hoped for a moment that the poltergeists would be exorcised some months ago, when County Judge Bill Elliott got himself a defrocked Episcopalian priest for a spiritual adviser, to hover in the shadows behind his chair, but it doesn't seem to have worked. You have the diapers there?"

"Surely there is more to it than that," I started.

Lucille contemplated me coolly, looking exquisite and infuriating, then she modeled her yellow uniform down the living room to light a cigarette at the mantelpiece. It made her look even more outrageous, a nun with make-up, smoking. "Look at yourself," she said. "You write an article in the paper that would move a heart of stone, and what happens? A guy comes zig-zagging down the street in a Model T, hops across the lawn with his hands on his head crying, 'Help!' and why? Because he's been pecked on the head by a bird. All he has remembered from your heartbreaking article is that you work in the Emergency Room. And so it goes, here in Houston."

"But look at the parcel thrown on the lawn!" Marjorie said. "I would say . . ."

"Yes, look at it," Lucille interrupted, with maddening composure. "A sinister car creeps past three times, throws a bomb, you two take a swan dive with a tea tray and what's inside? Diapers, and a T-shirt saying, 'Here comes the Mighty Mouse.' You folks may have a different sense of humor, but you'll have to admit that the incident would not quite fit into the biography of Dr. Schweitzer or Florence Nightingale."

"Have you had any reactions yet from anyone else?" I asked.

"A few," Lucille answered, evasively it seemed.

"What did they say?"

She stubbed out her cigarette in the ashtray on the coffee-table. I always knew Lucille had been there when, coming back from the University or the hospital, I found the ashtrays full of cigarettes that had barely been smoked. "Frankly, nothing," she answered, suddenly serious. "A lot of my neighbors take the *Chronicle*, they know I work in the hospital because they see me parade in this outfit in front of the house, as unobtrusively as a canary, yet nobody mentioned it when I said hello to them this morning, on my way here. I made a point of doing so because I wanted to know what their reaction was. Well, the answer is there was none. Yet I knew they had read it, I could tell. They looked—how shall I say—cagy."

After she had left for the hospital with the parcel, we felt a little deflated, and went for a walk in the park. We strolled along the banks of the bayou, looked at people picnicking, children romping in the grass among the trees with ecstatic dogs racing around them in skidding circles. We tried to feed peanuts to squirrels and sat watching a turtle, as it tried to edge its way up the sloping concrete banks of the river, blinding white in the sun. It was very hot; cheers and laughter and thumping splashes sounded from behind the screened fence of the swimming pool; a gaily colored kite danced high above the trees in the dazzling blue sky, among the small white clouds of spring on the prairie.

When we returned home, I looked in the mailbox to see if maybe someone had put a letter there in our absence, but no one had. The house was exactly as we had left it, exactly as it always was every Sunday afternoon. We played Scrabble and then we read the rest of the papers; we had a light meal in the garden at dusk and listened to the mocking birds starting their courtship in the treetops and on the telephone wires. Then we went indoors and watched television and, when we found it boring, we did some more reading. And all that time, all that endless, endless time, nothing happened, nobody called, no letters arrived, nothing was thrown onto our lawn. It was just a Sunday afternoon, in spring, in Houston.

3

THE NEXT MORNING I went to the hospital with a feeling of apprehension. I did not know what to expect; after I had been there an hour, I had to come to the conclusion that I should have expected nothing. Nobody mentioned the article, it seemed nobody had even read it. Then, in the middle of the morning, Mrs. Kowalski turned up. I had thought she was off for the day, but she came back from a lecture given for head nurses and supervisors by a mortician on how to show respect for the dead. The moment she saw me, she said with an Amazon's delight in pugilistics, "Socko, Mr. de Hartog! Splendid! My husband whooped when he read it. You've got yourself a fan there."

"What about yourself, Mrs. Kowalski?" I asked, feeling impertinent.

She looked at me; her expression changed as she related

her abstract enjoyment of fisticuffs to the reality of our Emergency Room. Then she said calmly, "I don't think it will make any difference, frankly. You cannot change this place; it changes *you*." Then she pulled some thumbtacks out of the cork announcement board over the doctors' desk and started to pin up a newspaper cutting that she took out of her pocket. I saw to my surprise that it was my letter.

"Let's give those handsome young butchers something to talk about," she said. "Now, would you mind taking the specimen box up to Three, and this time not forget to sign the register at the blood lab? Thank you."

As the day went on, more and more people read the cutting over the doctor's desk, and the reactions started. I was complimented by unexpected people, like two surgical interns who, until then, had never so much as acknowledged my existence. The two intimidating women behind the admissions desk were voluble in their approval, saying it had been high time somebody opened his mouth. Mrs. Birdland, who had recently been rehired, seemed self-conscious, almost embarrassed, as if she liked me personally but was unhappy about the letter. Maybe it was because all she could see was the threat to the status quo, an outside interference with her unobtrusive preoccupation with the patients. John Rivers, the orderly, liked the letter, mainly because he liked watching people's reactions to it as they stood reading, but he summed up what turned out to be the general feeling of the nursing staff when he said, "Fine, fine, you knock the bejesus out of those politicians. But do not expect us to help; they can't fire you, but they can fire us."

Toward evening, the hospital was buzzing with the controversy; as usual, this seemed to spawn rumors. Mrs. Willoughby, I heard, was indignant, Mrs. Masters noncommittal; most of the doctors approved of what I had said, only a few surgeons disagreed, as they could not see anything wrong with a hospital that provided them with so many interesting cases, and never interfered with OR.

When I came home that evening, there still were no letters. A few friends had telephoned, Marjorie said, but nobody unexpected. I called the paper and heard from Gilles that they had received no letters either; just one telegram, that turned out to be from the same lawyer who had telegraphed me the day before. Perhaps it was too soon to tell; but it began to look as if the whole thing had fizzled out before it had even started. At least, it gave us a good night's sleep, the deep, dreamless sleep of the deflated.

4

THEN, THAT TUESDAY, everything changed. The first mail brought eighteen letters; we sat on the floor, opening them, reading bits of them aloud to each other, like children opening presents at Christmas. The letters all said, "What can we do? Now that you've made the breach, let's do something." There was not one letter that sounded crazy or hateful. They were all from people deeply concerned with the hospital. Most of them said they had known about it but felt helpless; obviously here was the time and the chance to do something about it. Where could they go? What could they do?

I called the *Chronicle*. They had received more letters and were printing nine of them that night on their editorial page. If the selection they published was representative, they too had received only constructive, reasonable letters. Again all of them asked, "What do we do now?" The editor of the editorial page, Bob Cochran, invited me to come and meet him in his office; he would take me to a place where he thought we might find a group of prominent citizens to make up the panel I had suggested.

I had never quite realized how big the town was until I saw the offices of that paper, one of the three serving the town. It was bigger than any newspaper office I had known in Holland or even Paris, a huge beehive full of characters from Ben Hecht and Charles MacArthur's *The Front Page*, scores of men in shirt sleeves, sitting at old-fashioned desks littered with paper, ashtrays, typewriters and telephones. The noise in those halls seemed prohibitive to any concentrated thinking; the headquarters of the editorial page, although somewhat more luxurious, were no better as far as the din was concerned.

I took an instant liking to Bob Cochran, a youthful, intense man who seemed to personify that peculiar mixture of a crime reporter's ruthlessness and a passionate civic concern, typical of American journalism at its best. He too was in shirt sleeves, crumpled and disheveled with harassment; his secretary, however, sat juggling two telephones in alpine coolness, speaking into each of them in turn while making notes on a pad which, I felt sure, had nothing to do with either conversation. On the wall of the office were printed plans of the layout of coming editorial pages; I noticed that a large space was reserved for the hospital issue on each of them. On the opposite wall, next to the bookcase, I saw a few framed academic certificates, issued by Ivy League schools to Robert T. Cochran, Jr., which gave the office the aspect of a doctor's waiting room. "Let's get the heck out of here," he said, grabbing a coat, "before the whole hive starts buzzing out for lunch."

As we went down in the elevator and crossed the street to a garage building where he had parked his car, Bob Cochran told me about the place where we were going to have lunch. It was called the "Wednesday Club" and congregated in the home of a Mrs. Randolph, whom he called "the Eleanor Roosevelt of the liberal Texas Democrats." There would be anything from thirty to forty people present, all of them keenly interested in civic affairs.

It was nothing official, nothing organized, it was just the most progressive and intelligent group of civic-minded people in this town getting together informally. We might well find there the beginnings of a civic movement for helping the hospital.

His car turned out to be another sports car with tailguns for exhausts; as it was of an older vintage than Gilles's, it had the virile smell and elusive set of squeaks and rattles two-seaters acquire only after having been left out in the rain with the hood down often enough. He tried to explain Houston politics to me, while darting in and out of the noonday traffic like a panicking rollerskate finding itself separated from its mate. Finally we arrived outside a one story house in a suburb; I had to slam the outside of the door on my side before he could open his. His last words, on entering the Wednesday Club, were "Let's play it by ear."

We found a suite of rooms jampacked with people. They were helping themselves to food at a long table against the wall, sitting on folding chairs at communal dining-tables, or standing about in discussion-groups. My first thought was that this was a horrible thing to happen to anybody's home; it looked like one of those English manor houses, occupied during the war by semi-civilian groups like Psychological Warfare or Scientific-Survival-Analysis, commonly known as the Boffins. The houses had the same atmosphere of somebody's private living quarters having been turned into the permanent picnic grounds of a debating society. There was the same highly intellectual conversation, the same mess of paper napkins, paper plates and paper cups strewn about under the absentminded assumption that, this being somebody's home, there must be maids somewhere who would eventually clean everything up. Somewhere in this house, it seemed, there must be untidy bedrooms with unmade beds, Sheraton night tables with cigarette burns, beside lamps adapted for midnight reading by wrapping underwear around their lop-sided shades, and open boxes of dog biscuits for midnight snacks. The whole thing seemed, somehow, un-Texan.

Bob Cochran took me by the arm and guided me through the throng to a table in the corner, where an elderly lady with tired eyes and the weary hairdo of the female pontiff sat gazing at the milling mass of her visitors with an expression of reserve. She was flanked by two balding businessmen, who had managed to get hold of an ear each and were doing some high-pressure forging while the iron was hot. The smile with which she welcomed us proved that she had been listening to neither of them but thinking of something peaceful and innocent, like ducklings on a sunlit pond. Bob Cochran introduced me and her smile widened, while her canny eyes wrinkled benevolently for a scrutinizing look that proved she was not listening to Bob Cochran either. "Nice to have you, go and get yourselves something to eat, make yourselves at home," she said; it sounded as intimate and at the same time impersonal as a card bearing your fortune extracted from a machine.

"Let's do that," Bob Cochran said; as he guided me back toward the table with the food I realized that he had not let go of my arm since we arrived. We collected fruit salad, pickles, a candied yam, a deviled egg and a folding chair from the display and found an opening in the ranks through which we could worm our way to the edge of a table. The hubbub was bewildering and the beverage I had been handed in a paper beaker so burpy that I sat there hot under the collar, haunted by the thought that at the next nasal hiccup bubbles would stream from my nostrils. There were some charming girls, waving and gesturing at us across the table, taunting and soundless like the submarine mermaids of Florida's Weekie Wachee Springs behind the glass of their aquarium. Suddenly somebody started to hammer a glass; it created an interested silence. A man had risen at the largest of the tables and was now introducing the first speaker of the week: "Our friend, a young politician from England, will give us in a few expert words an idea of the reaction in Britain to its exclusion by France from the Common Market."

There was a smattering of applause; from a foxhole in which his sponsor had vanished rose a young Englishman, as unkempt as the Beatles, who proceeded in a voice plaintive with superciliousness to give a five-minute discourse during which I had the feeling that, at last, I understood why England was so fearfully amused at having crept through the needle's eye, though madly protesting against France's megalomania. It was a brilliant little speech and everybody obviously enjoyed it; but from the nonchalant applause I deduced that this level of entertainment was common at the lunches of the Wednesday Club. Then, there rose the first man again, and he announced the next attraction: "Our friend, a well-known Quaker professor recently from Holland, teaching playwriting after a life as a sailor, who will give a graphic picture of the Emergency Room in Jefferson Davis Hospital, where he now works as an orderly." There was some confused applause, as well there might be after that introduction, and I rose to tell the meadow of chewing faces, in which I suddenly found myself slowly pirouetting, some of the things I had told better in the paper. When it was over, the meadow applauded and I sat down again with a sense of relief; but it turned out there were to be questions.

The first came from a kind and concerned man who wanted to know why Quakers were always the first to grapple with these civic issues. I tried to answer his question lucidly and modestly, which turned out to be impossible on both counts. The next question was put by a short and obviously uncharmed lady in her sixties who asked, with the chafing voice of a district attorney, what standards I was applying to Jefferson Davis Hospital. What were the hospitals in Holland like? She had been to Europe several times and visited hospitals there that compared unfavorably with any she knew in the United States.

There was a sudden silence of interest and I realized that this was what everybody had come for: a weekly cock fight. I remembered in time that I had just tried to explain, futilely, how gentle and persuasive Quakers were; so, giving her a smile that expressed the power of positive thinking, I answered that she was right in implying that I had no business kicking up a fuss if Houston had decided to put up with any charity hospital, however backward, as long as it could point at a worse one in Saudi Arabia.

The lady, undaunted, was obviously not through with me, but as I had sat down she had lost sight of her opponent. While she was speaking to Hamlet's father's ghost, Bob Cochran whispered, to my relief, "Let's get out of here."

We did, after someone else had risen from the meadow. We passed the table where the lady of the house was eating pecan pie while listening impartially to the businessmen on either side of her, who each still had a full plate in front of him. She gave us a wide smile, while she again sized me up with a swift, appraising glance, then she said, "So nice to have you. Come back soon," and resumed eating. It was obvious that, if she had some prominent citizens available in her stable, she was not going to sell them to us. The issue of the Houston charity hospital, it seemed, harbored no promise for the liberal wing of the Democratic party in Texas.

Back in the sports car, the black leather seats of which were at boiling point after an hour in the noonday sun, we tried to discuss the experience of the past hour, at the tops of our voices; I gathered from Bob's shouts that he thought I should meet another person who would give me the background to the various political groups in Houston, before we went scouting any further for prospective members of a citizens' panel. I understood that he wanted us to have lunch the next day with a man called Gray, administrative assistant to County Judge Bill Elliott. When I asked him, shouting, if this was the defrocked priest I had heard about, his eyebrows rose in shocked astonishment. "Who told you that vicious story?" he cried. "Hartsell is a terrific guy, who left the priesthood because he was no longer satisfied with preaching at people. I don't quite know what he does on Judge Elliott's staff, but I know he is putting his faith into practice. You'll find him fascinating, and extremely knowledgeable." At that, he cut into another lane, in front of a cattle truck that told him, by two-tone horn, what it thought of him.

5

THE NEXT DAY, AT LUNCHTIME, I went back to the *Chronicle* building, found his secretary still telephoning, though wearing a different dress; she told me that Bob was waiting for me in Kelly's Restaurant across the street with the gentleman from the County Judge's office.

As I pushed open the swing doors of Kelly's Restaurant, I stepped back into memories of London. The main ingredient in the décor seemed to be red plush, but I could not be sure as it was steeped in semidarkness. There was a strong smell of beef and cigar smoke and the fishlike glints of red-and-gold-liveried flunkeys in the gloom; all else I could discern in the darkness was a tightly compressed herd of seated males. Then someone called my name and I turned toward the sound, colliding, as I did so, with a stretcher bearing a man-sized roast on a silver tray, pushed by a blood-spattered orderly wearing a chef's hat.

"Here!" the voice called, and my sleeve was grabbed. I sidled past the cortège and sat down beside someone I assumed to be Bob Cochran; all I could see of him was a pair of glasses reflecting the feeble gleam of coachhouse lanterns. "Meet Hartsell Gray," the voice said; as I stretched out my hand it was grasped by an invisible angler who, after a tentative squeeze, obviously did not like what he had caught and decided to throw it back in the water.

After I had sat there for a few minutes and ordered a Slenderella salad, on the recommendation of the administrative assistant to County Judge Bill Elliott, I began to discern his features. I had not been aware until then that I had a distinct mental picture of him; I had imagined somebody tall and thin and stoop-shouldered, with a hooked nose and burning eyes, hovering behind a magistrate's high-backed chair, a character by Aldous Huxley. Reality revealed itself as a bland, rotund youngish man in a seersucker suit whose face, though totally without expression, somehow conveyed resigned disenchantment. He turned out to be not very talkative; Bob told him about the luncheon of the previous day and he nodded, almost imperceptibly but knowledgeably. Bob worked hard to interest him; I realized that his enthusiasm for the hospital issue was not just that of a competitive journalist; it concerned him as a man.

I could not bring myself to conclude the same about the vague, faintly desultory young man across the table, who sat listening to us like a tired parish priest hearing an over-familiar spinster's confession. His hands, asleep on the table, looked surprisingly youthful; the essence of his presence would have been described by *Time* Magazine as "roly-poly." When Bob had told him all there was to tell and fallen silent our companion asked, flatly, "What are your immediate objectives?" dismissing all that had been said before as clumsy camouflage.

"Well, we want to see if we can get this panel of prominent citizens together. . . ." Bob Cochran started, but I interrupted him by saying, "To start with, we want the budget cut canceled." I spoke, because I felt that I had seen this scene a hundred times on the Late Show on television. "Let's go see Irish Mike," one of the characters had said, and here we were, seeing Irish Mike in the speakeasy that was his headquarters. The only way to deal with Irish Mike was to come clean; he would now answer, "Okay, what is it worth to you guys?"

But Irish Mike did nothing of the sort. He looked at me with his bland, disillusioned eyes and said, "You probably have already done that. But the distressing thing is that, as the money has to come from the general fund, they'll take it away from the orphans to give it to the hospital."

When Bob expressed shocked disbelief, the fat man explained patiently that there was a general fund in both the city's and the county's budget, from which all institutions of welfare had to be financed. That fund had a certain fixed amount of money in it, but it was like a half-inflated rubber ball: if you exerted enough pressure on one end, you could by doing so blow up the other. It depended on where public pressure was exerted which service was going to benefit for the coming year. With the increase in population, the fund had become totally inadequate, obviously the only real solution would be to increase it; but no politician in his right mind would risk his neck by putting that on his ticket, not in this town.

"Why not?" I asked. "We found there is a lot of concern and generosity in Houston."

His eyes seemed to get more tired as he gazed at me. For a moment, he looked as if he were about to say, "Sorry, boys, I'm going to have a nap. We'll talk about this later." But he rallied and said, in a tone as if he had told me this before, "Sure there is, but only for a neighbor in the literal sense of the word, a person with a face and a name and a hard-luck story that has been personally witnessed. The moment it concerns faceless people, an anonymous mass of misfits and freeloaders that have to be subsidized out of taxes, people here set their jaws and shake their

172

heads and refuse to pay a cent. This place is not merely a boom town, it is the closest thing to a gold rush since the Klondike. Its mystique is that every man came here to make a fortune and that if he fails he has only got himself to blame. To the Houstonian, welfare programs put a premium on failure; and if this attitude concerned just welfare, maybe something could be done about it. But it concerns everything. The sewage system in the city was declared unsafe years ago; now it will cost a hundred million dollars to put it right. Zoning has been voted down three times; anyone can buy a piece of land anywhere in the city and build on it whatever he likes. And why? All because of the mystique of the gold rush: let's strike it rich, quick, and get the hell out; anything goes, as long as it lasts out my time. But you cannot refuse to take moral responsibility for the community you live in without turning it into a jungle." His pale, disillusioned eyes suddenly singled me out. "In that jungle," he continued, coldly, "you arrived, yesterday: one apprentice missionary, starry-eyed, rolling up your sleeves, thinking: 'Leave it to me.' But you'll soon discover that you have become part of the jungle. Don't think I am joking. I looked at you when I said that the money for the hospital budget might be taken from the orphans. You thought, 'Well, the orphans are somebody else's business.' Wasn't that what you thought?"

I sat there, bewildered by the dawning realization that the pasty-faced, fatigued, roly-poly exterior was a disguise. "I . . . er . . . I suppose so," I said.

He looked at me for a moment, then he asked, "How big was the response to your article?"

"So far, about thirty-seven letters," I answered eagerly.

He smiled, without mirth or kindness. "Congratulations," he said. "Out of a million and a half inhabitants you have managed to reach thirty-seven, with a letter that anywhere else in this country would have wiped out both city and county governments. It would have done so unjustly, in my opinion, but it would have all the same. Here in Harris County it resulted in thirty-seven letters."

"Well, a few more," Bob hastened to add. "We received a good number at the paper."

"All right, a hundred letters. Two hundred letters. What do they say? Bravo, Mr. de Hartog? Thank you, *Houston Chronicle?* Thank God we have you in our midst; we commend you for your intestinal fortitude—that kind of thing?"

"More or less," Bob admitted.

"In other words: you got yourselves a scrapbook with letters telling you how wonderful you are. What the hell good is that going to do anybody, apart from being nice for you guys' egos? Is it going to bring about a hospital district? Is it going to raise the necessary funds for running both Jefferson Davis and the new hospital, when the time comes? Is it going to take this public facility, that should be a public responsibility, from the hands of Mr. Ben Taub, who has been treating it as his private hobby for thirty years because no one else in this town cared a damn about it? Can't you see that all you are doing is building a nice little monument for yourselves, like anyone else who has ever dabbled in charity in this city?"

"But, Hartsell," Bob Cochran protested good-naturedly, "honestly, this is oversimplifying matters. Look at the University of Houston, the Hermann Hospital, the M.D. Anderson Hospital, all those were started by some Houstonian with a civic spirit."

"All right," the fat man said, "look at them." He was completely sure of himself, he did not argue, he just provided information; at least, that seemed to be his own concept of what he was doing. But I was getting more impressed all the time with the passion and the determination behind his studiously dispassionate words. "You must look a little closer," he said, "and you'll discover that most

174

monuments of the civic spirit in this town have a man's name on their façade. The University of Houston has the name of Mr. Cullen and his sons plastered all over the campus. On the main building, you'll find scrolls hewn in marble with quotes from speeches by Mr. Cullen, and each of the buildings is named after one of his relatives. I would not call that a monument of civic concern. It means, simply, that some people can afford a sobbing marble angel on their grave, others a university. Those who cannot afford either are out of luck in this town."

"But what about people like Ben Taub?" Bob Cochran asked. "There's a rich man who for over thirty years has devoted himself to the welfare of the indigent sick. I don't see his name on any building. How does old Ben fit into your picture?"

I suddenly felt a juvenile excitement, a puerile pride that I had last felt when I was invited, a mate's apprentice, to join two senior officers for a drink ashore, and listened to them talking about the Old Man, whom I had never thought about in human terms before. To the orderly from the Emergency Room, to talk about "Old Ben" was a degree of familiarity with the Almighty unattained even in his daydreams.

"You'll have to admit that he cannot have a selfish interest in the charity hospital," Bob continued. "How could he?"

Hartsell Gray smiled. It suddenly made him look jolly and mischievous. "I'm sorry, folks," he said, "but I'll have to get back to the office. Anything else I can do for you?"

"What is a hospital district?" I asked.

"Bob will explain it to you," he replied. "Thanks for the lunch, Bob. See you around." He wriggled himself out of the seat and vanished in the semidarkness of the most expensive coachhouse in the world.

Bob did indeed explain it to me. I was not sure that I got it all straight; what it boiled down to seemed to be a separate taxing agency, like a school board. It all sounded involved and complicated and abstract, but then it could hardly be anything else at this level. It was the level that worried me, as I slowly made my way home along the hot crowded streets. Was it really impossible to deal with the hospital on a human basis, in the rarefied atmosphere of power politics? It seemed obvious that the fascinating, colorful figures of the elected government of Houston were manipulated by invisible, ancient powers, entrenched behind boggy moats and unscalable walls, so remote and hidden from view that nobody knew exactly who they were. Even Bob Cochran, it seemed to me, did not really know who they were, and whom they controlled. The only thing I knew was that in the heart of that big thicket of mystery and silence the real enemy was hidden. Maybe I would find myself face to face with him, one day.

6

LATER THAT DAY, as I was changing into my whites to go to the hospital, Bob Cochran called. "Listen," he said. "I have some letters here that will interest you. First, there is one from Dr. Olsen—you know, the Dean of the Medical School and Chief of Staff at Jeff Davis, who endorses what you wrote. Then there is a letter from your Quaker Meeting, very official and dignified, pledging complete support. But there is one, signed by eighteen student nurses, that I'm going to read to you. It will be in the paper tomorrow, but I want you to hear it now. It is from the whole freshman class of Jefferson Davis Hospital School of Nursing, and they all sign with their full names. Are you there?" I said I was. "Okay, here it is. 'As freshman student nurses at the old Jefferson Davis Hospital, we want to second the stand taken by Jan de Hartog in his editorial which appeared in your April 21st edition. We want to thank him for expressing so thoroughly the atmosphere and conditions which prevail at J.D. twenty-four hours a day. . . .' "

It was a long and articulate letter, moving in its courage. By writing this, all eighteen of those girls put their heads on the block, which no one else inside the hospital had been able to bring him or herself to do. The letter ended, "We know that a game is being played between the City of Houston and Harris County officials, but must the twenty-two people that comprise these teams use the sick of J.D. for their pigskin? We, like Mr. de Hartog, have seen the halls of the new city-county hospital and felt the waiting silence within its domain. How long before this silence is answered? How long before this wasted space is filled with the activity of saving human lives? We are not in a position to answer these questions, but we cry out to those who are."

"Well, what do you say to that?" Bob Cochran asked.

"Wonderful. It must have taken real guts to write that letter, and sign it."

"You bet. As far as I'm concerned, this settles it. I'm not going to let those eighteen girls down. We're going to keep up the fight on the editorial page until something gives. I don't know what, but something will have to give, sooner or later."

The letter from the student nurses was published in the *Houston Chronicle* the next day, signed with their eighteen names. Soon thereafter, City Hall announced that the hospital would be moved to the new building in the Medical Center within two weeks; nobody mentioned the jail ward any more, or the budget cut for that matter.

The eighteen girls had done it, and here they are, as they signed themselves in the paper: "The Freshman Class of Jefferson Davis Hospital School of Nursing: Margery Vaughan, Norma Berney, Judy Harper, Judy Dlabay,

Judy Matheson, Patricia A. Rhoderick, Ruth Hill, Dandy Talbert, Helen Schoellmann, Rachel Campos, Mary Joyce Franke, Eugenia Ybanez, Mary Resvanis, Martha Blomstrom, Barbara Lanier, Sandra Elliott, Peggy Claborn, Irene Bailey, S.N."

CHAPTER 5

I T S E E M E D a major victory. Everybody inside the
hospital was ecstatic—or almost everybody.

One of the young doctors that I knew from Emergency accosted me in the passage and asked, irritably, "I
thought you people were trained?"

"I beg your pardon?"

"I thought Women-in-Yellow with a blue band on their
caps were trained nurses' aides?"

"That's right."

"Well, you had better have yourselves trained again,
buddy, or at least that couple of broads in the Burns Ward.
They're worse than useless. What we need is properly
schooled, professional people, not sentimental housewives
puking in a corner." He marched off angrily, leaving me
behind in bewilderment. There was nobody else on duty
from our group, certainly not in the Burns Ward. I told
Mrs. Judd that I would be right back and hastily went upstairs to see for myself.

I found a nice, middle-aged woman, as pale as a sheet
and with all symptoms of acute nausea, staring at the huge
stainless steel bathtub filled with silicone in which a burnt
woman floated, surrounded by the waving algae of strips
of skin coming loose. It was an invention by somebody at

Baylor and seemed to be very effective, but apart from being a gruesome sight it stank the place down. The Woman-in-Yellow, manfully fighting her physical reaction, looked at me pleadingly as I came in. I saw, to my astonishment, that she had a blue stripe on her cap, like the ones issued to the members of our group after eight weeks of training. She told me that she was new to the hospital, that she had wanted to help patients, that Mrs. Willoughby had asked her if she had any nursing experience; when told that she had followed a first-aid course at high school during the Second World War, Mrs. Willoughby had issued the woman a uniform and a cap with a blue stripe, and sent her out on the floor. And she was not the only one: there were other ladies who had been similarly distinguished. She was not sure, however, that she liked this kind of work; maybe she would be happier at the information desk.

It seemed odd at first; but when more good-willing but untrained women were given blue stripes on their caps, it became obvious that this meant the end of the confidence our group had acquired from the side of the nursing staff and the doctors. It would have been ungenerous to conclude that Mrs. Willoughby intended to discredit the program, but she did in effect do so. When I suggested to her that her women recruits should be trained by the Red Cross before being sent onto the floors, she replied there would be no more Red Cross courses. The training program for volunteer nurses' aides and orderlies was discontinued because of the impending move to the new building. Obviously, under the circumstances, the nursing office could not undertake to supervise them, let alone give them clinical training. And there the matter rested.

2

AFTER THE SHORT EUPHORIA that followed the announcement of the move, the nursing staff inside the hospital woke up to the prospect of having to move everything, lock, stock and barrel, including patients, to the new building within ten days. The date for the move had been arranged, but nothing else; a few mornings later Mrs. Judd sought me out in Observation, as I was helping one of the doctors perform a spinal tap on a terrified old lady. It was totally unlike Mrs. Judd to come barging in on such a delicate operation, when one jerky movement by the patient could mean agony. I guessed at once that she was in a flap.

"Mr. de Hartog, please!" she asked, as if it were the end of a long ardent plea instead of the beginning of an order. "Could I see you *the moment* you are through here?"

When I joined her at the nurses' station after ten minutes, I found her bent over a drawing that she announced to be a plan of the Emergency Room in the new building. She had copied it from a blueprint, she said, but as in her version the Emergency Room in the new building seemed to get smaller and smaller toward the bottom of the paper until it ended in a point, I suspected that she, like my mother when drawing a bicycle, had drawn herself into a corner before she got to the second wheel.

"I must go over there this morning," she said nervously, "to determine the number of sinks, suture tables, instrument counters, closets and shelves. I thought that if you came with me we could draw into this plan, room by room, what we find there, with symbols, you see. Something like this . . ." She showed me a sort of Rosetta Stone with hieroglyphs: an eye for a sink, a capsized Roman III for a set of shelves, a stylized centipede for an instrument counter; by then she had obviously run out of realistic symbols and taken to nonrepresentational ones, that needed interpretation by the artist. She explained that a crossed knife and fork stood for an operating table, a pretzel for a suture table and the little severed human leg, complete with seven toes, for a plaster cast table. The pretzel, it turned out, was not a pretzel but the outcome of her effort to draw a suture knot.

She suggested that, as it seemed to be a quiet morning, we had better go at once before it turned into a busy one, as it was sure to do the moment we made it known we were about to leave. Mrs. Judd always gave me the feeling that the Emergency Room was watched by an eagle-eyed, mischievous young deity who, for want of anything better to do, took a juvenile delinquent's delight in causing multiple car wrecks, triggering guns accidentally and causing scaffoldings to collapse the moment he heard anybody whisper that "it looked like a quiet shift today." We sneaked out of the basement door with superstitious stealth, strolled nonchalantly to the station wagon, sidled into the front seat and made off. I had the impression that she tried to hide the floor plan she had drawn as we crossed the parking lot, although I was sure that even the young god, had he caught a glimpse of it, could never have guessed what it represented.

During the drive across town she leaned back in the front seat, eyes closed, looking very tired. I started to ask her if she had been putting in extra hours again, but decided to let her enjoy this moment of relative peace undisturbed. I had never been to the new hospital building before; when we arrived I saw a huge red stone edifice without any obvious shape or character other than that it seemed complicated and very big. It took us some time to find the Emergency Entrance; once we found it we discovered a note on the door saying it was locked and that only the Engineer's Entrance was open.

Mr. Gardner, one of the engineers, sat in a glass cubicle at the entrance to his department, glasses on the tip of his old nose, a pencil behind each ear, licking his fingers as he slowly turned the pages of a book marked *Specifications*. He was an imperturbable, lean old cow poke of the kind that sits loose-limbed and poker-faced on the heaving back of a bucking bull during a rodeo, and remains seated until the panting beast collapses with exhaustion, after which he walks away, teetering on high heels. He peered at us over the rim of his glases, his eyes pale and blue and filled with the calm of the prairie. "Don't tell me y'all want to change something now," he said. "It's too late for changes."

"Oh no, Mr. Gardner," Mrs. Judd said hastily, "I honestly would not know what to change. . . ."

"Well, well," Mr. Gardner croaked, in a strenuous effort to sound pleasant, "that sure makes you an exception, little lady. You're the first nurse who doesn't think she knows more than the architects. Do you have the key to Emergency?"

"No," Mrs. Judd confessed, "I know I should, but I . . . I've never been there yet."

Mr. Gardner's face, as he contemplated her motionlessly, froze in craggy disapproval. "Seems I counted my blessings too soon," he said dourly. Then he opened a drawer, selected a key and said, "Don't try to turn on the lights, because there ain't any."

"Oh, but how am I going to see?" Mrs Judd asked, trying to make it sound reasonable.

"There is light in the halls," Mr. Gardner replied. "As to the rooms, you'll just have to open the doors and guess." He returned pointedly to licking his fingers and turning the pages, with the resignation of a man who knows he is looking for something that he is not going to find.

"How do we get there from here?" Mrs. Judd asked, helplessly.

"Like anyone else," the Knight of the Wide Open Spaces replied, with a sideways nod of the head and without looking up from the pages. "By following yer nose, thataway."

"Well, Mr. de Hartog, I'm ready if you are," Mrs. Judd said manfully, after a short hesitation, and we entered gamely the twilit world of Kafka's Castle.

Endless, dimly lit corridors intersected with other endless, dimly lit corridors. After turning two corners we were hopelessly lost, and realized only then that we should have gone to the Emergency Room round the outside, which was why we had been given the key. We tried calling "Hello there! Is there someone? Hey! Yoo-hoo!" but nobody answered; not even an echo came back. It was one of the eeriest places I had ever seen; everything looked severely functional and meticulously planned and yet nothing made any sense. It was like a hell for bureaucrats, where they would be condemned to wander in all eternity, pointlessly, through the uncluttered mind of a computer, carrying folders. It seemed to us that we had been walking down the concrete intestines of Houston for hours when, suddenly, we hit upon another microbe: an electrician in khaki, his belt full of screwdrivers, two coils of shiny new cable on his shoulders.

"Oh hello, could you tell us please how we can get to the Emergency Room?" Mrs. Judd asked gaily.

"Sorry, miss," the man said, "I'm a stranger here myself," and he walked on in the direction from which we had come.

Mrs. Judd sighed; when I said, "Good thing he didn't ask us how to get to Mr. Gardner," she began to giggle hysterically. We strode bravely on and at the next corner found a sign with an arrow saying EMERGENCY ROOM.

"How about that?" Mrs. Judd said, "Wouldn't you think that man would have seen it when he came this way?"

But we had underestimated the bureaucratic mind. Following the direction of the arrow meticulously we walked for what seemed another ten minutes, then we came upon the same sign once more. It had to be the same sign, for now it pointed in the direction from whence we had come.

Or maybe it wasn't, maybe we had missed it; maybe, as Mrs. Judd suggested, giggling creepily, there was a hatch in the floor somewhere that we had overlooked. Then, rounding another corner, we came upon a telephone.

I picked it up, and heard music and laughter. I called "Hello! Hello there!" but no one answered. I juggled the cradle and the music stopped; in its stead there now sounded a high whining tone. I dialed a number, regardless, heard to my astonishment a bell ringing somewhere, thought it was in the telephone, but Mrs. Judd tapped on my shoulder, pointed and said, "There! Over there!" I put the telephone down; the ringing stopped.

"Oh, shucks! Now we've lost it," Mrs. Judd said.

I looked at her with a feeling of encroaching insanity. I wanted to explain that as I had dialed that number myself at random, it didn't make sense anyhow; but I had the uneasy feeling that this was not the point any more, that we were lost, not in the mind of a computer, but in that of Mrs. Judd's juvenile delinquent deity. Then, after three more corners that looked exactly alike, we suddenly found ourselves coming up behind a man sitting on a stool in front of a desk.

We approached him with the elation of marooned sailors spotting smoke. "Sir!" Mrs. Judd cried, "Sir, could you please . . ." The man turned round and peered at us over his glasses. It was Mr. Gardner. We were back where we had started.

By the time we had stumbled past him, trying to feign composure, I was giggling too. Maybe it was those conspiratory giggles, maybe it was the silent darkness of the vast empty hospital, but when we finally opened the door to the Emergency Room with the key we had been given, and entered its hollow, echoing hall, there was between us the sense of intimacy and frankness that might exist between two travelers who find themselves stranded in a deserted railway station. As we were standing at the empty admission desk, trying to work out where the entrance hall was situated on Mrs. Judd's Rorschach test, she suddenly said, "Nobody knows it yet, but I feel it wouldn't be fair if I didn't tell you. I'm going to resign."

I didn't stop to think why she should have thought it unfair not to tell me. I was completely stunned by the information. I couldn't believe my ears.

"You aren't serious!" I said, at last. "We can't do without you, certainly not at this point!"

She shrugged her shoulders and looked around the dark, vast, featureless place that was nothing yet, not even a hospital, nothing but a void on the first day of creation, at the dawn of light itself. "They don't need me," she said. "The hospital doesn't need anyone in particular. It just needs people. People, people; it eats people. It ate me." She turned her head with a smile to make it a joke, but it wasn't a joke. I looked at her thin, drawn face, drained of youth, strength, of life itself. Her gray eyes seemed huge and empty like a famished child's; all that was Mrs. Judd, the unique, the irreplaceable, the joyous, the compassionate, the untiring, the tender, seemed to have gone from that face, leaving nothing but weariness. I had never noticed how she had changed; I had not looked at her for months. You didn't look at one another in Emergency, any more than you looked at yourself in the mirrors that some mixed-up architect's apprentice had put over the scrub sinks in the Shock Rooms.

"You aren't ill, are you?" I asked.

She looked away, almost furtively; my question must have taken her by surprise. Then she answered, with a shrug of the shoulders, "Oh well, you might as well know, but let's keep this between ourselves. My husband has put his foot down. I've been running a temperature for weeks now. Nothing serious, you know, but just something I can't shake. I've had x-rays, I've had everything, and they found nothing. It isn't TB, it isn't anemia, it's . . . well,

I know what it is." She laughed self-consciously. "I'm just J.D. sick," she said.

I wanted to ask her what that was, but for some reason I felt reluctant to confess that I had no idea what she meant.

"I wouldn't have paid it any attention, even so," she continued, "but there is something that scares me. I want to tell you about it, because you never know. It may be useful to you some day, as it is to me now—I hope."

"Ah?" I said. I suddenly had an odd feeling as if, silently, unnoticed, a presence had joined us from the darkness.

"A friend of mine caught it some time ago," she said, with an effort to sound chatty and conversational, just a moment of relaxation before we got on with the job. "She was a nice girl, very outgoing you know, wonderful with the patients. . . . Gosh, that girl had energy! I remember how jealous I was. And then she fell ill one day, nothing special, you know. Like me, just a temperature, and sudden gushes of perspiration at the slightest exertion. Something like flu, but it wasn't flu. She went to bed for a few weeks and then, when it made no difference, she came back and kept going, and then, all of a sudden, she just folded up. It was the funniest thing, she just folded. I don't know how to put it—she was taken ill and went home and her parents put her to bed again and I went to see her for a chat one day, and the next day she was gone. Very odd. There was an autopsy, but they never found out what it was. She was just, how shall I say, burnt out." She laughed, but stopped when our eyes met. "J.D. sick, they call it. I'm sure that in this place, whatever its name may be one day, they'll call it 'Blank-blank sick.' It's nothing, nothing you can put your finger on. It just is the end of the road. You know: out of gas, engine stalls, finish." She sighed and pushed herself away from the counter, as if to start going after our break. But she continued, "She told me one thing that scared me. I don't know why, but it really scared me.

She said, 'Ann, if you should ever get that fever, it may be just a bout of flu. But if at the same time you find yourself thinking about your childhood all the time, that's when you have to get out. Then you *have* to get out, fast, for then it will be almost too late.' "

"Have you been thinking of your childhood?" I asked, with still that sense of another presence in the darkness of the Emergency Room.

"Yes," she said. "The funniest thing, I didn't realize it until . . . until very recently. I mean, I'd been thinking for weeks; little things you know, like how I'd like to get back to Corpus Christi, how I'd like to see Granny's house again, and sit on the swing on her porch again . . . That sort of thing, you know. And then, well, a moment ago, as we were walking through those corridors and suddenly came upon Mr. Gardner, I suddenly felt a terrible longing to go back home and visit my old school again. Isn't it silly?"

"Is that when you decided that you should get out?" I asked.

"No, no," she said, quickly. "I had decided days ago, I mean, ages. I promised my husband and, you know, when he really puts his foot down, well, that's it."

"Mrs. Judd," I said, on an impulse, "you asked me this once and I'd like to ask you now. Why did you start this work? I mean, what made you go and work in J.D.?"

It seemed as if a doubt, a sadness, deepened the dark lines of exhaustion in her haggard face.

"I don't mean to stop you from what you are planning to do," I hastened to say. "I just would like to know, for myself."

She thought for a moment, then she smiled and shrugged her shoulders and said, "Well, I don't know. *Somebody* has to do it."

"But why J.D.?" I insisted. "What made you go there, instead of to one of the other hospitals?"

She looked at me intently and thought for a moment, then she said, "The girl I told you about got me in there. She took me round one day, and when I had seen it I stayed. I stayed as long as I could. Well, I suppose there will be others." She had said it bravely, but I realized at that moment that she had gone already; that, like the girl who went before, she had given all she had to give and that now there was nothing left but ashes. "God," she said suddenly, looking about her in the unformed darkness of the Emergency Room. "I hope that whoever is going to work here will be kind."

She said it simply and sincerely, as just a passing thought, but I felt a deep solemnity, as if, with these words spoken softly in the darkness, Mrs. Judd had opened the hospital. No future speeches by mayors or judges, no ceremonies of inauguration would ever equal the moment when Mrs. Judd, at the end of her road, dedicated this house to kindness.

We stood for a moment in silence, then she said, "Well, let's see what we've got here," and walked away. She found a switch, turned on a solitary light in a long, empty corridor, and we went to work.

3

FOR THE REST of the morning we roamed, in mounting bewilderment and confusion, through a seemingly endless series of empty rooms, halls, passages, cubicles, alcoves and corridors, all interconnecting and interlocking with the perverse intricacy of a Chinese maze, as if our new Emergency Room had been designed by the puzzle editor of the *Hong Kong Times*. We frequently lost sight of each other and had to find our way back by sound. We discovered, to our alarm, that there was not a single suture table, operating table, GYN table, medicine cupboard, linen closet, or counter for instruments and suture trays in any of the rooms. When at last we felt that we had seen everything, we left, locked the door behind us, took the key back to Mr. Gardner and drove back to old J.D., which suddenly seemed to have taken on a nostalgic glow of coziness, warmth and familiarity.

We lost each other the moment we came in, as two ambulances stood in front of the Emergency Entrance, their red lights still flashing, which meant that the drivers and their assistants had rushed their stretchers inside in a hurry, and they only did so with Shock Room cases. I let Mrs. Judd out before I parked the car, and that was the last I saw of her. John Rivers beckoned me into Observation the moment he saw me, to help him restrain a highly-agitated young boy, the first to be brought into the ward from the multiple car wreck. I did not get out of there for the rest of the day; when I did, Mrs. Judd had gone.

But the image of her haggard face ashen with exhaustion, her huge, empty eyes drained of life, haunted me, and I went on hearing her words, as in a dream.

"God . . . I hope they will be kind."

CHAPTER 6

FTER THE MOVE was announced, the letters to
the paper, which had continued to arrive in increasing numbers, stopped. The clamor about the
scandal of the charity hospital, that had been taken over by
the television stations, faded out. *Time, Newsweek,* and
The Saturday Evening Post, who had had reporters on the
spot to interview people and collect photographs of conditions in the old hospital, canceled their stories. Within a
week, the charity hospital issue was back where it had been
for the past fifty years: under the carpet. Houston moved
on to other issues, such as the eighty-million-dollar bond
issued called by Judge Elliott, and whether the Domed Stadium should provide private offices for the managers of the
local sports clubs.

The people of Houston honestly and sincerely believed
that all was well now the hospital was to be moved to a
new building, and so they forgot about it with a sense of accomplishment. When we tried to point out to our acquaint-
ances that all was not well but worse than before, because
now two hospitals would have to be financed out of the
same budget, their answer was, "But hasn't the budget cut
been canceled?" We tried to explain that to cancel the cut
had not been enough, that the budget should be increased

dramatically, or we would soon be faced with a worse situation in the new hospital than the one that had caused the fuss about the old one. For J.D. was not going to be abandoned; it was to be used as a TB hospital, and its tenth floor would become the county Psychiatric Ward; the Obstetrics section would remain where it was, and so would the School of Nursing. To run this vastly expanded establishment with the same amount of money that had already proved inadequate to finance one hospital was to invite disaster.

Alarmed by the community's blithe assumption that the hospital issue had been settled, the hospital committee of the Houston Meeting decided to attack this dangerous misconception on two fronts. First, by appearing weekly in front of both the City Council and the County Commissioners' Court, to harass them about the inadequate budget and make people aware of the impending disaster unless it was increased to meet the need. Second, by starting a fund called *Mercy*, which had as its goal to collect sixty thousand dollars in voluntary contributions, to supplement the hospital budget with ten thousand dollars' worth of extra salaries each month over a period of six months. The figure had been quoted by Mrs. Masters, the Director of Nurses, as the absolute minimum required for supplementary nurses' aides and orderlies, if both hospitals were to be run with a skeleton staff. We assumed that, during those six months, the committee of prominent citizens we were still trying to assemble would come up with a humane and mature solution for the financing of both charity hospitals out of public funds.

But we discovered that, overnight, we had turned from crusaders into crackpots in the eyes of Houston. The soothing voices of public officials assured the citizenry, with a faint note of strained patience, that the issue was settled, at least for the next year or so; they seemed to hint that those who went on making a public nuisance of themselves proved thereby to be little better than publicity-seeking trouble-makers.

The reason for our undignified tenacity lay in the fact that the charity hospital had been made an official *Concern of the Meeting*. To Quakers, this is a momentous circumstance; you cannot make an issue a Meeting's concern and obligingly drop it when it starts to lose public sympathy. With the cautious, subtle canniness of three centuries of gentle persuasion, Friends are very wary of making anything an official concern of a Meeting; when they do, they stick with it until it has been settled to their consciences' satisfaction. In the early nineteenth century, many Meetings on the Eastern Seaboard made the abolition of slavery their official concern; as a result, whole communities had to pull up stakes and hazard West, leaving behind them prosperous plantations that could not be run profitably without slaves. It was the beginning of the Quaker migration to the Indian territories; it culminated in the Underground Railroad, most stations of which were manned by Friends who had migrated from the East. A Meeting that abandons a concern without having seen it through to the end is no longer a Meeting but a social club.

Priscilla took on the job of organizing the interpellations during the weekly public sessions at City Hall and County Court; one of our liveliest members, Debbie Nimick, became chairman of the Mercy Fund. She was a vivacious slip of a girl, referred to in the papers, demurely, as "a young Quaker housewife from Philadelphia." The Philadelphia part of her was obviously the top half, looking matronly and composed although she had a tendency to forget to take out her hairclips. The lower half of her person expressed the truth: she tramped about, untiringly, in bobby sox and slant-heeled old shoes that looked as if they had had a stroke; she even wore them to concerts in the Music Hall. She had taken on so many responsibilities, apart from providing a home for a husband whose composure was heroic and two small sons with a propensity for doing hand stands in the living room, that she rarely managed to do anything below the waist about her disguise as a young Quaker housewife from Philadelphia. She bonded herself as the chairman of the Mercy Fund, and thus added, to her already dizzying daily schedule run like a relay race, hours of telephoning with stodgy dignitaries and topheavy presidents of Women's Clubs, proclaiming these "periods of rest" by lying upside down on the stairs as she telephoned. So we had, in fact, two chairmen: one young Quaker housewife from Philadelphia, and one lovable, indefatigable but occasionally bewildering nut.

The moment the Mercy Fund was announced in the papers, a professional "fund raiser" got in touch with us and offered to organize the campaign for a fee of ten percent of the proceeds. When we hesitated, he pointed out that to get any money at all out of Houston was a devil of a job; to get it for the charity hospital was impossible. Nobody else would be able to get a nickel out of them for that purpose except him, because "he knew where the bodies were buried." Then a local lawyer, Ben Ramey, offered his office and his services gratis, and we accepted his offer with gratitude and relief.

2

THE MERCY FUND got off to a modest start; many contributions came in, but mostly in very small amounts. Five-dollar bills, dollar bills, even fifty-cent pieces and quarters, taped to a piece of paper and stuck in an envelope, were sent to Ben Ramey's office in the Shell Building. Many of the contributions were accompanied by letters wishing us luck, telling stories about old J.D. from the patients' point of view that sounded like memoirs from a Turkish prison. Most of the correspondents and the contributors lived in the poorest sections of Houston; only a few well-to-do people sent any money. After three weeks, all we had managed to raise was $1,573.19.

In the meantime, Priscilla and her group of women Friends had turned up regularly at the public meetings of the City Council and the County Commissioners' Court, raising questions about the charity hospital that required specific answers. During those first three weeks, the Mayor as well as the commissioners answered evasively, discussing the lovely new building, the trouble they had with the other body of local government in financing the move, each putting the blame for whatever might be wrong with the hospital budget on the other party. On one occasion, moments after the Mayor had muttered some evasive platitude in response to a plea for his assistance in raising the sixty thousand dollars in voluntary contributions, a woman rose in front of the Council to donate fifty thousand dollars for a rose garden. The Mayor graciously accepted the gift, lauding her civic pride as exemplary.

Finally the women Friends phrased some questions that could no longer be evaded, and put them, first of all, to the Mayor.

"Where does the money come from to finance the hospital?"

The answer was, "The taxpayers, through the City Council and Commissioners' Court."

"To whom does this money go?"

"To the Board of Managers at the hospital."

"Who appoints the Board of Managers?"

"The City Council appoints two-thirds, and the County Commissioners one-third."

"Who are they?"

The answer to that question caused some embarrassment; finally it was said that the City Council did not actually know the people involved, because it was so difficult to keep track of each one of them.

"Since you have appointed this board, is it not accountable for its actions to you?"

The answer obviously was "yes," but the Mayor tried to circumvent this by giving an ambiguous reply, in which he seemed to pass the buck to the County Commissioners, who were supposed to take care of the board.

So the women moved on to the County Commissioners' Court the next day, where they put the same questions and received the same answers until they came to the last one, when suddenly one of the Commissioners, a thin, white-haired man, leaped to his feet, flushed red with rage, and shouted at the questioners, "Will you ladies please leave this court alone! The commissioners know nothing about the Board of Managers or how long they hold office! They are there until they either leave or die! All they ever do is go to the Houston Country Club, have lunch, and talk about nothing, and if one of them says, 'What about this move?' then Ben Taub says, 'Let's not talk about that now,' and that's the last we hear of that!"

"How often do they meet?" Priscilla asked, unperturbed.

The commissioner answered angrily, "We don't know! None of us know!"

Priscilla persisted, "Don't you ever get reports?"

"No! We never get anything! We only pay the money! Why don't you go and sit in on a board meeting yourselves and find out, instead of coming here and pestering us with your questions? Go to that private club, and find out for yourselves what the true situation is! Go and find out!"

Shortly thereafter, one of the radio stations, which had taped a speech Debbie had made in front of the Commissioners' Court, telephoned her to say that they had been in touch with Mr. Taub to ask him about the Mercy Fund; he had answered that he knew nothing about it and that he could not accept any moneys raised. Debbie conferred with Ben Ramey, who advised her that, as this was a city-county institution, public funds were involved, which meant that contributions could certainly be made. So Debbie called Mr. Taub, had some trouble getting through to him, but managed to tell him she was the chairman of the Mercy Fund and informed him of Ben Ramey's advice. Mr. Taub answered that he was pleased that private citizens in the town were so interested in his hospital. Debbie remarked, "We feel the hospital is just as much ours as it is yours, Mr. Taub. That's why we are so concerned about it." After that he broke the connection.

Even so, some of the mystery that surrounded the city's attitude toward its charity hospital was now dispelled: obviously, Mr. Taub was the key figure. We discovered that there were three schools of thought about him in connection with the hospital; actually, they were not schools of thought but emotional attitudes. First of all, there were the members of Mr. Taub's own social stratum: the very rich, mainly second-generation, "permanent" Houstonians. To them he was the Dr. Schweitzer of Houston, an aging saint in the eyes of the women, a harmless old eccentric with a bee in his bonnet in the eyes of the men. Whenever we managed to corner one of these permanent Houstonians and started to talk about the hospital, they would first look for a way out, and when they realized there was none, they would blurt out, "Why tell me? Tell Ben! He's the one who looks after it! It's his baby!"

The second emotional attitude was that of some middle-class intellectuals who had met Mr. Taub on occasion and were aware of the fact that he was the sole ruler of the charity hospital, dominating the Board of Managers the way General de Gaulle dominates his Parliament, and treating the City Council and the Commissioners' Court the way the General treats his allies. They saw him as an essentially kind-hearted, civic-minded old man, maybe a little set in his ways, who, if he erred at all, did so with the best intentions. When we started to talk with them about ways and means of improving conditions in the hospital, their reaction was summed up in the words, "Lets go and tell old Ben about this; he gets so upset if anything goes on in connection with J.D. that he doesn't know about."

The third attitude toward Mr. Taub was that of those who were supposed to be his employers: the two local bodies of government. To them he was an insufferable dictator, but they would admit this only in private; there was nothing they could do about him at this point, so they might as well keep their wrath bottled up. They quoted the stubborn refusal of the Board of Managers to admit a Negro doctor to their ranks, or even inside the hospital, despite the fact that the majority of the patients were colored; most frequently they fumed at the intolerable circumstance that neither the City Council nor the County Commissioner's Court, although officially responsible for the hospital's operation, was able to exert any influence whatever upon the board, or even have a look at some of its books, among which a few had not been audited for thirty years. There were rumors of secret funds inside the hospital, of large sums of money vanishing mysteriously, all of it adding up to what was referred to as "The pirate's treasure in the cellars of J.D." But even his enemies could not help admitting, be it under pressure, that, whatever Mr. Taub might have done over the past thirty years in connection with the charity hospital, he had not done it for personal gain or fame. He was, and had always been, a cryptic figure in the background who rarely made a public statement and never appeared in the limelight. He might use the hospital for his soul's salvation or to satisfy a secret craving for power, but they could not think of any other ulterior motives.

Then, a few days before the move of the hospital to its new quarters in the Medical Center, something happened that took everybody by surprise and upset theories held for decades. The City Council and the Commissioners' Court, unable to agree on anything in connection with the charity hospital, had managed to squabble even over its name. One suggested "The Sam Houston Charity Hospital," the other "The Jesse P. Jones Mercy Hospital"; they arrived at a compromise by naming it "The City-County General Hospital"; this name was painted on big billboards at the entrances to the parking lots. Then, out of the blue, both bodies of government announced they had decided to call it the "Ben Taub General Hospital."

The newspapers reacted with eulogies; the man in the street reacted as he had in all cases pertaining to the charity hospital: with complete indifference. The nursing staff were delighted because it was universally assumed that Mr. Taub would take advantage of the situation by refusing to accept the honor until his conditions had been met as to the inadequate budget and the political ball game to which the hospital was subjected. It seemed a unique opportunity for a demonstration that, for once, would make this town sit up and take notice.

But Mr. Taub did not break the silence he had maintained for thirty years. He did not accept, he did not refuse; he reacted to this latest development with the same lofty condescension that had made him such a formidable power in the first place.

The hospital was ceremonially named: but, just as an unknown nurse had opened it with a few words spoken softly in the darkness, an unknown indigent wit gave the new building its popular name.

Nobody ever found out who first thought of it, but the Ben Taub General Hospital became known among the Negro population of Houston as "Uncle Taub's Cabin."

3

WHEN IT BECAME OBVIOUS that Mr. Taub was not in sympathy with the Mercy Fund, we decided that one of us would go to see him, to assure him that we did not intend to interfere with the running of the hospital in any way, that we had no political axe to grind, that all we were interested in was the well-being of the patients. Before we had appointed an emissary, chance decided for us.

The day before the move, Mrs. Kowalski and I went to stock the new Emergency Room. Reactions to her appointment as our new supervisor had been mixed; there was no doubt in anyone's mind that she had the necessary skill and authority, but most people thought that the patients would be the losers. In combination with Mrs. Judd's gentleness and unflagging motherly concern, Mrs. Kowalski's regimental sergeant-major's behavior had seemed salutary at times; but by itself it promised a different Emergency Room indeed, one where the patients would lay to attention as she came in.

Mrs. Kowalski had picked me to assist her when I came on that morning. She had been told that the Emergency Room was as good as ready, but she wanted to make sure of this and take over the first medicines and instruments at the same time. Removal trucks had been parked in front of Emergency for days, loading what seemed like incredible junk, considering it was going into a new building. There had been a scuffle between city and county again on the subject of the beds; one party had suggested the old beds should be moved, the other party had calculated that, as old Jefferson Davis Hospital was going to be the new TB hospital, it was cheaper to put new beds in empty rooms and leave the old ones where they were. We were happy that reason thus prevailed, for nobody had mentioned in the debate that the old beds in J.D. would fall apart the moment they were moved, as they were held together by surgical tape.

When Mrs. Kowalski and I drove up to Ben Taub General, she commented, "This proves that the old guy has no idea of the truth about his own hospital. If anybody would suggest calling it 'The Mopsy Kowalski General' I would flee town."It was the first time I heard the name by which she must be known to her family and friends; it was so wildly unsuited to the redheaded Valkyrie, whose glance could set seven-foot brutes trembling in their shoes, that it seemed to suggest she was leading a double life: Mopsy Jekyll and Nurse Hyde.

The Emergency Entrance was open. A removal truck stood parked outside it; two men in white overalls were unloading a gynecological table that must have been dug up from a forgotten storeroom in the basement of the old hospital. Its leatherette padding was chafed and torn, its chromium peeling, and it had only one stirrup. The men asked Mrs. Kowalski where she wanted them to put it; she examined it coldly. The engineer had the misfortune to turn up from the catacombs at that very moment.

"Mr. Gardner," she said with the prissy voice that always made everybody prick up his ears, for it meant the lighting of a fuse, "do you know about this thing?"

"What thing?" the old Texan asked, dourly.

"This antique instrument of torture here. There must be a mistake. I thought somebody had donated it to the police museum."

Mr. Gardner looked her up and down, unfazed, with dawning male appreciation. "No use getting fresh with me, Mrs. Potifar," he said, with a grin. "That there table is all you're going to get. If you don't like it, go to the administration. I just work here."

He teetered off, leaving Mrs. Kowalski momentarily at a loss, like a Brahma bull downed in a rodeo by an unarmed, bow-legged old cowboy. She consulted her floor-plan and directed the removal men to take the table with the single stirrup to Treatment Room 3. Then she performed her first act as supervisor of Emergency, by writing something in red pencil on a strip of surgical tape, which she then stuck onto the door. It said, ONE-LEGGED GYN PATIENTS ONLY.

When I laughed, she flashed me a black look and said, "I did not mean to be funny, Mr. de Hartog; this is for when the Administrator makes his rounds with the press. One thing everybody might as well realize here and now: as supervisor of this Emergency Room I am not going to be given the J.D. runaround."

I remembered Mrs. Judd and her gentle words spoken softly in the darkness with a fleeting feeling of betrayal, for suddenly my hopes for the Emergency Room were unreasonably raised. They turned out to be justified, at least in this instance: somebody from Mount Olympus saw the notice; the next day the table had two stirrups.

But when Mrs. Kowalski and I made the rounds that morning to see what had to be done to make ER operational, my raised hopes collapsed again. There was nothing: no place to put instrument trays and suture racks, no place to put sheets and linen; there were no storage cupboards in the Utility Room and the only counter space was the floor. But there was another detail that looked even more ominous: in old Jefferson Davis, the Observation Wards had been an integral part of Emergency, separated from the treatment section only by the short passage with the doctors' desk. So, although there was no nursing staff especially assigned to the patients in Observation, those in the treatment section were close at hand and a cry from in there could attract the attention of either a doctor at the desk or a nurse in the GYN room. In this new ER however, the Observation wards were separated from the treatment section by the entrance hall. In themselves the wards were very attractive and a great improvement on the old ones: the beds were new; there were two separate sections, one for men, one for women; in the back were a Utility Room and a kitchen where emergency meals could be prepared. There also were two isolation rooms for contagious diseases, a bathroom with the tub at stretcher height, two washrooms and a dressing room for the nurses. The only trouble was that we did not have the nurses. Apart from myself, who, even if I were to come in every day, could only cover one shift, there was nobody permanently assigned to Observation. The wards could not be used unless there was somebody stationed there, but where to find the people? Already, the Emergency Room was critically understaffed, as was the rest of the hospital; unless our campaign for supplementary salaries was successful it seemed unlikely that the Observation wards would ever be put to use. This clearly was nonsense; an Emergency Room without Observation was useless. Mrs. Kowalski stood, arms akimbo, behind the beautiful new nurses' desk, shaped like the keyboard of a cinema organ; she looked round, and said, "Okay, we'll solve it somehow. Now let's fix up the Shock Rooms and the Suture Rooms, for tomorrow morning at seven sharp we have to be operational."

We worked all day and well into the night, just the two of us, with nothing but our own transportation between the two hospitals to carry loads of suture trays, tray stands, medicine, bandages, IV bottles, IV stands. During all this, the Emergency Room in old J.D. was busy as usual, so we found ourselves in the schizophrenic situation of having to rob the old Emergency Room to fit out the new one. At everything we touched some doctor screamed, "No! Leave that alone! I need that! What the hell do you think you're doing?" When we told him we were fitting out the new Emergency Room for tomorrow, he said, "I don't care! This is where I'm working *now*! Leave that thing alone!"

We made four or five trips lugging things across; during these grueling hours I became filled with admiration for the indomitable Mrs. Kowalski. Her husband turned up at a given moment to take her out to dinner; as we had not eaten since seven that morning, except for a couple of bars of chocolate from the vending machine in the waiting room at J.D., I joined them for a quick meal in a nearby diner. Her husband was a quiet, humorous young man who turned out to be the only male not intimidated by the new supervisor of the Emergency Room, maybe because he knew Mopsy Jekyll and not Nurse Hyde. She behaved in his presence with the endearing snootiness of a woman secure in the knowledge that she can only get away with it as long as her husband lets her, whereas he behaved with the calm dignity of a young naval commander who is conscious of being calm and dignified. But occasionally, when she was not looking, he would gaze at her with the irresistible smugness of a young boy gazing at his new bicycle. For a dessert to our hasty meal, he wolfed down a king-size helping of lemon meringue pie which she had told him sternly not to order because it was six hundred calories; he had ordered it all the same, after telling her calmly to shut up. She went all feminine for a moment, feigning helplessness, pouting over her coffee, refusing the sugar with exaggerated politeness. She was a rare treat to behold for someone who had seen her clench three-hundred-pound wrestlers in a double nelson and slam hypos into their buttocks while they bellowed like bisons. He drove us back to the hospital, told her solicitously in the entrance to the Emergency Room not to overtire herself, she knew that she had to be careful. She kissed him demurely, promised she would take it real easy, gave him a shy little wave as he drove off, then she slammed open the door to the entrance hall and said, "I wonder if that old creep has come up with those stretchers yet. By God, he has not!" Her nostrils flared, her eyes flashed black lightning and she said, "All

204

right, Mr. de Hartog; would you mind? Round up Mr. Gardner, bring him here, and I'll take care of the rest."

I found Mr. Gardner and told him Mrs. Kowalski, that smashing redhead, wanted to see him. He followed me with alacrity and a smirk of virile self-confidence; when, for the rest of the night, he found himself pushing stretchers down corridors, panting and puffing, he would have believed as little as I did that there was one man in the world who could tell this hot-tempered bushwhacker to shut up, and *not* find himself pushing stretchers down corridors as a result. My hopes for the future of ER were raised once again.

Around midnight, she had managed to transform the new Emergency Room in Ben Taub General Hospital from a set of empty offices into an infirmary that could take care of at least one Shock Room case at a time, six suture cases and a normal number of ambulatory emergencies. She had used old stretchers for counters and forced Mr. Gardner to break two sets of shelves out of somebody's office for the linen, while a bookcase from the Women-in-Yellow headquarters, unguarded by their lioness after 5 P.M., found itself in the Utility Room as a storage cabinet, with pieces of surgical tape as nameplates for the classifications. On one of the stretchers left in the hall for patients lay Mr. Gardner, felled in a rodeo for the first time in his life.

When we were through, Mrs. Kowalski looked round with feminine satisfaction. "Well, that'll have to do for now," she said, touching up her hair, which looked as tidy after this stevedore's day as it had in the morning. "That leaves as our most pressing problem the unattended Observation Ward. Maybe I had better ask Mrs. Willoughby for some of her disposable women."

Like any pedantic professor, I was about to point out the correct expression was "women at her disposal," when it occurred to me that she had meant exactly what she said, for, indeed, she treated them that way.

After we had gone out, she locked the doors marked EMERGENCY ENTRANCE with a key and said, "Well, I suppose this is the last time these doors will ever be locked until we move to the next new building, another thirty years from now."

I wanted to remind her of Mr. Gardner, prostrate on a stretcher in the darkness, but concluded that he probably had his own key.

"All right, Mr. de Hartog, thank you and goodnight," she said, curvaceous silhouette against the bleak backdrop of the courtyard. "I'll just pop over to old J.D. and see how things are going there. See you in the morning."

"What time would you like me to come on?" I asked.

Her disembodied voice answered, gaily, from the darkness, "Oh, five o'clock will be fine."

Like all men, except one, I stood muttering strong language for a while in derisive defiance; to say "Good morning, Mrs. Kowalski! Long time no see," with a coward's smile at five o'clock the next morning.

4

THE MOVE went surprisingly well, considering the chaotic labyrinth of cranky customs and bureaucratic idiosyncrasies ingrained upon the hospital for thirty years. In the minds of those familiar with the situation the operation had loomed like the dislodging of an avalanche; but it came off with commendable smoothness. All the private ambulance companies of Houston cooperated gratis; a fleet of ambulances of all sizes, shapes and ages turned up at the appointed hour and began to transport patients in convoys of six cars to the new hospital. The full staff had been called out for the occasion and each convoy was accompanied by a nurse. Mrs. Kowalski left with the first convoy, carrying the narcotics box for the new Emergency Room. It was like carrying out the host from a church building; the moment that box was gone, the ER at old J.D. closed down for the first time in thirty years, and forever.

The first floor to be completely emptied of patients was Male Medicine. Like all other orderlies, I had been ferrying stretchers from the wards down the elevators to the ambulances. When the last bed was cleared on her floor, diminutive Miss Lucas, radiating elation, cast a last look round the ward where she had witnessed so much suffering and so many defeats. "Well," she said, unable to disguise her triumph, "at last my cockroaches will go hungry!"

As the elevator doors closed to take us down, this parting remark seemed to acquire a sudden momentousness, as if, unwittingly, with those few words she had closed the old hospital the way Mrs. Judd had opened the new.

I did not drive to the new hospital in one of the ambulances, but was to take the stationwagon, loaded with remnants of our supplies: four stretcher loads of IV bottles, boxes of instruments, chest-suction sets, bags of bandages and sterile flats.

I was the last of our crew to leave the old Emergency Room. I walked around the dark Observation Ward once more, its beds now bare and stripped of sheets, its curtains gone, its empty bedside tables gaping open. The silence, after decades of the incessant sounds of suffering, was ghostly. When I walked for the last time down that long corridor, Via Dolorosa of so many people, crushed, maimed, sick and broken, I looked up at the ceiling which all of them had seen as in a dream when they were rushed in here on ambulance stretchers. I stood there for a moment, thinking of all the prayers of despair and pain that had been whispered at that ceiling by the thousands of people who had passed here, lain here, waited here, waited for eternities of pain-twisted, nightmare-haunted, unending time. I remembered those I had seen rushed in here—the little girl that had been raped, the babies beaten by their parents, the innocents defiled, the defenseless tortured, the meek derided, the gentle brutalized—and I asked myself if I would ever understand.

Even as I thought that, it seemed as if some yearning, some homing instinct began to draw me towards the new place, the virgin ceiling, the empty ward that was even now being filled. A mysterious urging bade me go there, filled me with the absurd desire to start again to scoop out with my cupped hands the ocean of suffering, now withdrawn from this barren beach. As I slowly walked away, out into the sunlight, I reflected that, as mysterious as the enigma of man's suffering, was his urge to alleviate it.

5

WHEN I ARRIVED outside the new Emergency Room, I saw cameramen of the television stations taking shots for the night edition of the news. While unloading my car, I gathered from their converstion that they wanted to film a so-called first patient to enter the hospital; for some reason they did not want him to be a Negro. As there were no white patients forthcoming, one of the cameramen lay down on a stretcher, was covered with a sheet and carried inside, cameras whirring around him; one of his colleagues, in the nick of time, removed his cigar.

In Emergency, the first cases had already arrived. The broken-down benches in the waiting room, transferred from the old hospital, were already partly filled. After I had parked the station wagon, Mrs. Kowalski sent me on a stretcher hunt through the hospital. I managed to round up a couple outside the elevator on the fifth floor, when no one was looking; as I was pushing my catch in tandem across the main entrance hall in furtive haste, eager to vanish into the corridor that led to Emergency, I was stopped by a voice crying, "De Hartog! I want you to meet my wife! She read your article!"

To my astonishment, I recognized Dr. Kirby, Chief Resident in charge of Emergency, who until then had never betrayed he was aware of my existence. I was just about to shake hands with a charming young woman when a hush fell over the hall and everyone in it, as if, suddenly, we were bathed in a supernatural, seraphic light. I had never before in my life been so acutely aware of the onset of sudden communal reverence, familiar, I suppose, to members of the entourage of the Pope. In the sudden hush, I saw enter through the main door of the building a small cortège, made up of the Administrator, a bodyguard of minor officials, and other dark-suited males, unmistakably political dignitaries, who surrounded like a court of cardinals in mufti one of the most extraordinary human beings I had ever set eyes on.

He was a white-haired, immensely dignified old man who, slowly, with the slight insecurity of step of old age, walked into the building. The most striking part about him was the size of his head, which seemed disproportionately large for his frail, apprehensive body. It was a majestic head, with features of such innate nobility and authority that I knew at once who this was. He advanced toward the center of the hall in majestic isolation, despite the bureaucrats fussily scurrying around him; then he stood still and looked about him with immense dignity and at the same time an oddly humorous awareness of the ultimate futility of this historic moment. The Roman Emperor Claudius, noblest and most erudite of them all, must have entered the first temple dedicated to him after being declared a God by his wily adversaries of the Senate in exactly the same way that Mr. Ben Taub now entered the hospital named after him by his wily adversaries of County

Commissioners' Court and City Council. One look at that granite face with its craggy lines of wisdom, its urbane aloofness and its sphinxlike eyes, and it became obvious why he had not bothered to react to the honor bestowed upon him by the Lilliputians pretending to govern his city.

As we stood there, motionless under the spell of the turning of the hourglass of history, children's voices chirruped outside, doors banged open and in came the first convoy of ambulatory patients from Pediatrics, shepherded by Marjorie, Lucille and, to my surprise, Miss Lucas. There were about a dozen children, some of them in small wheelchairs, others on little crutches, swinging legs in plaster casts; each of the nurses carried two babies. The children raced, wheeled, hopped and limped past the Emperor standing motionless in the center of the hall; none of them noticed him, not even the women, preoccupied as they were with keeping control of their mercurial herd. One little Negro boy on crutches hobbled, with surprising alacrity, toward the candy machine, standing in the otherwise unfurnished hall in solitary, garish splendor. Lucille, despite the babies in her arms, lit out after him with a dash as graceful as that of a ballerina and said in her most sophisticated *Harper's Bazaar* voice, "George Washington! If you think that you can't be spanked because your buttocks are cased in plaster, you have a surprise coming!" She nudged him back toward the elevator, now filled with children; the last we saw was the picture on his back and the words HERE GOES THE MIGHTY MOUSE.

After the doors had slid shut and the floor numbers over them started to flash one by one, I realized that the luminous figure in the center of the hall had been dimmed to almost human candlepower by the little procession. As this was a chance too good to be missed, I excused myself to Mrs. Kirby and accosted Mr. Taub before he was guided on by his entourage for a tour of the hospital.

I introduced myself and asked if I might come and call

on him in the near future on behalf of the Houston Meeting of the Religious Society of Friends. He looked at me slowly with dark, impersonal eyes. They were indeed the eyes of a sphinx; behind them lay, so it seemed, no mere humanity, no terrestial schemes or ambitions, nothing but the starry night, the distant nebulae, the mind of God. The only person remotely like him I had ever met was Queen Wilhelmina of the Netherlands, who had ordered me into her presence after I arrived in England during the war. She had been a woman of unforgettable majesty, despite her disguise of a dowdy housewife; two generations of politicians had withered under her gaze, I myself felt profoundly uncomfortable under the crafty scrutiny of her pale, probing eyes. But even that gaze of utter perception had been unable to hide a comforting humanity, the humorous awareness of a grandiose but intensely feminine old politician. There was no such comforting humanity in the dispassionate gaze of M. Taub as he contemplated me. I now understood the County Commissioners' animosity toward this man, for, under that gaze of interstellar indifference, any political opponent was doomed to diminish gradually from councilman into carpetbagger, pipsqueak, grasshopper, flea, no-see'um, and, finally, nothing.

"I'll be pleased to talk with you," he said in a surprisingly courteous voice. "Why don't you give me a call one of these days, at my office?"

I said I would and thanked him; he rewarded me with a courteous little nod, said, "It will be my pleasure," with great charm, and turned away.

"Hi, friend," a voice said softly behind me.

I turned round and recognized Judge Elliott's gray eminence, Hartsell Gray.

"What are you doing here?" I asked, surprised.

"Rendering unto Caesar," he replied; then joined the cortège that slowly trooped down the corridor toward Emergency.

To everybody's surprise and relief, the move continued to go entirely according to schedule. That night, before darkness fell, all the patients from old J.D. were lying in new beds in the new hospital under new sheets; a cameraman from a television station filmed the deserted Observation Ward of the Emergency Room while a commentary, spoken off screen, pointed out that this proved why extra money for supplementary nursing staff was necessary. Here was a ward with forty beds that could not be used because the hospital did not have the people to staff it.

This adverse publicity, combined with the doctors' angry protest that they could not possibly run an Emergency Room without an Observation Ward, resulted in a sudden and somewhat panicky augmentation of the Emergency Room nursing staff. Indignant enquiries were made as to who had leaked the information about the unattended ward to the news media; nobody squealed. Mrs. Kowalski strolled down the aisle of her freshly conquered territory with her sexiest walk; no man had eyes for the Band-aids on her heels, chafed raw after thirty-six hours of labor, as a result of which she had presented the city of Houston, against odds, with an Emergency Room where it could bring its dying and its dead.

We never went back to old Jefferson Davis. A few nights later, in "Watchem," a column in the *Chronicle* that answered readers' questions, Marjorie found this query: "I hear that the old charity hospital on Allen Parkway is now used for tubercular patients. Could you tell me how intensively the old facility was cleaned before the new patients were moved in?" The answer read, "Old patients out: Monday; new patients in: Tuesday."

Miss Lucas's cockroaches had not gone hungry after all.

6

A FEW DAYS LATER, I went to visit Mr. Taub in his downtown office. I had been told that he was a tobacco merchant, and that he liked to do business in the old-fashioned way. Yet I was unprepared for what I found.

To step into his place of business was to step back into another century. Behind its unobtrusive contemporary façade lay a storehouse as romantic, nostalgic and irrevocably bygone as the great plantations of the Mississippi delta. It looked as if it had not changed since the Confederacy and remained oblivious of any changes in the world outside since. First of all, there was the smell: the warm, spicy smell of vast quantities of cured tobacco, an old-fashioned smell, because every office in Houston of any size was air-conditioned to a point where they all shared the same sterile, dehumidified, chilled atmosphere of a morgue.

Mr. Taub's store was not air-conditioned. Huge old-fashioned fans, suspended from the ceiling, swished somnolently overhead with the childhood sound of the sails of a windmill, scything the summer air. The walls and the floors of cypress wood were smoked to a dark gold hue; shelves, reaching to the ceiling, were jammed with samples of tobacco, jars and flasks, chubby tubs with old-fashioned names painted on them in Victorian lettering like PERUQUE and LATAKIA. The dark warehouse in the back of the store looked huge and dusty, full of secrets and treasures of spice and leaf, like the hold of an East Indian trader.

Behind a wooden counter sat a white lady in an ageless dress, writing in a ledger with pen and ink. Beside her, a display of cigar boxes seemed to be waiting to be picked up by wasp-waisted gentlemen with waxed mustaches, as indeed did she. The pictures on the boxes recalled the era in which the Czar of all the Russias dedicated photographs of himself to Wilhelm the Short-Armed Kaiser, signing them

213

Your doting Nicky. They showed pink, busty girls in Spanish mantillas peeping naughtily under plump, succulent arms or prudishly covering their mouths with fans, leaving the pink promise of their bosoms innocently revealed. The names were equally nostalgic, like *Primas Señoritas* and *La Passionaria de Habaña;* other boxes, bearing the stern countenances of bewigged kings and princes staring haughtily from garlands of tiny dancing Indians, were labeled *Charles II* and *William III.* What the elated little Indians seemed to be celebrating was that all their majesties' wars, murders, plots and passions had amounted to in the end was to have a cigar named after them.

The unconcerned confusion of the wares on the counter and the samples on the shelves suggested the friendly atmosphere of a village store, where a man could buy a pack of pipe cleaners and a ten-cent cigar and imported English cigarettes by the shipload and prime Virginia cured leaf by the freight car. A few old Negro hands were rummaging in the background, wheeling old-fashioned dollies, whisking the dust off bales with a huge green feather duster. My sense of receding into the past deepened when one of them, in answer to my question as to where I could find Mr. Taub, answered, "Mister Ben is in there, sir." Somehow it would have sounded better had he said, "Sir Ben is in there, mister."

Between two high sets of shelves, heavy with dark parcels and dusty samples, smelling like a garden full of night-flowering tobacco, was an open door, leading to a small office. Behind a simple desk, cluttered with cozy junk, sat Mr. Ben, in shirtsleeves, as impressive and incongruous in these surroundings as if I had stumbled upon Moses coming down a mountain carrying two tables while on my way to a ski lift. I knew even before we started that Gilles had been right, when he had called me "a babe in the woods." I had sat earnestly listening to many theories, explanations and philosophies concerning the enigma of

Houston's attitude toward its charity hospital; I now knew that I could have saved myself the trouble. Thirty years ago, the city had deposited its conscience in Ben Taub's personal strongbox, and that was where it remained until this day. Everything to do with the hospital began and ended at this desk.

When Mr. Taub and I talked, we talked courteously like Southern gentlemen, but while we sat chatting amiably about harmless generalities, the whole confusing picture of recent events slowly seemed to clarify. There had obviously been a time when the Quaker volunteers fitted into his scheme of things; my letter to the *Chronicle* and the ensuing rumpus had reinforced the stand taken by Dr. Olsen, Dean of the Medical School, in his interview with the *Houston Press* in January, which Mr. Taub must have authorized, if not suggested. We had helped to achieve his objective, which had been the cancelation of any budget cut or plans for selling the new hospital, and to put both City Council and Commissioners' Court under public pressure, to make them fly at each other's throats again. It was all ridiculously simple, once you had the key to the enigma: the courteous old man behind that desk. As long as he could keep the two bodies of local government that were supposed to control him fighting each other, there was no danger that they would ever challenge the Board of Managers of which he was the chairman. The board was obviously nothing but a ventriloquist's dummy on his knee; one look at the man was sufficient to make anyone realize that he could never be the chairman of any board, but only what he was born to be: a monarch, holding court.

As we talked on, something else became apparent. He was a sincere and dedicated guardian of what he regarded as his wards: the destitute Negroes of Houston. The fact that he was unaware he had turned into an anachronism was not his fault; like Albert Schweitzer, he had saved the honor if not the soul of his generation. It was the immortal tragedy of Man that both of them had become relics of the past by surviving the generation they had saved. What made Albert Schweitzer an anachronism was not the fact that his hospital was backward, unhygienic and dirty, but that he refused to train native nursing personnel as, in his words, the Negro was not ready for it; and it soon became apparent that Mr. Taub concurred in this opinion.

When finally he and I began to talk business, I was overcome by an immense respect for the man and an eerie sense of having wandered through a mirror, back into the past. He talked about the Negro as if we were still carrying the White Man's Burden, as if Lincoln had just been shot and Stanley were still looking for Livingstone in darkest Africa. He told humorous stories about childlike, uninhibited Negro wenches who had come to his hospital six years in a row to have a baby, each time from a different father; he told me how he had chatted with one of them as she lay in his maternity ward and how he had asked, "Jenny, did you do this for money?" "No, Mister Ben," she had answered, "Ah does this for lurve." So he had advised her that she should charge her next lover money and give it to him, to help pay for the hospital.

The anecdote conveyed everything: his sincere concern for the poor, his concept of himself as the great white father and of his beloved Negroes as jolly, amoral Stone Age creatures producing seasonal litters of pickaninnies for him to look after. He had done so for thirty years with patience, understanding and an unflagging sense of responsibility; nobody could deter him or get round him, nobody could trick him into a position where the rapacious rascals of the political mafia in this town could get between him and the helpless mass of big-hearted, pea-brained sick people with whose care he was entrusted. He said that nobody in Houston cared about the charity hospital, but he did not have an inkling that he was partly to blame for this himself. If thirty years ago the city had handed its conscience over to him, now anybody daring to arouse it without his permission was an enemy of the helpless dependent on his care. For, by doing so, that person introduced an element of emotion into the conflict that interfered with his own plans for the future of the charity hospital. He knew this city, he knew its people; he had set out to improve the care for the indigent sick more than thirty years ago and never had he committed the error of increasing the speed of progress to where it might become controversial. In matters of public welfare, the only permanent results in this town were achieved at the speed of a glacier; compared to the charity hospital of thirty years ago, even Jefferson Davis had looked like a City of Hope. The new building, with its comfortable beds, its marvelous equipment, its glorious possibilities, was the result of a lifetime of tenacious dedication to the cause of the sick pauper in this town, and nothing—no power, no money, no threat of violence, no temptation, not even the subtle lure of naming that hospital after him—could provoke him into accelerating, recklessly, the speed of his steady encroachment, the irrevocable progress of the glacier. And so, thanking me for my interest in behalf of his people, he now suggested that I go home, wherever that might be, and leave the hospital to him.

When I asked him, man to man, why he refused to endorse the Mercy Fund, thus giving people to understand that it was suspect, he answered with the question, "Why did you people tell those lies about my hospital?"

"Lies?" I replied, astounded. "What lies?"

"The conditions you described are not true, and you know it."

"But, Mr. Taub . . ." I said, not believing my ears, "how can you say this? You know the hospital yourself!"

"Exactly!" he answered. "I know the hospital better than anyone else, better than any volunteer orderly or student nurse. The conditions you described do not exist, for I have never seen them."

As I sat staring at him, incredulously, it dawned on me that he must be right. He probably had never seen what conditions were like. No man could enter the hospital the way I had seen him enter—like Moses descending Mount Zion—and expect to look around at his ease, unnoticed. I had heard it said that the moment the word came that Mr. Taub had arrived in the hospital, people raced round the floors whisking top sheets off the beds and throwing on clean ones, leaving the patients to lie in the filth underneath. He had, on one occasion, walked through the waiting room of the Emergency Clinic in old J.D., addressed at random a man on the benches, asking how long he had waited; when the answer was "three hours" he had ordered the Administrator accompanying him to call the doctor in charge. When the surgical resident turned up, bewildered and preoccupied, wondering why the hell he had been called out of the Shock Room, he was indignantly shown the man who had waited three hours, and ordered to attend to him at once. The doctor had not mentioned that others had been waiting for as long as twenty-four hours; he had said, "Certainly, sir. Thank you, sir. Goodbye, sir," and gone back to his work, leaving Mr. Taub and his court to move on with an air of accomplishment.

I realized that the real difference between our two worlds was that he did not work inside the hospital, whereas I did. The two worlds were irreconcilable, even inside the hospital. Mrs. Willoughby and her Women-in-Yellow knew as little about the truth of the hospital as he. One of these Women had written to the *Chronicle* about *The abuse of Mercy*, stating that, after working in old J.D. behind a desk for many hours, she had become convinced that there were a number of Negroes who profited undeservingly from the services provided. None of us nursing volunteers had quarreled with her on that score, because we did not sit behind desks; but when she had gone on to write, *"I have yet to see a bed propped up with a chair or to see patients lying on filthy sheets, and I have moved freely and unannounced on every floor of the hospital at various times of the day as I delivered mail or packages that were brought to the Information Desk,"* she had received a call from Priscilla and Debbie which had ended with her collapsing in tears and asking how she could make amends. If an obviously dedicated woman could deliver mail and packages to patients without seeing anything wrong, how could a man who arrived preceded by a host of angels blowing trumpets be expected to see the truth? He was not to blame; he would never know the truth until he put on a scrub suit and joined us at work, not for a day or a week, but for months.

But, surely, even he must be aware that the state of cleanliness in his hospital was not up to minimum standards? Those storm troopers might manage to whisk off dirty top sheets and replace them with fresh ones in a matter of minutes, they could not clean floors that had not been washed for weeks. When I asked him about this, he answered, "You should go and see how those people live at home. Compared to the state of their own homes, the hospital is a luxury hotel."

He said it innocently, without malice; it was Schweitzer's answer, the answer of the past. Why give them a bed-bath? They never take a bath at home. Why brush their teeth? They never brush them at home. Why comb their hair? They never comb it themselves. It meant condemning the illiterate and the damned to remain illiterate, and be damned.

But who was I to judge him? All I could do in good conscience was to get up and thank him for the time he had given me, and hope for the best. We parted courteously; as I clasped his old dry hand, he said, unexpectedly, "I am convinced that you are an honorable man. Why can't you leave the political side of the hospital to me?"

It was an important moment. I let it slip by, for I simply did not know what to say. The temptation to give in to him was very strong; I was acutely aware that he had given thirty years of his life to a political struggle in which we had been engaged only a month. I wanted to say that I was convinced he was an honorable man too, and that the most intelligent thing would be for us all to sit down together and explore the possibilities for cooperation. But I knew it was too late for that, too late in his life and, in my own case, also in mine. However much I might secretly yearn to submit to such a venerable father figure and hand over my conscience to him as the city had done thirty years before, I was a man now. So I smiled and shook his hand once more and left the little office and crossed the dark warm warehouse perfumed with the scents of Dixie and said goodbye to the lady behind the counter, her cigars, her pipe cleaners and her packages of imported British cigarettes. The last I saw was the old Negro with the green feather duster, staring after me like a cigar store Indian with his headdress in his hand.

When I stood in the hot, roaring street once more, it all seemed to have been a dream, a jumbled rehash of Southern novels half remembered. But one thing remained as I slowly walked to the parking lot on the shady side of the street. The whole thing might be remembered as a pilgrimage to a shrine of the magnificent, melancholy soul of the deep South, if it had not been for his one remark, "It is not true, for I have not seen it."

Neither as Friends, nor as volunteer orderlies and nurses' aides in the hospital that bore his name, should we rest until he had.

7

W<small>HEN I CAME HOME</small>, I found Marjorie in the back garden. She was squatting in a patch of weeds that had once been a flower bed, doing something with a metal claw and an out-size spoon which looked new and shiny. On the lawn behind her lay a gaily colored piece of cardboard to which the tools had obviously been stapled. *"Transform Your Backyard into a Luscious Eden in a Jiffy"* it said. *"Scientifically Designed Miniature Spade and Hoe, Success Guaranteed or your Money Cheerfully Refunded."* Around her sat three neighborhood dogs, intently watching, as if she were digging up bones for them. All three dogs started to bark furiously the moment I appeared, defending her garden, prancing backward vociferously as I went toward her. When I bent over to kiss her, they sat down with a sigh of boredom. For some reason, my kissing her always seemed to depress dogs.

"How did it go?" she asked.

I told her, following her into the kitchen, talking all the time, while she poured out two glasses of lemonade that we took back into the garden. When finally we sat in the rattan chairs, warding off wasps who thought that a glass of lemonade on a hot day was a good idea too, I wound up my report by saying, "As it is obvious that he is the one who makes all final decisions, the only one hope for the Mercy Fund would be to get his cooperation. But he is not going to give that, unless we can somehow open his eyes to the truth about his own hospital. How are we going to do that?"

She sat in silence for a while, watching a wasp drink lemonade from her glass, while a spaniel with long ears full of burrs, his chin on her chair, gazed up at her with insufferable adulation. I sat waiting for her comment with growing impatience when the son of our neighbor, a professor in engineering, came grinding toward us on his tricycle, got stuck in the grass and sat staring at us motionless for a while with his hands on the handlebars. Then he climbed off his machine, toddled toward her and, from a distance of six feet, stood still to stare at her with somber intensity, legs crossed, hands in pants, in urgent need to go to the bathroom. What with the drinking wasp, the mooning dog and the staring toddler, I began to feel outnumbered; I was about to say something fatuous when it occurred to me how typical this scene was of her. At first sight, she seemed just a standard English girl with all the mannerisms of a proper British education, the kind of girl that bores find themselves left with at parties. It was only after watching her, unobserved, for quite a while that you began to discern the real person behind the correct exterior, the bland British behavior, the impeccable manners, the maddening moderation. Only animals, toddlers, babies in the Newborn Nursery and sick old women in Female Medicine saw it at once. I had rarely caught a glimpse of her on the floors; we seldom came across each other in the hospital. But a few images remained in my memory: her gently stroking the hair of a crying girl in a bed by a window; her giving a back rub to a wrinkled, ancient human skeleton that lay moaning quaveringly with luxurious pleasure. I remembered her coming home from the hospital, her face drawn with tiredness but around her an inexpressible, tranquil tenderness, saying, "I had such a sad old lady to look after tonight, a ninety-three-year-old leper," to continue in the same tone of calm serenity, "Yes, thank you, darling, I would love a glass of something. Look in the fridge, there may be some cranberry juice left." And now, there I sat, jealous of a wasp, a spaniel and a child that had to go to the bathroom, imperiously waiting for her comment on my summing up of all the reasons that made our defeat inevitable at the hands of that bizarre combination of guardian angel and evil genius, the invincible Ben Taub.

Then, for no reason at all, it occurred to me that I sat waiting for an answer that had already been given. Whatever she might eventually say, she embodied the answer herself. For one moment, as we sat there in silence, I saw, as in a glass darkly, that the only power on earth stronger than the harsh paternalism of the absentee White Father was the power that had guided the hand that stroked the crying girl's hair.

"Darling," I said, "could you please take our little visitor to the bathroom? I can't stand his agony any longer."

And then I found all of them staring at me: wife, dog and boy, three pairs of eyes gazing with shocked reproach at the bully that would not let a wasp drink, a spaniel swoon, his wife think or a three-year-old boy squeeze his own pinny in peace.

It obviously was not my day.

CHAPTER 7

A FEW DAYS LATER, at a meeting of the hospital committee, Debbie told us that the River Oaks Methodist Church had canceled a speaking engagement on the subject of the Mercy Fund, for which one of us had been invited. We had been giving quite a few speeches after the Mercy Fund started, to try to raise money; we had spoken at coffees and fraternity meetings, to social clubs and sewing circles. The net results had been slender, but at least we had been listened to with patient, though vaguely commiserative sympathy. The cancelation by the River Oaks Methodist Church was ominous.

Four weeks had gone by, the Mercy Fund now contained three thousand dollars toward the sixty that we had set as our goal; the professional fund raiser had been proven right when he said it was impossible to raise money for the charity hospital in Houston. Now that our efforts were being sabotaged behind the scenes by invisible powers, to continue our campaign began to look like mere obstinacy. While the discussion floundered, one of our members, a boy called Bob Cogswell who worked as a volunteer orderly in Male Medicine, calmly announced that he was so outraged by the town's indifference to the misery of the patients in the hospital that he had started a hunger strike in protest. We discovered, to our alarm, that he had already gone forty-eight hours without food and that he planned to go on fasting until the people of Houston had filled the Mercy Fund, even if it meant the end of him. He felt he had to do whatever he could; he had no money; all he could contribute was himself.

After he told us this, we sat for a moment in uncomfortable silence; nobody knew quite what to say. He was one of our least colorful members, a quiet, rather mousy young man with glasses and a crewcut and the stern manner of the congenitally shy. I had considered him to be the least concerned of our four men now working in the hospital; I had seen him once or twice in Male Medicine as I brought a patient up from Emergency; he had struck me as dexterous and active, but not particularly kind. And now, there he sat—obviously highly embarrassed, looking more stern than ever; and here we sat—stunned by the sudden realization that we had not known him at all.

It took our combined powers of persuasion to make him at least postpone his plan a few weeks. We were greatly relieved when, finally, he agreed to do so; we suddenly knew him well enough to realize that he would indeed have fasted to death, and we had to come to know Houston well enough to realize that it would not have cared if he did. But he achieved this much: not one of us dared come up with the obvious and sensible suggestion that we should admit defeat.

I drove home after the meeting along the dark freeway, part of the rippling river of red taillights underneath the stars. Again I saw the glorious vision of Houston ablaze with light, shrine of hope and promise, scintillating like a jewel case in the night, and suddenly I felt a deep, wordless loathing, an unutterable contempt for that fatuous town with its callous disregard for humanity and compassion, its shabby soul. But I remembered in time not to fall into the familiar trap of anger and indignation; with a conscious effort of will I tried to transform the destructive energy boiling inside me into a creative one by the old Quaker device of concentrating on "that of God" in the city, rather than that of the devil.

It worked, but not quite in the way I had intended. As by magic, my anger against the heartless city turned round and faced me. I suddenly no longer glowered at a town with such self-righteous fury, but at a mirror. A moment ago I had been outraged at the thought that, after all the pointless self-sacrifices of the past like Mrs. Judd's and her nameless friend's, now a boy was ready to starve himself to death to redeem this town's indifference to human suffering; then, in a flash, the question faced me: "What have *you* done?" Well, for heaven's sakes! I had worked in the Emergency Room for nine months; I had written an article throbbing with compassion. . . . A laconic voice seemed to say calmly, from that radiant town, "Bully for you."

It came as an utter surprise. Instead of feeling a better man, I felt worse. Instead of being mad at Houston, which was not an altogether unpleasant sensation, I now was mad at myself, which was something else again. I tried to shrug the whole matter off, but I found to my alarm that I was unable to do so. While I drove home, one thing imposed itself on me with clarity. If I really was involved in this thing, and not just toying with it, it was now my turn to make a gesture of commitment that had some reality to it, were it only for my own peace of mind. My work as an orderly was not enough, it had not been enough for Bob Cogswell. And I was the crusader who had opened his big mouth in the paper and hollered his wrath. I had to do *something*, something that would show, unequivocally, that I was prepared to go out on a limb. Writing that article had not been going out on a limb at all; the only real risk I had ever run was being hit on the head by a package of diapers. If Mrs. Judd's haunting face, and now Bob

Cogswell's, made any sense at all to me, then I should, rather than sit in a warm sitz bath of poetic indignation and tut-tut about heartless Houston, come out with a concrete gesture of commitment, or forever hold my peace. And then, suddenly, everything fell into place. All at once, the whole plan was there, as if it had been waiting in the wings.

Hubert Mewhinney, wit of the *Houston Post*, had called Houston "a whisky and trombone town," and he was right. Never mind how many museums for modern art, concert halls and universities they might build, this was a gamblers' town. If the boys in the backroom would not respond to a cry from the heart, they might respond to a bet thrown onto the gaming table. It was pointless to appeal to them as humanitarians, for even they knew that this was not what they were. I should appeal to them as what they knew themselves to be: crap shooters.

At home, I found a sandwich under a plate on the kitchen table and a note from Marjorie propped up against a glass of milk: *"Dearest, I'll probably just miss you but I have been called to old J.D.; somebody did not show up in Premature tonight. I'll try not to be too late. Love, M. (Now EAT this! Not just cookies!)"*

I went upstairs to my study, sat down at the typewriter and wrote a letter to the *Houston Chronicle*, saying that, as a bet with the community, I herewith put ten thousand dollars on the gaming table, being one month's supplementary wages for lower-echelon nursing staff in the charity hospital, on condition that the town matched this with fifty thousand of its own within thirty days. If not, I would pocket my ten thousand and take my business elsewhere.

It was in the best style of the Mississippi steamboats; the only snag was that I did not have ten thousand dollars. The nest egg that all authors are supposed to have was considerably less in my case. The only way to raise the money was to borrow it from someone; and what better stimulus could there be to a local civic effort than to borrow the money in Houston? Let somebody join me in the gamble. A new play of mine was about to be tried out on the campus of the University of Houston, so they could see there was still some fire underneath the pot; I added, as casually as I knew how, that I hoped somebody in this town would loan me the ten thousand dollars with, for collateral, my future earnings as a playwright. When I had finished, I wondered what Marjorie would say to this; in anticipation I went down to the kitchen, ate the sandwich and drank the milk.

She came home late that night, smelling of babies, and very tired. I did not read her the letter; I just told her its main points.

She looked at me in blank astonishment.

"What on earth gave you that hare-brained idea?"

I told her how, ever since my first visit to the new hospital with Mrs. Judd, I had been haunted by the thought of those two girls who had given everything; then I told her about Bob Cogswell and his fast.

She listened intently; finally she said, "I don't know much about gambling, but I have been trying to understand. All I can see is that you are planning to bet this town that they won't pay any money, is that right?"

"That's right."

"In other words, if you win the bet, you lose your money. Is that right?"

"That's right."

"But, because you don't have the money, you ask them to loan it to you, so you bet them that they won't give you any money with their own money—is that right?"

"There you go again!" I said, impatiently. "You've lost the thread again."

"I'm sorry," she said, "but I'm honestly trying to understand. The way people who read your letter will try to understand."

I sighed and rubbed my eyes and asked, wearily, "All

right, sweetie, just tell me: what do *you* read from that letter? Let's take it from there."

"Oh, the letter itself is clear enough," she said. "There can be no doubt that it's written by a man who is hopping mad with the whole town of Houston for doing nothing about their charity hospital after he told them to do something. Now he is shaking his fists at them, telling them they are sinners and damned, while passing the collection plate at the same time. Isn't that about it?"

"Not quite," I said, with self-control. "I have put ten thousand dollars on that collection plate myself, if I may remind you."

"But, sweetheart," she said with tenderness, putting her hand on mine, "you haven't, you haven't *got* ten thousand dollars. You want *them* to put ten thousand dollars on the plate and agree it is yours, otherwise there won't be a game. Can't you see?"

"Against interest!" I cried. "I'll pay them a normal interest, and give them my future earnings as a playwright for security!"

She looked at me intently, in a last, strained effort to understand. She obviously did in the end, because she smiled.

"Thank heaven," I said, "you're beginning to see the light. Are you?"

"Oh, I've seen it all along," she said, smiling. "If you want to play poker with the boys of Houston, with the hospital as a pretext, by all means. Who knows, maybe their thinking is as muddled as yours. But what happens if they don't take you on?"

"Then I'll have to borrow the money in Europe," I said. "Would that be okay with you?"

"I don't know," she said. "If you ask me: 'Do you mind losing ten thousand dollars?' I scream. But I am so completely out of my depth in this thing that all I can do is accept your, well, I don't know . . ."

"My judgment."

"Your destiny, rather, I suppose. We agreed, the night you wrote that first letter, that there would be more to it than just your writing a letter to the editor. We knew there would be consequences we could not foresee, and I was ready to face them. If this is one of them, so be it."

"All right," I said, with the small, bizarre sensation of being an impostor who had taken advantage of a trusting woman. "What about some Ovaltine?"

We had our Ovaltine, and so to bed.

2

THE STORY of the Dutchman betting Houston one to five that it did not care a damn about its charity hospital, and risking ten grand in the wager, became an item for caustic commentators in the papers and on television. The general reaction was one of benevolent disbelief. When Judge Elliott stated in an interview, with obvious sincerity, that to him the hospital issue was so serious and so personal that he would cut his wrist over it, one commentator observed that what with the Judge's blood and Mr. de Hartog's confederate money the future of the charity hospital looked bright.

I was forced to the conclusion that the whisky-and-trombone town would take me seriously only after it had bitten my silver dollars one by one and dropped them on the bar, to hear if they rang true; obviously, they would not believe me until I had substantiated my claim in public. But no gambler came forward to put his money on my future as a playwright. A week later, the play I had composed for my students to demonstrate the conception, birth, growth and first production of a Broadway success was performed in the campus theatre for a limited season of three days, and so thoroughly trounced by the critics of all papers that further appeals to civic-minded Houstonians to invest their money in my future as a playwright seemed inopportune. In a way, I was glad that the play no longer figured in the already fairly confused picture; I appealed for the loan in Europe, by cable, explaining the circumstances, and received the reply that the money would be forwarded at once, at four percent.

So far, my bet with the town had failed to result in an appreciable increase in the contributions to the Mercy Fund. Again, the majority came from the poorest sectors of the city, the Negro and the Mexican quarters, most of them anonymous. Obviously, the gamblers were waiting to see the color of my money. So, when my check from Europe arrived, I decided to put it in escrow with the Houston Bank and Trust Company, and to do so publicly. Television stations and newspapers were informed that I would be handing over the check to the Chairman of the Board of the bank at ten o'clock the next morning; an accountant, highly regarded in town, helped set up the appointment in a theatrical way. I was to arrive in front of the bank in my car, the television cameras would film me as I walked up to the entrance, then I would go in. Once inside, I would wait for the cameramen to run ahead of me to the second floor; there they would take up position in the Chairman of the Board's private office and film the handing over of the check. The episode would end with a close-up of the check, showing the amount clearly to assure everybody that I had indeed, as the saying went, put my money where my mouth was.

The morning turned out to be ideal for outdoor camera work. Marjorie, who had been fairly leery of the whole procedure, insisted all the same that I put on my good summer suit for the occasion. I had not worn that good summer suit for a couple of years; obviously I had put on some weight in the meantime; I still fitted into the pants, but it was a tight squeeze. With the check in my breast pocket I set out for the bank, on the late side to give the cameramen ample chance to get there before me. I did not feel exactly like Count Leo Tolstoy; on the other hand, I did not feel exactly like one of the Ringling Brothers either. Without misgivings other than whether my shirt was blue enough for the cameras, I drove to my destiny.

Twice I had been the subject of a demonstration how God, if He interferes in human affairs at all, tends to deal with those who glance in the mirror in passing to see if their halo is showing. Any other biped of moderate intelligence would have suspected, after the incident of the bomb and the actor pecked on the head, that he was in for some more of the same, but not I.

I arrived in front of the Houston Bank and Trust Company, a square black marble building reminiscent of Mecca's Ka'Ba. The television cameramen were there, and I dallied for a moment, fussing with my seatbelt to give them a chance to focus. Then I opened the door, carefully avoiding any acknowledgment of their presence, and strolled toward the glass doors of the bank, pretending not to notice the massive gaze of a crowd of secretaries who peered down at me from the windows of the second floor. I wanted the cameras to get a good look as I opened the door to the bank, so, instead of pushing it open by hand, I did so with my shoulder, to give them a frontal view of their subject. Maybe it was that unusual strain, maybe it was just metal fatigue, but as I pressed the door to go in, the zipper on my pants burst open from top to bottom, affording the cameras a frontal view of such generosity that the ten thousand dollars were peanuts in comparison.

The first intimation I had of something being wrong was a sudden sense of relief around the hips; then one of the cameramen seemed to go into a nosedive with his instrument, barely catching it before it hit the sidewalk. I looked down, saw with heart-stopping horror what had happened, looked up, saw the mesmerized gaze of the massed secretaries on the second floor, and sought refuge in the gesture of Adam in Paradise on Medieval paintings.

The cameraman of Channel 11, who had collapsed with laughter and dropped his cigar in the process, came to my aid. He suggested that I take off my jacket and drape it over my arm before going in. I did want to go in, didn't I? Surely I didn't expect them to wait around for me to go home and change my pants? So let's get cracking, pardner, and make the best of it; ha ha, hee hee, hoo hoo.

Mortified, I took off my jacket, draped it over my arm, let the cameramen enter first and then I moved, no longer nonchalantly, into the building.

I had to wait at the top of the stairs until they had installed themselves in the office of the Chairman of the Board. I went to great pains not to betray how conscious I was of the titters and the snickers among the secretaries. Then someone in the doorway of the Chairman's office whistled on his fingers, and I marched.

The office was big and impressive. Behind a big glass desk rose a short old man, asking, nervously, "Listen, does Ben know of this?"

"Smile, Mr. Chairman!" one of the boys cried. "That's it! Now shake him by the hand!"

While the cameras whirred, I stretched out a hand to him across the desk, pressing my jacket against my midriff with the other, and said, "How do you do, sir?"

The Chairman of the Board went on shaking my hand, asking, "This okay? This the way you want it? Can I stop now?"

"You can stop," a voice answered. "We got that fine."

We both sat down, opposite each other. His desk was empty except for a pen tray, a spotless blotter and a plastic prism, each facet of which showed a color snapshot of a grinning baby, in various stages of teething.

"What's the matter?" the Chairman asked, solicitously. "Got a stomach ache?"

I answered "No, no. I—er—I just had a mishap with my

pants, that's all."

"You mean, you bust your fly?" he asked, concerned. He opened a drawer. "Here," he said, "take these, go to my bathroom, right over there, and see if you can fix it." He handed me a handful of paper clips.

I went into his private bathroom, while the newsmen blew their noses. Inside, in the isolation of a marble toilet lined with mirrors, I looked at myself, my pants, the paper clips, and finally got God's message.

When it was all over, and the gentlemen of the news media had left, the Chairman and I signed a sober document stating that my ten thousand dollars would be put in escrow for thirty days as from the date of signing; they would be paid into the Mercy Fund as soon as it was proved, to the satisfaction of the Houston Bank and Trust Company, that said fund contained fifty thousand dollars or more. When the signatures had been blotted we shook hands, and I left the building like a guest leaving a burning hotel.

3

THAT NIGHT we watched television full of apprehension, switching from channel to channel to catch the episode on each of the three newscasts. We saw, to our relief, that none of them had used their Rabelaisian footage. The next morning Channel 11 called, and invited me over for a chat.

Channel 11 was the CBS station, and not affiliated with a newspaper as were the other two. It used its independence profitably by tackling issues that the other stations, for reasons too delicate to mention, avoided. "The boys at 11" were a tough lot of characters, certainly the newsroom; their director, a tall handsome hustler called Nick Gearhart, offered the station's full cooperation in our drive, on condition I would come clean and name the culprit. Surely the filthy mess inside that hospital was somebody's fault; all right, whose was it? When I said that it was nobody's fault except maybe his own, for not noticing sooner that there was something wrong with Jeff Davis Hospital, like everyone else in Houston, he lost his temper. He said there was no point in trying to be smarter than he; there must be somebody inside that hospital who thrived on secrecy and silence—all right, *who* was it? What had he done? When had he done it? Where could he be found?

With that question, he touched upon the essence of our campaign. As Friends, we had at first refused to blame anyone on principle; as time went on we had realized that indeed there was no one to blame for the deplorable conditions inside the charity hospital except the people of the town themselves. Their huge indifference over fifty years and their refusal to provide even a minimal sum of money to run the place in a humane fashion meant that no one in control of the hospital itself ever had a fighting chance to do a proper job. In the face of Houston's attitude toward its indigent sick, as revealed to us during our campaign, Mrs. Willoughby's dogged perseverance of twenty-four years became impressive; and even those who did not agree with the autocratic way in which Mr. Taub wielded his power had to admit that he had performed a miracle with the meager means at his disposal; the new hospital was a monument to his unshakable determination. Even the City Council and the Commissioners' Court could no longer be saddled with the blame; as elected people's representatives, all they could do, when all was said and done, was to implement the people's wishes. It was the people of Houston that wished their charity hospital to be run as a human dog pound that merely kept the dead and the dying off the streets; if Nick Gearhart wanted to denounce them to themselves, he was welcome to it.

But Nick Gearhart was not going to be put off that

easily. He was convinced there was a villain somewhere, trying to hide from the righteous wrath of public opinion, and he was going to ferret him out. He tried to rattle my composure by engaging me in a breath-taking slanging match. The boys in the newsroom, undisturbed, went on hammering on their typewriters; his secretary sat polishing her nails, while waiting for something in our conversation worth taking down. Our heated dialogue reached its crisis when I said, in the middle of an argument, "You may think, 'Oh well, he's just a nice guy . . .'" He bellowed, "I do *not* think you're a nice guy! For all I know, you may be a conniving bastard! For all I know, you may be doing this as a publicity stunt to sell your lousy books!"

All I could answer was, "So what? What difference would it make to the patients in the hospital what my motives are, so long as we get the money to relieve their misery?"

For some reason, this convinced him. He suddenly slumped down in a chair, that looked as if it had seen him coming, and lit a cigarette. When he continued, he sounded calm and pleasant, as if all that went before had not been. "Well, where do we go from here?" he asked. "You want fifty thousand dollars? We'll get you fifty thousand dollars. What else do you want?"

I was convinced that he meant what he said. To collect fifty thousand dollars must be no problem for a station with the power and the sheer hutzpah of Channel 11.

They too found out in due course that they might be able to raise fifty thousand dollars in Houston for anything under the sun, but not for the charity hospital. Their campaign was generous, thorough and professional; it made no impact whatsoever.

The Mercy Fund, after six weeks, contained four thousand dollars.

4

THE INVITATIONS to speak on the subject of the hospital to clubs and coffees petered out too, after that cancelation by the River Oaks Methodist Church. This time we really felt like admitting defeat, but there was one speaking engagement left which we intended to keep, unless they canceled that one too. It was to be to a group of matrons in a River Oaks Garden Club; if we wanted to find ourselves in the heart of enemy territory, there was our chance.

It was not canceled; Lucille, Debbie and I turned up in advance of the appointed hour and thus had ample opportunity to be intimidated by the overwhelming noise of a hundred and fifty women gossping on their feet, drinking coffee. Finally I faced them as the first speaker, after the chairs had finished scraping, the cups and saucers ceased to clatter and the chairman had introduced me with a bright but slightly apprehensive little speech, like a woman who had rashly agreed to smash a bottle to christen a barge.

I made our final appeal for funds on behalf of the charity hospital to our fellow citizens of Houston. I told them how we had first got into the hospital, what we had found there, what we had done; how we had made it a concern of the Meeting and worked anonymously and in silence until the day of the budget cut. I told them that the move to the new hospital had changed nothing, that it was only a matter of time before the new hospital would be in the same deplorable condition as the old one had been, unless the community provided more money for nurses' aides, orderlies and housekeeping staff. I said that Houston was fortunate in having one great citizen, who for thirty years had taken care of the indigent sick on everybody's behalf: Mr. Ben Taub. . . .

Here I had to pause for applause.

I continued by saying that the hospital, so deservedly

named after him, should be a monument to the memory of his selfless devotion. . . .

I had to pause for applause again.

I concluded by saying that unless the community saw to it that this hospital was given the money to comply with minimum standards of patient care, it would turn from a monument to our great citizen into a desecration of his memory.

I paused, but this time there was no applause. I announced that there would now be a short interval, during which the ladies would have the opportunity to contribute to the Mercy Fund, which intended to help provide minimum acceptable nursing care for the patients at Ben Taub General over a period of six months. This was a stop-gap measure to give the people of Houston a chance to decide, calmly and coolly, how to pay for their two charity hospitals out of public funds so as to ensure a treatment of their indigent sick that would be commensurate with the times. After the interval there would be an opportunity to put questions.

For ten minutes, amidst a babel of voices and clattering crockery, I sat watching Debbie and Lucille at their little table in the back, receiving donations. When the interval was over and all the ladies had ranged themselves once more in rows in front of the rostrum, I was handed a folded slip of paper by Debbie with on it the total of the contributions received. I announced, after creating a silence by staring at the paper incredulously, that the one hundred and fifty ladies present, inhabitants of the richest neighborhood in the richest city in the world, had contributed toward the alleviation of intolerable conditions in their charity hospital the sum of eleven dollars. I also announced that now we would be happy to answer any questions they might care to put on the subject.

As I sat waiting for the first question, I registered to my own amazement that I did not feel any anger or animosity, but relief. At last, we had done all we could; now we could go back into the hospital and be anonymous orderlies and nurses' aides again. I hoped we would all soon forget about this embarrassing excursion into evangelism.

The ladies and I sat for a few minutes observing one another with amused interest; then, somewhere in the center, a young matron rose and said, with the unmistakable voice of breeding and affluence, "I gather that you are surprised at the small amount of money you have received today."

I answered that indeed this was so, but that this surprise did not imply judgment. It was the prerogative of every individual to act upon his own conscience. We had felt that we could not let our neighbors condone by ignorance a situation that we personally considered to be intolerable. The fact that their opinion did not concur with ours was immaterial.

"I realize that this is a period set aside for questions," the young woman said. "But I wonder whether you would allow me to explain to you good people why the amount is so small." She then proceeded to explain, with frequent nods and sounds of approval from her audience, that people who lived in this neighborhood were hounded by requests for money for charity to a point where they had been forced to close their ears. She wondered if she could bring home to us how this had come about; she asked us to try to identify ourselves with a couple, ready to contribute to worthy causes, who felt that the fact that they had more money than most people imposed certain obligations. But she doubted if we had any idea of the devious, offensive and unscrupulous means that were used by some individuals and organizations to blackmail them into contributing to their causes. It seemed that as long as someone was soliciting money for a charitable purpose, this gave him or her the idea that the end hallowed the means. She was sure that she spoke for the majority of those present that morning when she said that her husband and she had been forced to decide to ignore all further appeals for charity. They had set aside a certain amount per year and now referred all requests to their attorneys, who could distribute that amount as they saw fit. From that day on, they had found peace because, and here she laughed apologetically, it had relieved them of being exposed to the unspeakable obscenity of the exploitation of the blind, the maimed, the mad, the orphaned, the famished, the dying that, she assured us with earnest sincerity, was as bad in River Oaks as it was in Calcutta.

She was rewarded by a prolonged applause. But she did not sit down as I had expected her to. She waited until the applause died down, then she continued, "This does not mean that we do not care about this hospital. We care very much; we have all known about that awful place on Allen Parkway for many years and each one of us here, I am sure, has secretly felt the urge to do something but has been unable to find a way of doing so. And you know how it is: you have these impulses, but when you find that you can't do anything about them, they pass and you forget. I don't know about the others here, but I feel that today I have to make up my mind. I do agree with you that conditions in our charity hospital are a challenge to each one of us individually. I want to meet that challenge, but I do not want to meet it the way you suggest. I do not want to pay money; I do not want to buy peace of mind. I want to do what you people did. I want to be trained as a nurses' aide, and go in there myself."

In the sudden silence that followed, something happened to the nape of my neck. All I could do was stare at her in disbelief.

"Could you tell me what the work is like?" she asked, matter-of-factly. "How long would I have to be in training? What does it entail?"

Debbie, who was sitting in the front row, rose and said

cheerfully, "Well, as a nurses' aide myself, I think I can give you that answer . . ." and she proceeded, in obvious eagerness to exploit this incredible windfall, to give the ladies a version of our work on the floors that sounded like an episode from *The Nurses* on television.

I suddenly felt that this would not do, that the young woman who had stood up and stated that she wanted to go in there deserved better than that. She deserved the truth.

"I'm sorry, Debbie," I said, "but I feel that this is the moment to put our cards on the table."

I turned to the young woman standing there among the matrons, and said, "Madam, you will be trained for eight weeks, four weeks of theory, four weeks of clinical training on the floors, and for what? To carry bedpans for sick old Negroes."

In the shocked silence that followed, a deadpan voice said from the back of the room, "Attaboy." It was Lucille.

"But, Jan!" Debbie said, hastily. "Don't let's look at it from that angle, let's . . ."

But the girl in the crowd said calmly, "I would like to hear Mr. de Hartog's version, if you don't mind."

"All right," I said. "You will find in that hospital the poorest of the poor. You will find the pauper relations of your maids, that even they themselves are ashamed of. You will be expected to serve them, not just to help them, to *serve* them. You will be expected to feed them, to wash them, to dispose of their excreta, to clean them when they are incontinent. You will come home to River Oaks, haunted by the stench of sweat and excrement and pus and death that you will be unable to get out of your nostrils. You will see madness, suicide, despair, cruelty, and you will not be able to do a thing about it, other than hold their hand and wash them and comb their hair and feed them and inhale their dying breath. It will undo all the work and expense of your hairdresser and your beautician. Your face will begin to show lines that cannot be erased by cream or treatment, for they will be lines of sorrow; and your only reward for all this, the only one, will be those lines. For they will be the credentials of your humanity."

There was a silence in which I looked at her with the feeling that, behind me, all the sick, the desperate and the helpless of Houston were silently ranged, that I had spoken for Mr. Hood, who had died of necrosis of the feet, for Miss Lucas' patients who had been tortured by cockroaches, for the one-legged old man bleeding from the rectum whom I had sent naked to his death on the back seat of a broken-down car. "I am sorry," I said. "But you wanted the truth."

There was a stillness in that room that I shall never forget; then she asked calmly, "Where can I enlist?"

From the back of the room came Lucille's voice, saying, "Right here, ma'am." She added, over the hubbub that started, "Anybody else who feels like earning those credentials, come and see me. The training is free."

When it was all over, we stared at her list with a feeling of unreality. We had harvested, from the richest fifty square miles in the world, eleven dollars, and five volunteer nurses' aides.

CHAPTER 8

THE ENLARGED hospital committee met in emergency session. This included all the Quakers working inside the hospital and Lucille, who had turned into an illustration of a New York rabbi's dour remark that some of his best Jews were Friends.

We discussed the situation from all angles and our conclusion was unanimous: we should no longer solicit money, we should go for volunteers. Out of that meeting came the slogan of our new campaign: *We don't want your money, we want you!*

If indeed the people of Houston could be moved to offer their services rather than their money, this might transform the hospital. If we could recruit enough volunteer nurses' aides and orderlies to go in every day and take care of the patients' basic needs, they would introduce an element of humanity and individual care that might indeed make Mrs. Masters' dream come true and turn Houston's charity hospital into a model of its kind.

There were a few massive roadblocks to be surmounted. The first was that neither Mrs. Masters nor Mrs. Willoughby was prepared to start a new training program for volunteer nurses' aides; even if they should agree to do so, they were at such immutable loggerheads about who was to have the ultimate authority that they now stood facing each other like two snowplows on a narrow road, each of them refusing to budge an inch. A volunteer nursing corps could hope to succeed only if a third authority was created inside the hospital; the logical solution, proven practical elsewhere, was to hand the whole program over to the Red Cross, ask them to train, organize and supervise all voluntary nursing personnel inside the hospital, and put these, in Red Cross uniform, at the disposal of the Nursing Office, which would deploy them as it saw fit.

We agreed on this as our objective; we decided, however, to find out first what response a campaign for volunteer nurses would get from the community before approaching the Red Cross and asking them to take over. Everybody present volunteered to take part in the new campaign; the Mercy Fund was to continue as its central office, Debbie, as its chairman, would coordinate the speakers, Lucille and Priscilla corral the new volunteers, if any, and register them on the spot.

My first speaking assignment was a small Negro church in the northern section of town. Debbie had organized it; her occasional housekeeper, Mrs. Johnson, was in the choir and so, it turned out, were all her children and grandchildren. The church was a minute, ramshackle structure, as hot as an oven and filled to capacity with about thirty people. Twelve kitchen chairs on a platform, with white pillow slips over their backs to protect the gowns of the choir, surrounded an overstuffed armchair covered with red velvet, facing the congregation. The church was filling up as we arrived; when more humanity had been packed within its walls than had seemed possible, the minister came in from the back and sat down in the red velvet armchair.

He was a gray-haired, wizened old man of great dignity; as he sat down in his armchair the choir exploded in jubilation and the congregation started to stamp and chant, clapping its hands with growing abandon. As a tribal chieftain receiving homage from his people he gazed at the waving arms, the clapping hands, the shaking shoulders with a calm, contemplative stare of black melancholy eyes; as I watched him sitting there, tranquil amidst the commotion, I was reminded of Mr. Taub and his Roman emperor's concept of the white man's burden. After the choir and the congregation had sung three songs that would have made even the stodgiest Dutch Reformed elder feel like turning cartwheels at the feet of the Lord, I was beckoned to rise and address the congregation.

I cleared my throat nervously, and started to say that probably everyone present was familiar with old Jefferson Davis Hospital. I felt absurdly startled when the congregation responded, "Yeah, yeah!" I continued that it had been a place of shame and sorrow for a generation, but that now the time had come to change this. "Amen!" the congregation chanted, "Tell 'em, brother! Tell 'em!" Encouraged beyond proportion, and washed along by the ground swell of the congregation's emotional participation, I made a stirring appeal for volunteers to help the sick who could not help themselves. The days were gone, I cried, that the Negro community should leave this to the white man. It was a great joke to call the hospital "Uncle Taub's Cabin," but we must not forget that Uncle Tom had been a Negro. This hospital was the only hospital in town where Negro volunteers would be welcome to work as nurses' aides and orderlies, alongside their white fellow citizens. If this challenge to participate in a communal work of mercy was left unanswered, it would be a negation of the spirit of the times, and also of the spirit of the Son of Man, whose praise they had just sung with a passion fit to bust the window panes. Each man was at liberty, as an individual and sole master of his destiny, to think this over and turn it down. But each man had to be aware that he was now faced with a choice, a choice that could not be postponed any longer, but had to be made *today!* (Yeah, yeah!)

This morning! (Amen! Yes, brother!) NOW! and, packing the wallop of a prophet, I hit the Bible on the pulpit with a bang. The congregation burst into a rousing, cheering, hand-clapping, rafter-rattling song; the only one who remained unaffected by my eloquence was the minister, sitting motionless on his red plush throne with the regal serenity of a Pharaoh. When the singing and the shouting finally died down, he lifted one pale hand and said, "That was a beautiful speech. Now, let's hear it again."

For a second I stood there, speechless and utterly taken aback. Then our eyes met in quiet combat and I realized that here was another Mr. Taub, resolved not to succumb to any shapeless emotional nonsense.

So I made the speech again, this time without any revivalist hoopla. Had the first been intended to arouse, the second set out to inform. The fiery climax of my sermon, that had brought about such explosive exultation, seemed to become a little embarrassing in retrospect, as I ended by calmly and unemotionally answering a series of factual questions about the Red Cross training, the price of uniforms and the different types of nursing care, that varied with each floor.

When it was all over, the minister called for a collection. The proceeds would go to the Mercy Fund; if any brother or sister wanted to volunteer they should give their names and addresses, after the service, to Mrs. Nimick.

The collection brought in $24.50, and two volunteers added their names to the five from River Oaks on Lucille's list. The minister invited me into his office after the final benediction; there we sat talking for a while in an atmosphere of realism. He approved of the volunteer nursing corps, he said, and he was going to give it his cooperation. This did not amount to much, he added with a smile, for he was dying of cancer and would not live out the summer. But he would arrange that, this fall, I would get an invitation to address the association of ministers of his area, to solicit their cooperation.

I had never before sat opposite a man who so matter-of-factly took his own imminent death into account while planning the future. It was only when our talk was over that I realized why he could be so detached. He had so completely identified himself with the struggle of his people for human dignity that in those singing, handclapping, jubilant masses, striving toward the light, he had found his immortality. When we said farewell and I took his soft old hand in mind, I had the uncanny feeling that I stood hand in hand with the future, the way I had stood hand in hand with the past when I said goodbye to Mr. Taub. His office had looked as simple and as unassuming as this one; the main difference was that the children on the publicity calendar from a funeral home that hung over the Reverend Wilson's desk were Negro, whereas the bosomy belles on Mr. Taub's cigar boxes had been Caucasian.

2

MY NEXT ASSIGNMENT seemed a complete contrast: I was sent to address a luncheon of the Junior Chamber of Commerce. The Houston Jaycees had the reputation of being extreme right wing; although they were made up of fifteen hundred young men from all over town and all sorts of business enterprises, the ruling clique, I had been warned, was rabidly segregationist.

When I stood facing them: a hall full of suspicious, unforthcoming young men, noisily eating, I knew, even before I started, that what I had been told about them beforehand was beside the point. The point seemed to be their youth, and their eagerness to become involved in programs of public service. I saw them size me up through narrowed eyes, take in my weatherbeaten face and sailor's eyes, unable to equate them with the weighted-down jacket with bulging pockets and the baggy pants of the professor. And suddenly I was overcome again by the same sense of excitement that I had felt when I first roamed the streets of this city. It seemed as if, at last, I stood face to face with the personification of Houston: a young man, yawning in pajamas with sleepy eyes and tousled hair in front of his bathroom mirror in the morning; the true Houstonian, average age twenty-seven, unkempt, furry-tongued, reluctant to start a new day of work, yet ahead of schedule on things like the largest domed stadium in the world. The Domed Stadium had become a symbol of the city: it was so preposterously huge that one of its problems had turned out to be the formation of thunderclouds underneath its cupola in the torrid heat of a normal summer day. In human terms, this meant that Billy Graham, who was invited to open the stadium with a mammoth revival meeting in the fall, was in actual danger of being struck by indoor lightning. An aerial photograph of the half-finished stadium looked so hauntingly like the ruins of the Coliseum in Rome that the analogy became compelling. If only I could bring home to these reluctant and suspicious young men that their charity hospital should be as much an object of their pride as the Domed Stadium, then they might create a link, across two thousand years of history, between their young city and that metropolis of antiquity, where citizens had formed similar groups of anonymous men to help the poor, the sick and the stricken. In Florence of the Middle Ages, the Brothers of St. John had done the same; I was convinced that it had been those nameless men who made the suns of their cities shine with such brilliance that their rays reached into this very hall, where I now stood facing their glum-faced reincarnations.

I had been allotted five minutes for my talk. I told them

as succinctly as possible about old Jefferson Davis, how we had become involved with it, and how we had discovered by trial and error that only a group, united in purpose and disciplined in dedication, could do any good at all. And if a group was the answer, this should be the Jaycees. They could contribute something that no other group could: enthusiasm. They had the vision to realize that it was in their power to change the charity hospital from a place of shame into a place of pride. Here was a chance for them and their wives to go in as orderlies and nurses' aides and change the face of the city. I realized that there were men present who felt strongly and even bitterly about integration, but this did not enter into it. A segregationist was not by that definition a brute or a sadist who needed slaves to trample on to bolster his paranoiac ego. Those among them who said to the Negro, "I will never integrate," would surely, as honorable men, say in the same breath, "But if you fall ill in loneliness or are lying helpless by the road, I will lift you up and carry you and nurse you myself." Suddenly, frighteningly, this was answered with a burst of applause. I knew at that moment that I had spoken their own minds.

My five minutes were up, but no one protested when I continued by telling them what to expect inside the hospital. I told them with the same frankness as I had told the women in River Oaks. Each man had to decide for himself if he thought he could face this kind of trial; but he need not worry about his wife. Although she was sure to start by saying she could never face a bedpan, she was equally sure, after a while, to scoff at the faintheartedness of the next group of trainees about to go in.

Their response was typical of the city. There and then, they appointed a committee, complete with chairman, to analyze the project and report back to the membership. The committee would submit a detailed training program for members of the Junior Chamber of Commerce and their wives who wanted to go into the charity hospital as volunteer orderlies and nurses' aides, the first group to be limited to a hundred.

The whole thing was settled by acclamation with a minimum of fuss, the way decisions of equal magnitude must once have been settled among the few autocrats who had ruled the city before it became a metropolis, of whom the great Ben Taub was the last survivor.

I came out of the meeting that I had entered with trepidation with a great confidence in the future of the hospital. I was sure that Mr. Taub, after thirty years of lonely dictatorship, would welcome these young men and women when they came to reclaim Houston's conscience, which the citizens of three decades ago had deposited with him.

3

OBVIOUSLY, after the entry of the Jaycees and their vast potential in numbers, the time had come to inform the Red Cross. We had been rounding up, almost casually, a lot of volunteers to be trained. While I was canvassing among the Negro working class and its opposite in River Oaks, others had been recruiting at neighborhood coffees, church sewing circles, the Teamsters' Union and the striking oil workers of the Shell Company in Pasadena.

When we finally went to see Mrs. Bannerman, our former instructor, at the Red Cross Head Office and told her what we had done, she looked round our circle, we thought, with alarm. But suddenly, to our utter surprise, she uttered a high whoop of joy, a yahooing Texas prairie yodel, utterly incongruous on the part of this stern and forceful woman of whom we were all still secretly in awe.

"Wait till I tell our Chapter Manager!" she cried, getting

up at once, and knocking on a door; Debbie and I were invited inside for a conference with the local director of the Red Cross.

We were welcomed by a surprisingly sophisticated and urbane gentleman, with the deceptive bonhomie of a rear-admiral of the Royal Navy. As he sat chatting amiably in his swivel chair behind his executive's desk, he somehow managed to make us aware of the full extent of the immense power he represented in the way a Convoy Commander had done when I sat in front of his desk, twenty years before, in the company of seventeen others. For two decades I had tried to remember what the charming, convivial gentleman had chatted about so chummily before broaching the subject of the impending operation; as I sat in front of the desk of the amiable chapter manager of the American Red Cross in Houston, I remembered: it had been snooker, one of the more boring British forms of billiards, to which the admiral had referred as "A wild game straight from the Arabian Nights." Then, suddenly, as had been the case twenty years before, we were talking about the impending operation. The Red Cross had, of course, the manager continued, known of conditions inside the hospital for many years. He was delighted that at last the people of this city were responding to an intolerable situation with a desire to do something, rather than go on talking. However—and here his voice sounded exactly as the admiral's had when he used that same word—there was a snag. The Red Cross would be delighted to train any eligible applicant, it could take care of a virtually unlimited number, but the snag was that the Red Cross could not offer its services; they had to be requested, in this case by the hospital. The reason for this ruling was that the Red Cross had been created to fill a need, not to crusade. It could not operate under circumstances where its presence might be resented; the moment it became controversial, and thus politically involved, it had to disengage itself at once. So, until we had seen the Administrator, or preferably Mr. Taub himself, and explained to him why the Red Cross had to wait for their invitation before it could start training applicants, there was nothing he could do.

Only as we left and he saw us, courteously, to the door of his office, did he express how he really felt about the Red Cross starting a voluntary nursing corps inside the charity hospital. "If you people can bring this off," he said, "you will be realizing a dream that many of us in this building have had for years. So, good luck."

4

IT WAS DECIDED that I should go to see Mr. Taub, as I was the only one of us who knew him. I went with high hopes, for I felt that, although our previous conversation had been somewhat frustrating, it had achieved one thing: each of us was now convinced that he was dealing with an honorable man. Even so, I had prepared a bit of holy blackmail that, I thought, might help, just in case he should prove reluctant to commit himself.

After I had been ushered into the presence of Mr. Ben once again by his employee with the green feather duster, I told him that the Red Cross could provide the hospital with a virtually unlimited number of volunteer nurses' aides and orderlies, which would not cost the hospital a cent as they would be organized, trained and supervised by the Red Cross.

His reaction seemed to be one of stony disapproval. He sat there, across that village storekeeper's desk, with the weary grimness of Pontius Pilate, proconsul of Palestine, listening to the latest envoy from the nihilists who surrounded that carpenter with religious megalomania. He was not going to distinguish me with a dissertation on either his personal philosophy or the principles of imperial government; all he said was, "Thank you for the information."

When I did not accept this dismissal but persisted, "May I take it that you welcome the offer?" his large, heavy-lidded aristocrat's eyes rested on me pensively for a moment. In them, I could discern no emotion, neither sympathy nor antipathy. All I saw, again, was what the astronauts must see when they gaze out of the portholes of their spacecraft into the interstellar void. Then he said, "It is not up to me to decide. I am only the Chairman of the Board. A request like that must come from the administration."

It was my turn to let my eyes rest upon him, giving him, I hoped, as impersonal a view of the ocean as he had given me of outer space. I realized that, like everybody else connected with the hospital who had not found refuge within a cohesive group, he was afflicted with the disaster syndrome. He sat there with the utter certainty that he was the only one who was dedicated, determined, experienced, concerned and incorruptible enough to cope with the calamity of the charity hospital. And, indeed, the mere fact that during the past thirty years he had been the only powerful individual in Houston who cared about the sick paupers made his lonely silhouette rise out of the rat race of the past in awesome humanity. But by now he had become so thoroughly convinced that there never would be anyone else who cared about them that any outsider who dared to raise his voice on the subject seemed to interfere with his plan for creeping progress at the speed of a glacier, and had to be circumvented or slowly crushed. Seen from his point of view, the very idea of allowing a few hundred busybodies from the community to roam the floors of his hospital was ludicrous. I sympathized with him; what a month it must have been. First, he had a hospital named after him which, despite its flattering aspect, implied a challenge to resign as Chairman of the Board or expose himself to censure for turning a public institution into a personal monument. Now a hot-eyed fanatic sat breathing adenoidal fire at him, planning to invade his hospital with hundreds of snooping taxpayers who all called it "their" hospital, and to add insult to outrage the man had the gall to suggest that he request this invasion himself by official invitation. I could not blame him for deciding, behind his granite mask of self-control, that he would see me in hell first. Considering that sixteen people of my ilk had managed to raise such a rumpus after working there as so-called nurses' aides and orderlies for a few months, he must have a realistic picture of what would happen were he to allow hundreds of us into the hospital. I had to admit that his reasoning was absolutely right; only it was not a matter of whose reasoning was right, but what was best for the patients.

"Sir," I said, "we feel as responsible for the patients in that hospital as you do; like you, we cannot rest until we have done whatever we can to improve their lot. As it is now obvious that the people of Houston do not want to make a financial sacrifice to hire extra nursing help, and as you have just made it obvious that you are not prepared to accept the offer of the Red Cross for voluntary staff, we must try and raise the money to hire sufficient professional staff elsewhere. The only way I personally can contribute to this is by writing a series of articles about the hospital in the international press, to solicit contributions abroad. I realize that the papers in Europe may be eager to publish such an appeal for the sick paupers of the richest city in the world out of considerations that are not exclusively charitable; but I know that if, for instance, I tell the people of Holland how the indigent sick are treated in the hospital that bears your name, they will be sending food parcels to Houston within a week. So—how about letting the Red Cross in?"

I thought I saw a flicker of something in his night-black, melancholy eyes, but I was mistaken. It took more than a clumsy attempt at blackmail to shake the last survivor of the picaresque era when Houston had been called Murder Town, U.S.A.

"Thank you," he said. "I appreciate your interest."

I had thought that, by now, I really had come to know this city. How foolish I was to have remained unaware of such a glaring and decisive aspect of its character. Contrary to its nervous sister of the plains, the city of Dallas, forever fussily agonizing over her image, Houston did not care a damn what anybody said. So some foreign newspapers were going to scream with glee about medieval conditions in the charity hospital of the richest city in the world. Who cared, if he had enough money to buy them all, supposing he could be bothered?

As I stood outside on the hot pavement, and the last whiff of the sensuous scent of Dixie evaporated in the blast-furnace of the noonday sun, I had to conclude, calmly and unemotionally, that we had reached the end of our tether. He had proved too much for fifteen successive generations of professional politicians; what in the world had made us assume that he would give in to a handful of Gentle Persuaders, one of whom had now ended by clumsily brandishing a Quaker gun?

We had better face it: the Red Cross would never get into Ben Taub General Hospital in Houston, not in this century.

5

BUT IT WAS DECIDED, by those who make bouncing back a way of life, that we had one more chance. I went to see Dr. Olsen, Dean of the Medical School of Baylor University, in his office in the Medical Center.

It was a scalding hot day; the interior of the new building seemed icy when I entered its dimly lit lobby. Maybe it was the heat, maybe it was the cool dignity of that lobby, but I was reminded of the government buildings in the Dutch East Indies before the war. They had felt and looked like this; as if they had always been there and would be there forever, indestructible monuments to the unchanging moguls of bureaucracy. Romans, Venetians, English, Dutch, French, Spaniards, Americans—it seemed as if this cool palace of scribes and secretaries had never changed and never closed. Odd, that my first association with Dr. Olsen's setting should be a political one; less odd, when I faced him in his office.

He was a tall, thin man in a light blue tropical suit, younger than I had expected. As he rose behind his desk and held out his hand in greeting, there emanated from him, despite his diplomatic smile, a Scandinavian frostiness. He looked as out of place against the background of scorched palms and boiling spirals of heat outside as the Dutch had looked in Indonesia, and chances were that he was just as efficient an administrator as they had been, while the going was good.

It was obvious, from the start, that the patients were an abstraction to him, and they could hardly be anything else as he rarely came to see them; his students, however, were anything but an abstraction. If the ice-cold man with the impeccable manners I faced had any passion at all, it was to make this the best medical school in the country.

He told me that he had been involved in a politically controlled city-county hospital up North, and that this experience had revealed to him the ultimate horror of putting a teaching hospital at the mercy of political appointees and seat-hugging bureaucrats. So no one could appreciate more keenly than he the genius of Mr. Taub, who for thirty years had kept city and county from ganging up against the hospital board by keeping them at loggerheads.

He reacted to the idea of training civilians to serve as volunteer nurses' aides with reserve. He agreed that the very fact this was a teaching hospital made it imperative that the patients should receive the best possible nursing care, but this care should be given by professional nurses, not amateurs. When I asked him why the small number of professionals could not be supplemented by trained amateurs he tried to freeze me with a glance of long-suffering patience and the terse words, "Maybe you have to be a professional to appreciate that this goes without saying." Then he added, "What's more, I do not think that the teaching of medical students should be made a public spectacle." Translated into layman's language, this meant that a student should be allowed to make an honest surgical mistake and say, "Whoops! Sorry!" without setting some sentimental housewife in a pinafore screaming across the operating table. Obviously his ideal teaching hospital was a maximum security laboratory, like the ones in which nuclear physicists enjoy their jealously guarded privacy to experiment and, occasionally, blunder. I felt more convinced than ever that we were badly needed, to complement Baylor's educational zeal with some sheer emotional concern for the patients. But for the moment, so it seemed, we were in conflict. He was not going to crusade for the admission of the Red Cross to the hospital, certainly not if by doing so he risked evoking the ire of Mr. Taub.

It was distasteful to me, because of the civilized and dispassionate level on which he had kept the discussion, to attempt my blackmail, but it seemed the last chance. When I mentioned that I might have to appeal for contributions in Europe, via a series of articles on the Houston charity hospital, something unexpected happened. He looked at me through narrowed eyes, and then his unemotional assistant governor's face broke into a grin that somehow halved his age and doubled his humanity.

257

"How did Mr. Taub react to that suggestion?" he asked, still in that official tone, which suddenly sounded incongruous.

"I don't think it worried him unduly," I confessed. "I had the feeling that all I had done was squirt at him with a water pistol."

"H'm." He clasped his hands behind his back and went to look out the window. "All right," he said, with his back to me. "If the Red Cross should suggest such a training program, and my opinion should be asked, it will be favorable on condition that the people who are to do the volunteering are carefully screened as to age, education and emotional maturity."

"I'm afraid the Red Cross cannot suggest this program off its own bat," I said.

He turned round; his Scandinavian eyes searched mine with sudden precision. "You mean the Red Cross has to be invited?"

"I'm afraid so. Do you feel you could do this?"

"I am sorry," he replied. "But anything to do with the nursing staff is beyond my province. Baylor staffs the hospital with physicians only. I am not even a full member of the Board of Managers, I merely sit in on their meetings, ex officio. All I can do is advise. And there is no way of telling whether my advice will be heeded."

"Then who makes the final decisions?"

"In this case, it would be the Administrator," he replied, blandly. I looked at him just as blandly. His grin was just underneath the surface. I began to like Dr. Olsen; his was the kind of witty wiliness that explained the miracle of evolution. But whether we liked each other or not, it was obvious that he lacked the power to force the issue in this matter, and he was not going to try. He was, above all, a realist. But the mountaintop where Mr. Taub lived began to look bleak and lonely; rarely had I felt around any man more respect and less love.

"All right," I said. "I'll see what the Administrator has to say. In the meantime, thanks for your encouragement."

He held out a thin, cold hand. "Don't worry," he said blandly. "It will all work out one day."

I waited for his wink, but that was that. We parted almost like Japanese. Baylor's future looked good to me; that of our program somber.

6

THE SAME NIGHT, in Observation, I was tackled by three senior medical students, with the suddenness of a hold-up.

Maybe they had their own grapevine inside the Medical School, maybe it was just that the time was ripe for the moment of truth. I knew the three of them only by sight.

"Listen, mister," one of them started, "you have been throwing your weight around in this hospital for quite a while now, and now we hear you are planning to bring in a lot of women. Is that so?"

I said, "Trained women."

"Why?"

"To provide the patients with the nursing care they lack."

"I don't mean that. What is your personal interest in this?"

"What do you mean?"

"Come on, you must have a personal angle. Everybody has. You're not just some do-gooder, you obviously are in here for a purpose. Don't give us any crap about being here for the sake of the patients; what's in this for you, personally?"

"Excuse me," I said. "But what business is that of yours?"

"We just want to know."

"Out of professional interest?"

"We want to know all the facts before we make up our minds whose side we're on."

Looking from one to the other, at their tough and yet youthfully vulnerable faces, I felt the same sensation as when I had stood facing the young men of the Junior Chamber of Commerce. I realized that they and I were in this together, that we were sharing the same point in space and time, and that together we made up this thing called Houston.

"Of course I have a personal objective," I said, "and I'll tell you what it is, although it's nobody's business but mine, and maybe my brother's."

They looked at me with a new awareness, as if until that moment they had only seen an abstraction, a symptom of outside interference in the world they claimed as their own. Now they became aware of a man, with a brother.

"A couple of years ago, my mother died of cancer of the stomach," I said. "My brother and I nursed her ourselves. Neither of us had any experience, but at the time there were not enough nurses available in the hospital in Holland, so we took it on. We had no idea what we were letting ourselves in for. It was a nightmare, and at the end she died in a way that made us doubt the existence of a God of love. For why must a woman like this, who had always given more than she received, be turned into a raving, screaming wreck, while a crook we knew had been allowed to die in his sleep? To that question, I had no answer. Not at the time."

"Don't tell me you have the answer now," one of them said, matter-of-factly.

"No," I replied. "But because of the way she died, I am here now. The idea of going in for this work would never have occurred to me otherwise. I can't judge if my being here has done much good, but occasionally I have been able to give someone lying here the feeling that I cared about making him as comfortable as I could. And I know that if my mother had been given the choice between dying in her sleep, or going through what she did and by doing so making the last hours of some tramp in Texas less bleak and lonely, she would have chosen the latter. That just happened to be the person she was. I don't know if that answers your question, but it answered mine."

They stood for a moment undecided; then the first one said, "Okay, granted you are sincere, I still think you are trying to change things too fast. There has been a great improvement in this hospital compared to twenty years ago. There is even a great improvement between this place and old J.D. Why must you, all of a sudden, rock the boat? Tell me that."

"I'll tell you, once you tell me whose boat I am rocking," I answered. "The only boat I am interested in is the one with the patients in it."

"You honestly think the patients will be more comfortable once you flood this place with amateurs, flapping around, commiserating, getting in everybody's way?"

I looked at him with a sense of fellowship. How often had I sat at messroom tables on board freighters and oceangoing tugboats, shooting my mouth off like that? I remembered with nostalgia and envy the feeling of comradeship and security it gave to be part of a crew, of a team doing the same work, with the same interests.

"I think trained volunteers could help a great deal," I said. "They could keep the patients clean, the beds made, the water pitchers filled, the bedpans emptied. They could hold the hands of female patients who are being prodded and poked by medical students. That would help."

"Ah, I see. You think we're callous, do you?" another one asked, aggressively.

"You're damn right, I do," I answered, as I had done so often at the messroom table. Where were they now, those friends of yore? Some of them were dead, some had made good, all of us had one thing in common: our youth was gone.

"Don't give us that crap of having to be emotionally involved with each patient," the young man said hotly. "You can't get involved with these people. You'd go crazy, and what's more: they won't let you."

"There is a difference between getting emotionally involved or calling patients 'Mr.' or 'Mrs.' to start with. This practice of calling everybody John or Mary or Buddy or Honey is degrading. And I'm not sure whom it degrades more, the patients or you."

"You have pretty strong ideas, for a volunteer orderly," said the third young man, who so far had not spoken at all.

I looked at him. I had dealt with his kind before. I knew I should understand him, and love his unique, irreplaceable soul, but the hell with it. "Get off my back, friend," I said. "I am forty-nine years old. I have been through a war, I've commanded ships. Occasionally, my Quakerly meekness feels like an affectation. Like now."

"Gentlemen, gentlemen," the oldest of the three said, echoing all the pacifying chief engineers of my youth. "Let's get to work, and wish the man luck." Then he said, touching my shoulder. "Okay, bring on the girls, Hartog. We'll teach 'em."

"He's more likely to think they'll teach *us*," the young wireless operator scoffed, with a thin smile.

"Glad you got the message," I said; then I beat it back to my bedpans before I undid whatever good I might have done.

But I realized after this conversation that, had we managed to get the Red Cross in, not only Dean Olsen but also his doctors would have been on our side. I wondered if those who drew up that ruling had realized it could be used to keep a town full of volunteer nurses separated from a hospital full of neglected patients. It seemed ludicrous to any sane person that a hospital, so urgently in need of help, could be given this help only on condition it asked for it. But then, maybe there were things I did not know. All I really knew, after all, were the patients.

7

LATER THAT NIGHT, when the after-dinner drunks started to create their havoc on the streets of Houston, and husbands coming home from work started to shoot sluggish lovers and faithless wives, we ran out of stretchers in Emergency. I had two secret caches of stretchers, one in the bathroom in Observation, the other in the passage between the rows of Treatment Rooms of the day clinic, dark and deserted at this hour of the night. Some rustler had made off with the one in the bathroom, so, grumbling crankily in solitary indignation, I padded on my soundless rubber soles into the dark passage. As I entered it, I almost gave a squeal of fright when I collided with an old Negress who came shuffling out of the darkness. She had no business being there, and the way she had startled me seemed to make her feel guilty, for she hastily shuffled past me into the main corridor. I turned to ask her what she was looking for when I heard her accost someone.

"Hey, mistah," she called, "where do I find the Emergency Room?"

"Go down this hall, then you turn left until you get to another hall, then you turn . . . Tell you what, I'll take you there. You'd never find it."

"Yeah," she said. "A person sure can lose her way in here. It ain't like the old place."

"Sure ain't," the male voice said. "Most of the time, I don't know where the heck I'm going myself."

The voice sounded familiar; I peered round the corner to see who it was. To my amazement I recognized the squat back and dark blue business suit of the Administrator.

As I wheeled my secret stretcher to Emergency, I ruminated upon the incident. It was totally unexpected from the Administrator as I knew him. There had been, in their short conversation, an odd element of kinship, as if they shared the same memories and felt equally lonely in the new world. It again went to show that you should never decide you knew all about a man.

The incident made up my mind for me. As soon as I could leave the floor for a moment, I went to see him. It was long after business hours; the administrative section was dark, but I saw light in his office. I approached it discreetly, my soles soundless in the silence.

When I appeared ghostlike in the open doorway, I saw him sitting behind his desk, his head in his hands. It was an image of such lonely weariness that, suddenly embarrassed, I sneaked back a few steps, coughed and walked toward the doorway once more, knocking on the post when I got there.

"Come in," he said.

"Good evening, sir," I said. "Could I have a word with you?"

"Sure. Sit down."

I sat down in the visitor's chair, that still had a pricetag hanging beneath its seat.

"Well," he started, "how are you making out?" His voice was jovial, but not nearly as relaxed as it had been when he talked to the old Negress.

"We are making out fine," I replied, "but we've come up against a roadblock of sorts."

"Is that so?" he said, still with that air of casualness, but his eyes hardened and his hands on the blotter became still. I had always had the feeling that he looked familiar; now, as I saw him wearily gather his wits about him for another walk on a tightrope between two conflicting interests I realized who the man was he reminded me of: the Director of the Amsterdam Municipal Theatre Company, at the beginning of the German occupation. He had been the only director who had made the company show a profit, which meant that he was condemned by the artistic pundits as "commercial" before the war. Under the occupation he had found himself faced with a choice between resigning and leaving the company to its fate, and trying to keep as many actors as possible employed and out of forced labor in Germany, thereby accepting the onus of collaboration. Being the man he was, he had chosen the second alternative. There was no doubt that he prevented many personal tragedies during the few years he stayed in office, but after the war he was dragged in front of one of those tribunals that everybody now tries to forget and sentenced to one year's inactivity, branded a traitor. Within the year he was revindicated, but that was not the point. The point was that, knowing what lay ahead of him, he had made his choice.

Well, here sat his counterpart, twenty years later, in Houston, Texas: as foxy, as weary, and as aware of the fact that whatever way it worked out he could not win. I knew nothing about the man behind the desk, other than that I had seen him scurry past a few times in old J.D. with what had then looked like unseemly haste. I still knew nothing about him, but I began to suspect that his reasons for sitting there were more worthy of my respect than I had supposed them to be.

I told him that we had the applicants, the assurance of the Red Cross that they would train and supervise a corps of volunteers inside the hospital, but that the hospital had to invite them officially. And this, obviously, the hospital was not prepared to do.

"What makes you think so?" he asked.

"I have been to see Mr. Taub and Dr. Olsen."

"And now you are seeing me," he said, without a smile.

He looked even more like the old theatre director in Amsterdam now. To divine what went on behind that mask would be fruitless. "That's right," I said.

"Why?"

It had been a harmless little question, yet my extrasensory antenna seemed to discern a small secretive signal, urging me to listen, to exclude all other sounds. "Because I thought maybe you could help," I answered innocuously.

"What makes you think so? I am only the Administrator. This is a matter for the Board of Managers to decide."

Although he had said it with formality, the signal was very strong now. If only I read him right.

"Suppose I were to ask you what our next move should be?" I ventured, unsure of myself the moment I had spoken. I knew I was making a mess of it, but I could not help myself, as I had no idea what I was dealing with. If only I knew whose side he was on, that of the patients or that of the powers. "What would your advice be?"

He shrugged his shoulders. "What advice can I give you, other than to put it in writing? Let the Red Cross write me a letter, in which they tell me what they have to offer, then I'll forward it to the Board of Managers."

"That's the point," I said. "They cannot do so. You have to ask for their help."

"I see," he said.

He had said it blandly, but with a hint of relief. If I had not heard him talk to that old Negress and seen him walk her to the Emergency Room, I would have left it at that, convinced that all he worried about was his position. In that case, knowing that Mr. Taub was against this, his main consideration would be not to get involved.

"How much money did you collect in the end?" he asked, to make conversation.

"About four thousand dollars," I replied. "That, at least, the hospital can look forward to."

"Ah?" he asked, with polite interest. "I thought you had

given the money to the Red Cross."

"No," I said. "No. We haven't done anything with it yet."

"Well," he said, "as I say, let them write me a letter and I'll take it from there. Hurry back now." He reached out a pudgy hand, I shook it and left with a feeling of faint disgust.

Only as I got into my car three hours later, at the end of the shift, put the key into the ignition and was about to start the engine, the penny dropped. I sat there, motionless, mouth open, for a moment; then I muttered, "Well, I'll be damned!"

I started the engine, backed out of the lot, swung into the park with too much acceleration; it was all I could do to keep myself from honking the horn. I sped down the winding lanes underneath the old oak trees draped with Spanish moss, along the bayou; when finally I arrived home I drove into the garage with such speed that the tires screeched as I braked. I burst into the kitchen, grabbed Marjorie round the waist and spun her round, shouting: "I've got it! I've got it!"

I put her down, caught my breath, and told her incoherently that we must write a letter to all the contributors to the Mercy Fund, ask their permission to change the money's destination, and instead of giving it to the hospital as a piddling supplement to one monthly budget we should donate it to the Red Cross, with the provision that it might only be used for the training and the supervision of a volunteer nursing corps in Ben Taub General Hospital.

"Why?" she asked.

I remembered in time how stupid I had been myself, not to see at once the solution that the Administrator had handed me on a platter. "This means," I explained, "that the Red Cross can write to the hospital administration, saying they have received a grant for this purpose and asking what it wants them to do with it!"

"So?"

"So the Red Cross is no longer stymied by the ruling that forced it to wait until it was invited in, which gave the hospital the chance to hold up this thing indefinitely!"

She looked at me with a frown, then a smile of understanding dawned on her face, but before she was able to comment she sniffed, hurriedly opened the oven and said, "Quick, put a pad on the table! We have cheese soufflé tonight!"

I knew by experience how she reacted to a soufflé that fell, so I hastily put the pad on the table and watched the dish emerge from the oven with apprehension. Once we sat down for our meal I was so relieved that when we said grace it all seemed to blend into one prayer of gratitude: the hospital, the soufflé, and her faith and constancy rewarded.

CHAPTER 9

ONCE AGAIN, we sat in front of the Convoy Commander's desk in the Red Cross chapter house in downtown Houston. Again he gave us the pleasant chatty preamble that precedes any briefing; only veterans know from experience that the chattier the preamble, the tougher the briefing. We had given him a copy of the letter we had sent to all contributors to the Mercy Fund; the Director of Nursing Services had given him her report, the Chairman of Nursing Services her opinion. Now it was up to him.

I had always been fascinated, and in my younger years depressed, by the capacity of commanders-in-chief for convincing their staffs that the present objective was decisive to the course of the war and hence to the future of all mankind, whereas at the next briefing, after the objective had been attained, they referred to it as "our initial little skirmish, which on the whole came off fairly successfully."

The manager of the Houston chapter of the Red Cross ran true to type, down to the word "skirmish." As I sat listening to his shrewd analysis, in one of those monologues commanders-in-chief refer to as discussions, I felt an excitement mingled with nostalgia. At last a breach had been made in the wall of secrecy and agoraphobia surrounding the hospital; as I sat there, looking at the intently listening officers in their blue-and-white uniforms, I realized not only that once the Red Cross had moved into the hospital it would never be the same again, but also that the Friends had no place in the operations now under discussion. My nostalgic feeling of farewell came from the realization that we had become redundant, now that the initial skirmish had been won. The days of barnstorming and haranguing crowds by torchlight were over; no more inflammatory letters by firebrands or rousing calls for action by rabblerousers. The letter from the Red Cross to the hospital was to be couched in correct and cautious officialese, and signed by the chapter chairman, Judge Hunt, whose prestige and reputation in Houston equaled that of Mr. Taub. For the time being, the appeal for volunteers would be suspended. About a hundred and twenty-five applications had been received so far, more than enough to make up a first contingent. Public appearances or other public appeals should be canceled until further notice; more emotional excitement at this point would jeopardize the chances of the Board of Managers granting the admission of the Red Cross volunteers.

At the end of the meeting I had to confess that there was one more speaking engagement I must fill, because to cancel it at this point would be impossible. The following Saturday, I was to address a group of oilworkers at La Porte; a good deal of work had already been done to organize this meeting. The Convoy Commander said, with a smile, "Why, of course, if you are committed, I can quite see how this would be difficult. How many people would you have to disappoint?"

I answered, with unconvincing humility, "Three thousand." In the silence that followed, I added reassuringly, "After that, my wife and I are due to leave for Europe. I have to do some work there that might take several months."

"Lucky you!" Mrs. Bannerman said, spontaneously. "I'd

love to go to Europe. But you will be back, won't you?"

"I expect so," I said, "but I don't quite know when. I have leave of absence from the University for the first semester, so it might be as late as November."

"You had better leave a forwarding address," Mrs. Bannerman continued. "We may come up against some unforeseen complications and need your help."

I was grateful to her for this kindness; but then, we had been in this together for some time now, ever since she started training our first group in old J.D.

"Splendid," the Commander said. "Are you planning to leave soon?"

"The day after that meeting at La Porte," I answered. "I'm sorry I can't cancel it, but I'm sure you understand."

He gave me a true admiral's smile and said, with unsettling insight, "Of course I do."

I had not realized it was so obvious that I wanted a last fling at being Savonarola, before I cleared the stage. The temptation had been irresistible, three thousand was a lot of people. The meeting was being organized by a formidable woman, secretary of a local of one of the unions; she had rounded up her dogies with the brashness of a Texas drover. Nothing seemed to stop her, nothing scared her; she had secured the big dance hall at La Porte gratis, by calling the councilman who owned it via the marine operator on board his yacht during the weekend. She had commandeered Boy Scouts to go from door to door, handing out stenciled invitations. We ourselves had a taste of the way in which she operated when Marjorie was interrupted during a telephone conversation by the operator saying, "Madam, I have an emergency call for you." For a heart-stopping moment she thought that I had been the victim of an accident; then the lady from La Porte was on the line. "Listen, honey," she asked, "has the man got transportation for Satiday night?" When assured that I had, she closed the emergency call by saying, "Okeedoke.

You make sure he gets there, hear? Seven o'clock sharp. These are not the kind of critters to keep waiting. Take it easy now. See you around."

It might not have been quite the ticket, but it obviously was the kind of femininity that achieved things.

2

I PREPARED my swan song with thoroughness. It was to be a simple but poignant farewell, a sober résumé of the recent past and a short but solemn vision of the future. I leafed for inspiration through King William of Orange's Farewell to Parliament, and the Gettysburg Address. As I sat writing in the silent seclusion of my study, I heard the sonorous phrases ring out underneath the echoing dome of that dancehall on the bay, and three thousand people applaud with thunderous cheers.

When the day arrived, the speech was rehearsed to perfection; but it was one thing to mumble those sonorous phrases in the shower or while striding along the banks of the bayou; to face the reality of three thousand people jam-packed in keyed-up expectation was another. The secretary had warned me to expect tremendous enthusiasm, all the oilworkers had been rooting for us, everyone had seen me on television, copies of the paper with my letter had been torn from hand to hand. These were the men that would make the difference, these were the masses about to rise and swipe that blubber-buttocked Board of Managers into the bay.

Debbie's husband Gus drove the car, Debbie and Lucille went with me, bringing handbills with my letter to the *Chronicle* and four heavy boxes, each containing a thousand application forms for training.

Never in my life had I been so nervous on my way to a

bull ring, with the possible exception of my examination for mate of ocean-going tugboats, on which occasion the German Zeppelin had appeared over Amsterdam. This I had considered to be a good omen. Now I looked morosely out the window of the car as it sped along the Gulf Freeway hoping for an omen, while sweat moistened my palms and my throat went dry. When finally we approached the dancehall of La Porte, ablaze with lights against the backdrop of the moonlit bay, I was ready to chicken out in a faked bout of the flu, but I knew that this was the ultimate moment of truth; now I had to stand up and witness in the face of history, or forever hold my peace.

We drove into the parking lot that had apparently been closed to prevent a traffic jam; with the feeling of being an observer looking down on myself that must be common to all candidates entering a hall for their examination, or mounting the steps to the scaffold, I walked with quaking calves to the garishly illuminated entrance of the building.

It only occurred to me that something was amiss when, in the vast expanse of the lobby, we found nobody except for our female Texan drover sheathed in a shimmering silver shift and an unhappy fidgeting man who turned out to be her husband. The doors to the ballroom were open, but it seemed to be steeped in darkness and incongruously quiet. The only other person I could discern was a man in armless white overalls and a chef's hat preparing a gargantuan quantity of popcorn in a booth.

"What's the matter?" Debbie asked. "Where is everybody?"

Our silver-sheathed friend answered, on the verge of tears, "I cain't understand it! I cain't understand it! There's nobody, there's only three people sitting in there!" Then she added, with painful sincerity, "I could run straight out to the bal-cony and shoot a bullet through mah hi-yed."

While my companions expressed shocked incredulity, I found myself grotesquely unaffected. I just stood there, idly wondering what part of her anatomy she intended to shoot the bullet through, and concluded it was her head.

We entered the hollow void of the darkened hall. Outside, beyond the open doors to the balcony, sounded the sibilant whisper of the surf on the beach of the bay. In the auditorium, sprinkled in the darkness like asteroids in interstellar space, sat three dim shapes. Their attitude of devotion was suggestive of a Quaker meeting, and I realized, once more, that indeed I stood in the presence of God. I remembered the bomb with the diapers, the actor's bird, the latter-day Count Tolstoy's fly; this occasion clearly fitted into that category. Either the woman was a raving lunatic, or I was being subjected to the same divine twitting as when I had stood looking at myself in the mirror of that private bathroom with a handful of paperclips. "Well," I said, "we might as well go and sit out on the balcony, considering there are only—how many?—ten of us."

"Nine," said Gus, who was a statistician.

"I am including the man in the popcorn stand," I said. "He might as well join us if he feels like it."

And so we shuffled out onto the verandah overlooking the bay. We pushed two tables together and drew up chairs and sat down. The sound of the surf was louder here; the heat was humid and sticky. Shouting over the surf, I began a little speech on the hospital issue, not the one I had rehearsed, but simply the bare facts. I had just started when out of the dark cave of the deserted ballroom a couple emerged. The man wore a ten-gallon hat and dandy boots, the woman a clinging flesh-colored dress and elbow-length white gloves.

"Mind if we join you folks?" the man asked. "Are you talking about the hospital?" When I said we were, he added, "My wife here knew the old one, as an LVN, so we thought we'd drop by and hear what the new one's like."

We drew up chairs for them and I continued my shouted soliloquy about Miss Lucas and the cockroaches. I had barely started a description of Male Medicine as it had been at night in old J.D. when the lady in the flesh-colored dress, so clinging that she seemed to sit across from me with nothing but her gloves on in the moonlight, cried in a strident, quarrelsome voice, "What nonsense! I've worked in that place for my training and I thought it was real nice!"

I thought I must have misunderstood her because of the surf; sturdy little waves went on stubbornly crashing on the beach and flattening with hisses. "Pardon?" I shouted. "You mean you saw nothing wrong with Male Medicine in Jeff Davis?"

"I sure did not!" she yelled. "I thought it was real interesting. A fine, fine school for a girl who wants to take up nursing for a living."

"But, madam," I protested, more for the sake of sanity than that of argument, "you must have seen the patients? How can you say . . ."

"You're darn tootin' right I saw the patients!" she bellowed belligerently. "And I just loved them! I loved them to bits! Once you got to know them, those little ol' niggers were real cute!"

I stared at her, dumbfounded, with the sudden suspicion that the vast dark ballroom, the three thousand supporters who turned out to be three, the pounding surf, the stifling heat and the ghostly presence of the popcorn man with his tall white hat in the moonlight were a midsummer night's dream, and that this couple of djinns that had come spinning out of the darkness were not a ten-gallon-hatted man in dandy boots and his wife in elbow-length gloves, but Ben Taub and Mrs. Willoughby with a spell thrown over them, bidding me get the hell out of their forest.

As I sat there, fighting the urge to burst into giggles, there came across the glimmering blackness of the bay the

deep-throated call of a ship's horn. I looked and saw, beyond the tall white hat of the popcorn man, the star-
studded silhouette of a freighter ghost by on the horizon.
It was like a call to sanity, the imperative honking of a
pilot goose waking up his dreaming flock, drifting like
large white buds on the still black water. Again the fog
horn hooted its deep, throaty call across the bay, and I felt
like spreading my wings and following my fellows on the
Atlantic flyway toward our distant home. Then, just as I
was about to take off with a cry of liberation, I saw old
Mr. Hood sitting slumped on his stretcher, his black dead
feet sticking over the edge, a grimy aspirin in his outstretched hand. So I turned away from that vision of
freedom slowly setting out to sea, and said, "I am sorry to
say that, in my opinion, it is people like you who are to
blame for the sad place we call our charity hospital. If
you, who worked on the floors, have seen nothing but
cute little old niggers whom you loved to bits for a living,
we might as well pack up."

I heard the woman gasp across the table and Lucille hiss
to Debbie in her stage whisper, "Let's get him out of here."
Then the husband with the ten-gallon hat and the dandy
boots said gallantly, "Listen, mister, that's not the way to
speak to a lady!"

"I am sorry," I said cheerfully, with the self-confidence
of a soldier going into battle, convinced that the only bullet
he need worry about is the one that has his name on it, "I
do not intend to insult the lady, but having worked there
too, I cannot let her get away with this."

"What are you? Some kind of a nut?" the woman
shouted, getting up. "I've never been so insulted in my
life! I'm getting out of here! To say such things about a
place where I learned so much and where I had such fun
and where everybody loved me! Yes!" She slammed her
chair down at the table. "They loved me! And I loved
them!"

276

I suddenly felt ashamed. "I'm sorry," I said.

She staggered, as one of her heels went down a crack between the planks of the balcony. Her husband grabbed her round the waist, and for a moment they stood poised in the moonlight like a burlesque dancing couple, sprung from a cake at a gangster's convention. Then she said, "Let's go, honey, I need a drink!" and they stumbled off into the darkness, leaving our small gathering behind in thoughtful silence, listening to the waves.

I wanted to explain to them that what they had just witnessed was a characteristic example of the disaster syndrome, but the wash of the freighter heading out to sea had now reached the beach, pounding it with a staccato surf. Before it had abated, the specter of the popcorn man started to flagellate himself like a dervish, crying, "Here they come!"

"What's the matter with him?" Lucille inquired with professional interest. A flat Texas voice answered dryly, "Skeeters." It was our organizer's husband, and it was all he said that night.

After this, there seemed to be little point in continuing the meeting. Everybody got up and started toward the dark ballroom, Gus and I lugging the boxes with the four thousand application forms.

In the car, on our way home, we tried to rationalize the events of that evening. We all had a go at it, but each of us ended up in a quagmire of irrationality. There was no explanation for anything that had happened that night, unless you accepted the axiom of a Supreme Being and attributed to that Being a sense of humor. Burdened with the perpetual doubt of my generation, I could not attach sufficient importance to myself as an individual to warrant sidetracking the Mind of God into such an elaborate practical joke, involving three thousand men, a bossy woman, a seventeen-thousand-ton freighter and enough popcorn to have fed the multitude on the shores of the Lake of Galilee.

If the power that guided the hand that stroked the crying girl's hair had any message to convey that night, Lucille summed it up when she said, stubbing out with jangling bracelet a cigarette she had barely smoked, "Well, it just goes to show that you can't win 'em all."

3

WHEN I ARRIVED in Emergency for my last shift before leaving, I found it in a mess. I had not planned to go, but Miss Lucas had called me in.

The regular eleven to seven shift had not come on, probably because the whole schedule had been changed once more; everybody thought it was his night off. Miss Lucas, pulled from Male Medicine and obviously in a dilly of a flap, skated in and out of all those interlocking rooms with a great show of briskness but her eyes had the hint of panic typical of anybody working in ER for the first time. Two student nurses, obviously roused from their sleep in the dormitory behind old J.D. and whisked across town by taxi, were being brave; a reluctant orderly had been pulled from the psychiatric floor.

The four of them had a hard time coping with just the Treatment section of Emergency. The attendant in the Utility Room had not turned up either, so one of the student nurses started washing up and sterilizing instruments in the autoclave before the Suture Rooms would run out of trays; this left nobody to cover Observation. I went in there, found most of the beds occupied and the empty ones unmade. I took the charts off the desk by the door and started to make the rounds; then a Shock Room case arrived across the hall and the orderly came to ask me where he could find the prep tray. To explain to him where it was inside the Chinese puzzle would take longer than taking him there myself, so I left Observation for a moment.

I was away for over three hours. It was the night after payday, the bars in town had closed, and screaming ambulances kept on bringing in the revelers. By two o'clock in the morning our eighth Shock Room case was brought in; interns and students were suturing in the corridors, a resident was putting in a chest tube in the Utility Room. This last Shock Room case caused a row between the Surgical Resident and a sheriff from the county jail, for the patient was a prisoner who had been brought in for suturing a few hours earlier after being knifed in a brawl in the drunk tank in jail; when the intern was through with him the man had tried to escape in the confusion and been shot by the sheriff in the parking lot as he was about to make off with somebody's car. Now they rushed him back into the Shock Room, and the resident gave the gunslinger a piece of his mind, asking what the hell he meant by making more work on a night when the staff was already run ragged? This was all they needed: to have sutured patients gunned down as they left the building.

It was a night of many such rows. Somebody was letting it rip in the other Shock Room as I came out; I found Miss Lucas, eyes flashing, fists clenched, bawling out a policeman who stood gaping at a naked woman patient prostrate on the Shock Room table, shot through the thigh. She told him to take his leering mug out of there; he had no business standing around while female patients were being treated; if he was interested in ogling naked women he should go out and buy himself a magazine. She looked as if she had just landed on a broomstick in this Walpurgis Night; the policeman, muttering manfully, agreed to leave but not before he had shackled the woman to the operating table with a set of handcuffs. At this, Miss Lucas streaked into the passage, shrieking like a five-point fire alarm, to call in the Surgical Resident so he might tell this

279

crazy cop that she could not put an IV in the arm of a patient who was handcuffed.

Amidst the chaos, I saw a chance to have a quick look at Observation before being forced back into the madhouse, where irate interns in bloody aprons stood bellowing, "Orderly! Orderly!" in the doorways of their shops, like burgled butchers yelling for the police. I was just crossing the entrance hall when a baby boy was carried in by his mother, herself no more than a child.

It was one of those cases that occasionally arrive in the midst of bedlam and that suddenly bring about a hush, as they somehow break the hypnotic spell of blood and violence. She stumbled to the reception desk, panting with fright and exhaustion, and whispered, "He beat him, my husband beat him. . . . A doctor, quick, a doctor . . ." She was followed by an elderly policeman in bifocals holding a clipboard, and an unemotional Texan-hatted detective, both of whom wanted to take down her statement.

I took the crying child over from her and carried it to the Poison Room, a small cubicle with only one table, where a doctor would be able to examine him in relative peace. The little boy, as he lay naked on the table, was a terrible and enraging sight. The brute that had assaulted him must have kicked him across the room, flung him against the wall, pressed him down on a redhot stove. His head was bruised and blue, his eyes closed and swollen, his nose bleeding, his lower lip torn, his body covered with welts and lacerations. One little arm was broken, his left hip dislocated, his right thigh covered with third-degree burns, his little penis blue and broken. His mother, deadly pale and trembling with fright, stammered heartbreakingly, "He couldn't help it, Hank couldn't help it, he's a sick boy, he needs help, he is so terribly nervous. . . ."

The child moaned plaintively, "Mama . . ."

The Medical Resident came in, cursing; when he saw the little boy he fell silent. He stood looking at him, motionless for a moment; then he called, "Miss Lucas! You'd better come and give me a hand."

When she came in and saw the child, a strange, sudden tranquillity smoothed out her harrowed face, her tense, harassed body. I saw her, in front of my own eyes, transformed from an aggressive waspish head nurse into someone so gentle and serene that she seemed the embodiment of the miracle of mercy. She went toward the child, took its groping little hand in hers and whispered something. The boy whimpered a little and became still.

She straightened up and looked at the hand she held in hers. "I believe there is a broken finger here too," she said calmly to the doctor.

"All right," he said. "We'd better start working him up. Would you gentlemen mind taking the air for a moment, so we can have some room here?"

"Doc, I've got to get a statement from this woman," the Texan-hatted dick said. "This was assault with intent."

"Later," the doctor said. "Come back later."

"Heck, doc . . ."

But the doctor interrupted him. "Orderly," he said, with a sideways nod at the door.

I put my hand on the shoulder of the detective and said, "Come on, let's leave them to it. They won't be long." To the policeman I said, "All right?"

The grandfatherly policeman had been staring at the little boy all the time. Now he said, like a man called out of a dream, "Yes, sure. Sure thing."

The three of us went out into the corridor which seemed much quieter now; the passage of the little boy had drawn a wake of silence. "Who did it?" the policeman asked.

"His stepfather," the detective answered, "with a gun butt and a skillet. He also threw him on the stove. Must be a madman."

The policeman nodded. "Sure," he said. "Sure thing."

One of the interns or medical students came toward me

and said, "Mr. de Hartog, we would like to help in the ward over there with all those beds, but we don't know what to do. It seems they have plenty of people around this end now."

I looked at him in bewilderment; they could not be students. The one who had addressed me looked familiar, but so did everybody around here. I noticed they were not wearing scrub suits but white trousers and white shirts. "Who are you?" I asked.

"My name is Bill Jepson," the talkative one said. "I am the chairman of the hospital committee of the Jaycees. He's Frank, public relations officer. Frank Balthazar."

"What are you doing here?" I asked, astounded; I had seen them on and off all night. Jepson's shirt was spattered with blood.

"We thought we'd come and have a look around," he said. "Frank brought a tape recorder so we could record some sounds to play back to the membership."

"Nobody stopped you?" I asked. "I mean, you just walked in and started handling patients?"

"Yep," he said laconically. "But we didn't do anything fancy. I was sick once, when that guy was brought in with his leg back to front and the bone sticking out. After that I was okay. You, Frank?"

Frank said he was okay too.

"How about speaking a few words into our tape recorder?" Jepson said. "Maybe we can use it on our Jaycee radio program. We have to give this project some publicity, you know, if we want volunteers."

"Tell you what," I said. "Why don't you come with me into Observation and put up your tape recorder there? We'll make some beds and put some patients on the bedpan and record some really realistic noises."

"Like what?" Frank asked.

"Like me telling you how to make a bed and put somebody on a bedpan," I said.

They said fine, as long as it was the real thing; so we went into Observation. It was a chaos. Merely to see those patients lying there without anyone having paid any attention to them for God knew how many hours made you sick at heart. There was no excuse for this. Nothing anyone could say, no arguments of economy or politics could justify this stupid callousness. I did not know where to start; the moment we came in, people started to call feebly from all directions. The first thing to do was to make the rounds quickly to see if there were any crucial emergencies, like oxygen failures or coma.

There were not, but some of them seemed awfully sick. The two young men followed me, shocked into silence by what they saw. Most of the patients had soiled their beds, none of them had anything to drink, virtually all the IV bottles had run dry. The most urgent thing was to get those IV's going again, if so indicated on the charts. The changing of IV bottles should only be done by RN's or LVN's, not by orderlies or nurses' aides; if the liquid was turned on without the air having been expelled from the feeding tube this could kill the patient. Mrs. Judd had impressed this upon me the very first day in Observation at old J.D. But, once I knew my way around, it had been tacitly assumed that I could be trusted with the job when there was no one else to do it. I showed the two young men how to change the sheets on a bed with a patient in it, and how to wash those who were incontinent; then I let them loose in the male section and started to change IV bottles, give iced water to those who were allowed to drink, bring out the bedpans and the urinals, check the suction machines; we were just beginning to see the light when the door to the hall was opened by Miss Lucas, holding up an IV bottle, to let the resident pass carrying the little boy, followed by his deadly white, dazed mother.

"Have you a bed for him?" the doctor asked. "Put him somewhere near your desk. I want him watched continuously."

I had to tell him that even if he put the little boy near the desk, there was nobody to watch him unless we pulled someone from another floor. I found him a clean bed up the aisle in the male section, and the doctor gently put the little boy down. He looked wan and drowsy, his broken arm was in a cast, a finger of the other hand in splints, his burnt thigh bandaged, his welts and bruises painted with Mecressin and his lip sutured. Miss Lucas suspended the IV bottle from the stand at the head of his bed, then she asked, "Is there a chair for his mother?"

I had to tell her that there were no chairs in Observation at all; a voice behind me said, "I know where to get one," and I saw Bill Jepson run off at a trot. Frank Balthazar stood looking down at the child in disbelief.

"Okay," the resident said. "I want him watched, vital signs taken every hour. I don't care a goddamn how you do it, or who does it, just as long as somebody watches him and calls me or the head nurse the moment there is a change." He did not wait for the answer, but turned away and left.

Miss Lucas and I looked at each other in dismay. The mother could obviously not be trusted to watch him properly; the only solution was that I check on him frequently while taking care of the others in Observation. I was about to suggest this, when Bill Jepson came running back with a chair for the mother. I had no idea where he had found it, but one thing was certain: it belonged somewhere else. The mother, faint with fatigue and shock, slumped down on it gratefully.

"The next bed is free," Frank said. "Why don't we put her on it? I'll sit on the chair and watch him."

Miss Lucas looked at him, then she asked quietly, "Do you know what to watch for?"

"No," said Frank. "I have no idea, but can't you tell me?"

"Sure," she replied, as if she had time on her hands. "First of all, watch his respiration. . . ."

As Bill Jepson and I walked away from the bed, I asked him, "Can you manage the other bedpans by yourself?"

"Manage?" he said, jauntily. "It's a ball. I found the solution, you know. I don't think of it as crap. I think of it as plasticine. How does that sound?"

"Sounds fine," I said, "as long as you don't get carried away to the point where you want to knead a little elephant."

He laughed. "Hell, that might be just the thing," he said. "A souvenir for you, from an apprentice in the Twilight Zone."

I glanced at his white face, his bloodless lips; I knew exactly how he felt and how it helped to make these wisecracks. "Are you planning to come back here?" I asked off-handedly.

"You mean to work? You're damn right I am. You can't spend a night in this place and not come back. You'd never forgive yourself. Don't you see?"

"I do," I said. "But you should get some training first, or you'll be in trouble."

"Isn't that what I am getting right now?" he asked. "I mean, you already started teaching me. Why can't I just come back for a couple of weeks or a month and work alongside you? Wouldn't that do?"

"It might," I replied, "but I'm leaving tomorrow."

"Where?"

"Europe."

We stood by the bedside of his next patient. "Hi there," I said. "How are you doing?"

The big Negro in the bed looked at me with jaundiced eyes, a look of total detachment, and said in a low, husky voice, "Yessir."

I looked at his chart; it said gunshot perforating the abdomen from the back, and I recognized him. He was the prisoner who had tried to escape earlier that night. He was on call to go up for surgery but no one seemed to be in any great hurry. I had better go and see Miss Lucas about him.

I said to Bill Jepson, "You'd better move on to the next patient. I'll check on this one."

"Would I have to be trained by the Red Cross?" he asked.

"That's right," I said.

"When does their course start?"

"They are sending a letter to the hospital, and it depends on the answer. The hospital might take some time to reply, so maybe you could drop by here occasionally to find out if they have."

"Whom do I see?"

"The Administrator, I'd say. Just call on him."

"You bet I will," he said. "I'll come back here, trained, if I've got to wear out that guy's Bigelow to do it."

"That's the spirit," I said innocently; having thus instigated some Quakerly mayhem, I went to see Miss Lucas about the man shot in the back.

The two Jaycees stayed on until the dawn; by then the Treatment Section had calmed down; the student nurse from the Utility Room came to take over Frank Balthazar's wake by the bedside of the little boy. I was ready to go home; Miss Lucas was obviously tired too; she came to Observation to see if there was any coffee going in the kitchen.

She looked absolutely done in, with dark rings round her eyes, the cold sweat of exhaustion on her forehead. She had heard we were assembling volunteers for a Red Cross training course; she said it would be wonderful if it succeeded, it could transform the hospital. We had never talked personally before; I discovered she was not as tough and short-tempered as she appeared. I was about to go back into the ward when she said, "You know there are powers in this hospital who would do anything to stop the Red Cross coming in, don't you?"

I said, cautiously, that I knew some people had reservations about it.

"No, no," she said, "not reservations. And not people, either. You know what Saint Paul writes? 'For we wrestle not against flesh and blood, but against principalities, against powers, against the rulers of the darkness of this world.' You must be prepared for them to fight you with all they've got. They'll never show themselves, you'll never see them. One moment you'll think it is this person, the next someone else. It shifts, it takes hold first of this person, then of that person, it's like a moving shadow. It is an evil spirit; all we can do is put on the armor of God."

She had looked very tired; now she sounded it. I could not help seeing the world of old J.D. the way she had seen it, passionate, fragile girl with an indomitable will, flinging herself at the barbed-wire defenses of a faceless bureaucracy, tearing herself to shreds.

"You are coming back, are you?" she asked.

"Yes," I said. "But it is better if I stay away now for a while, and let them work it out among themselves."

"Shall I make you a prediction?" she said. "I predict that the Red Cross will never get in here, not until those powers are defeated. They have been entrenched for too many years. They could not survive in the daylight, and the arrival of the Red Cross in this place would mean letting the daylight in. They'll fight with any weapons, they'll go to any length, do anything at all, because they are fighting for their lives. Don't underestimate them; believe me, you will really need the armor of God, as Saint Paul describes it. 'Stand therefore, having your loins girt about with truth, and having on the breastplate of righteousness. . . .' "

It was strange; again I had that sensation of being lifted out of time and place, of taking part in a moment that had existed, somewhere in this galaxy of stars and their circling planets, for a long time, as when I had seen Mrs. Judd with her arm around the shoulders of Mr. Hood, that first day in Emergency. Miss Lucas closed her eyes in a strenuous effort to remember the words which she whispered into the restless silence of the Observation Ward, where the people lay whose sentinel she was: the little boy, bruised and broken, the Negro prisoner, shot in the back.

". . . Taking the shield of Faith, wherewith ye shall be able to quench all the fiery darts of the wicked. And take the helmet of salvation, and the sword of the Spirit, which is the word of God."

She sighed, as if she had taken a deep draught of cool water, and opened her eyes. "That's what I try to say to myself when I see things I cannot stand. So, when your day comes, think of it: the armor of God. If you think of it desperately, if you really need it, you'll find it's there. But don't forget: 'We wrestle not against flesh and blood.' Don't ever think it is a person; it's a spirit." Then she frowned and said, "Sorry, I forgot: are you a Christian? Oh, of course," she answered herself, "you are a Quaker. I don't suppose that's too different from a Mormon, is it?"

"I don't know," I said. "I don't know any Mormons."

"I'm a Mormon," she said, with a smile.

"In that case," I replied, gallantly, "I can truthfully say that there is no difference at all."

She gave me a searching look, and I thought she was about to say something else, something from deep down within her, for that was the way she looked. But then she smiled, quickly and shyly, said, "Goodbye," and slipped out. I listened to the rapid rustle of her skirt down the aisle, until it was gone. Then I heard, in the silence of the ward, a weak voice call, "Please . . . somebody . . . please . . ."

288

I could not make out where it came from. All my patients seemed to be if not asleep, at least at rest. Then I heard it again. "Please . . . please . . ." I realized it came from behind the curtain to my left.

I had completely forgotten about that bed. It was rarely used: one isolated bed, opposite the corner where we kept the dirty linen hoppers. I went to open the curtain and found, in a tangled bed soaked with urine, a bald old man with a Slavic face, bristling with a beard several days old. He had two IV's, both of which had run dry; one arm, taped to a board, was bulging with infiltration, the needle stuck upright in the back of a swollen hand. He was a pitiful sight and obviously in great pain. "Please . . ." he whispered, "please help me . . ."

I said, "Okay. I'll be right back," and went to get clean sheets, basin, soap, towel, fresh gown, Foley bottle, tube, external catheter, surgical tape. I loaded it all onto the medication trolley, checked his chart and discovered that his IV's were to be continued; I would have to call in Miss Lucas to do it. As I pushed my trolley past the bed with the little boy, the student nurse whispered, "Do you need any help?"

She looked young, dedicated and very sleepy, on her chair between the two beds. The little boy lay very still, a comatose stillness. His mother, asleep on the other bed, lay as if she had fallen from a great height.

"Thanks," I answered, in a whisper. "Maybe you could go and call the head nurse for me. I have an IV that has infiltrated; she'll have to change the needle. How is he?"

She looked uncertain and a little worried. "I don't know. He's very quiet. I think the nurse should have a look at him too when she comes."

I said, "Good idea. You know who it is? Miss Lucas is her name."

"Thank you," she said, still in a whisper. "Will you watch him for me while I'm gone?"

I pointed to the bed with the bald old man. "I'll be right there. Leave the curtain open, so I can see him."

She got up, stiffly, and teetered off toward the hall; I pushed my trolley and pulled up beside the old man's bed.

We had quite a time together, changing his sheets, cleaning him, giving him a bedbath, putting on his catheter and the new gown. As I worked, he told me, haltingly and in a heavy accent, that he was a goose farmer and had been in Texas for fifty years after immigrating from Poland. His two daughters lived up North, his wife had died a year ago, the farm had gone down and could he have two pillows? His wife always had given him two pillows, he could not sleep on just one. He reveled in the sheer luxury of being washed and dried and powdered like a baby and put in clean linen and having a catheter put on so he need not worry about soiling the bed. In the end I was as grateful to him as he was to me; to have brought home to me so poignantly the preciousness of simple comforts was a sobering experience.

When finally he lay back, eyes closed and smiling, his old Polish head blissfully resting on that second pillow, he suddenly talked about death. He was about to go, he said, and he did not mind; we all had to go sometime. But it was nice to go gently, with somebody friendly on the platform to wave goodby to as you went. I fussed around him a little while longer, chatting as I cleared up; when finally he seemed to be falling asleep, I prepared to leave on tiptoe. He opened his eyes and saw me at the foot of his bed.

"Will you be back?" he asked.

"No," I replied. "I'm sorry. My leave starts tomorrow. I really am sorry. I enjoyed talking to you."

"Never mind," he said with a smile, closing his eyes again. "I won't be around long enough to miss you." Then he composed himself for sleep and I drew the curtain around him.

On my way out, I checked with the student nurse that

Miss Lucas would be in to take care of his IV; then, at last, I stepped outside into the early sunlight. As I walked toward my car, I stopped to look around at the doors marked EMER-GENCY ENTRANCE. I remembered Mrs. Kowalski locking them for the last time, for maybe another thirty years. I was suddenly overcome by a deep sense of loss.

"I won't be around long enough to miss you." I realized that I would miss him terribly. I had the sudden premoni-tion that I would miss Emergency very much. Life would seem empty and shallow without this place of pain and sorrow, where I had been able to do so little. I knew I would miss them, more than I could possibly foresee; and as I stood there, looking at the doors, I knew also that they would not miss me.

Only the present counted beyond those doors; no memo-ries could live there for long. Already we had almost for-gotten Mrs. Judd, who had given all she had; the moment I turned away and drove off into the morning mist, hang-ing shroudlike between the trees of the park, my footsteps would be washed away by the next tide of suffering to swamp the beach where I had walked awhile.

CHAPTER **10**

A ND SO the long summer started. Before sailing for Europe and all the demands that awaited us there, we had planned to spend three weeks on the island of Nantucket, as a vacation. The hospital business had made us late, so all we had left was a week.

We spent those days in the house of Hanna Monaghan, fiery old Quaker. She was one of the last handful of Friends on Nantucket, that once had been a Quaker stronghold; but she generated, all by herself, enough energy to light up the town. When the Quaker movement started, in the middle of the seventeenth century, it had been a band of spiritual firebrands, whose aggressive outspokenness was always getting them into trouble; many of them had died in jail, several had been hanged in New England. Since those early days the movement had changed character, but Hanna Monaghan had not. To hear her refer to our dignified, dedicated leadership as "those Mandarins in Philadelphia" was a surprising but somehow welcome change from the present-day process of friendly persuasion by which so many decisions were gently postponed. There seemed to be a link between this outspoken, outrageous old woman and the youngest generation of Friends; both had the same restless spirit, the same intemperate urge for action, the

292

same impatience with quietist lack of practice. Her bonnet was a veritable beehive, as is the case with most people of character and originality. The queen bee in her bonnet was her contention that the first committee to be appointed in the history of the Quaker movement, the so-called "Ellwood committee" that had edited the Journals of George Fox after his death and expurgated them before publication, had been the first emanation of the spirit she had battled singlehanded from the age of toothbrace and pigtails. Her contention was that the committee had cut the soul out of George Fox; during the long evenings, drowsily lounging in her sagging lawn-chairs in the back garden, we would listen to her holding forth, inspiringly and endearingly, about "Dear George," who was as real to her as a neighbor. When darkness fell and her frail silhouette was outlined against the pale green evening sky, with Venus rising over her shoulder like the star of Bethlehem, there came a moment when past and future seemed inexorably entangled, when the fiery prophet who had started the Friends on their way seemed to have been called Bob Cogswell, and the earnest young orderly who had wanted to fast unto death for the sake of his patients seemed to be called George Fox. Were I a weighty Friend in Philadelphia, shouldering the load of the society, I would probably be at a loss too as to what to do about her interference. But as an orderly in Houston I would be at a loss as to what to do without her inspiration.

Life away from the hospital turned out to be more barren than we had expected. We aimlessly walked the cobblestoned streets of the quaint little town, went for hikes on the moors with other people's dogs and had ice cream twice a day, once in each of the two drugstores, discussing lengthily whether we preferred the lemon here or the ginget next door. We took hours to read the paper, and were frequently beset by long, long yawns. We went to bed early and slept late, but our sleep was troubled by shapeless dreams made up out of loose, distorted images of Pedi and Observation. We telephoned Debbie one night to ask for news; she told us the Red Cross had sent the letter and was now waiting for a reply. Well, it was something; but it did not alleviate that feeling of emptiness and aimless waiting.

One of our dear friends, Margaret Ernst, was admitted to the Nantucket Cottage Hospital and we went to see her. To be back inside a hospital was an unexpectedly exciting experience; when the matron offered to show us around, we accepted greedily. We were shown the floors, the nurses' quarters, the dining hall, the laundry; finally, to the awed amazement of two solitary Women-in-Pink, we were shown the Operating Room, which seemed to be a signal honor. The hospital had looked like a wish dream; the staff outnumbered the patients, it was swarming with RN's, the atmosphere was one of concern, care and attention; I had never been in such a joyous hospital before. When we stood gazing at the operating table in the center of a room half the size of one of the Shock Rooms in Houston, it looked like a weary pilgrim's vision of journey's end: so meticulously arranged, so sternly sterile, that we did not dare advance further than the threshold. After a few moments of reverent silence, the matron said, "Well, we had better leave; we are expecting a case any moment." When I asked her what kind of case, she answered, "A circumcision."

First, as we walked back to Hanna's hotbed of Quakerly rebellion along the cobbled streets, we laughed at the contrast; then it penetrated to us what Houston had done to our standards. This, after all, was the way a hospital was supposed to be run, in the civilized world.

I HAD ALWAYS thought of Holland as my home, but coming back after this year in Texas I discovered it was a sailor's home: a haven of peace, prosperity and provincialism,
secure, sedate and set in its ways. It was a glorious country
and all of me that was child and boy and midshipmite,
gangling youth and pimply dreamer, urbane debater and
tongue-tied lover, all of young Jan lay there. Maybe I
would come back to it one day and walk the lanes of my
childhood and look down from the bridge, where I had
stood as a boy, at the still silver water that once mirrored
my dreams. But while I still had within me the call of the
wild, still lay listening to the wind whistling in the rigging
of ships at the quay, yearning for the sea, I must go back
to that town in the prairie, back to the battlefield where,
this much I knew, the forces were ranged for today's Armageddon, eternal field of honor for the humanity of man,
shifting perpetually around and across the globe like a
speck of sunlight, point of focus of the eyes of God.

The night before the ship sailed for Europe, we had
spoken to Lucille on the telephone. She had told us on that
occasion that the Red Cross had received an answer from
the hospital: they would appoint a committee to study the
advisability of admitting a corps of Red Cross volunteer
nurses' aides and orderlies. That had been three months ago;
now Lucille wrote that Mrs. Willoughby had said openly
that "the Red Cross will never be allowed to set foot in this
hospital" because "our by-laws state that all volunteers inside this building must wear yellow uniforms." Lucille suggested that maybe it would be a good idea if I reactivated
my plan to write a series of articles on the Houston charity
hospital for the European papers, as it was now obvious
that the Red Cross was being given the J.D. runaround.

It seemed unbelievable. Whatever way we looked at it,

ever allowance we made for the ponderousness of bureaucratic deliberations, it seemed incredible that a hospital
understaffed, deteriorating into squalor for sheer lack of
help, should refuse to accept an enthusiastic corps of
volunteers, trained and supervised by an organization as in-
ternationally respected as the Red Cross. What in the name
of God could motivate someone to consciously, deliberately
douse the spark of compassion that had shone for one moment in the heart of a metropolis? What considerations of
prestige or power or personal petulance could prompt people, supposedly concerned with alleviating the suffering of
the helpless, to deny so cynically the essence of their calling?

The most generous, conciliatory answer was to explain it
via the disaster syndrome. But if I faced myself in truth, I
had to confess I no longer believed in it. To refuse the offer
from the Red Cross, to refuse the helping hand from the
community after all those years of hypocritical cant about
nobody taking any notice of their poor hospital, could
never be justified. It seemed that here, for once, there was no
chance for the gentle spirit of love to do its magic work.
With those articles I could force the issue, of that I was certain. Considering that everything else had failed, this seemed
justified. As I had explained to Mr. Taub: the Nursing Office had stated that it could not properly care for its patients, not even to minimal standards, with the staff at its
disposal. The citizens of Houston refused to supply the
funds needed for professional help. Now that the hospital
itself refused to accept the help of trained volunteers, there
was only one solution left: to appeal for those funds elsewhere.

My European agents sounded out a few of the leading
magazines in France, Germany, Italy and Holland; when
the response was eager, they drew up a contract for me to
sign in which I agreed to write a series of six articles on the
Houston charity hospital, and the magazines agreed to act
as local collection agencies for contributions to the Mercy

Fund. But I hesitated to sign the contract. Discussing the hospital with friends in Europe, I had become alarmed by the mood I gauged in most of them. Even if I kept my articles as positive as possible and staunchly continued to refuse to blame anybody in particular, it was obvious that if I were to write them with the intention of raising money I had to be fairly explicit about conditions in the hospital; I was afraid that my appeal for compassion might result, beyond my control, in a bout of sanctimonious Yankee-baiting.

But what else could I do? What other hope was there to defeat those powers ranged between the city and its sick paupers, custodians of its soul?

Marjorie said, "Wait and see, let's cross that bridge when we get to it." But then, she had never really been involved in the clash of battle. When I went out to speak to those churches, unions, committees and clubs, she had worked in the hospital. Her secret was a spirit of gentleness, kindness and faith in her fellow men; but could that spirit win battles? Could it wrestle, not against flesh and blood, but against "the principalities, the powers, the rulers of the darkness of the world, the wickedness in high places"? Or could she be what she was only under the protection of my shield? Was her peaceable kingdom only possible after the battle had been won, the breach made, the beachhead established?

I did not know, I simply did not know. And I needed the answer, for time was running out.

3

THE DAY BEFORE we were to return to America I went with my brother to my parents' grave. It was in a big cemetery south of Amsterdam, across the water from our old family home. Between the familiar house and the unfamiliar garden of the dead lay the canal: a myriad memories of swimming and skating, of sailing little boats, of a boy's hand slowly splashing in the water, imagining it to be the sound of the sea. Outside the solid iron gates of the cemetery I had tried out my first bicycle, and solemnly, in the pitch darkness at the final strokes of midnight of some forgotten year, held hands with a scared, spindly girl to whom I recited poems about "Dead Buddha Drifting Down the Yellow River with a Butterfly on His Knee," at which she had irreverently giggled. So now she was married to a scientist.

Inside the gates, the birds were rustling in the willows; our footsteps crunched on the gravel in the peaceful silence of the dead. The cemetery was large, the graves close together, winding lane wound into winding lane; it took us some time to reach the large polished stone with the two names that meant more to us than we could express, except in the words "Mamma" and "Pappa."

To stand there together, two middle-aged men in awkward silence, with unexpected tears running down our faces, now weathered and worn, was more upsetting than we could possibly have foreseen. It had seemed such an appropriate idea, a last homage of filial loyalty before we parted once more to thread our thinning lifelines across the globe. We had not known that we would be so deeply moved, feel so close together and so lost in sudden, unbearable loneliness. We had last stood there when she was buried, and as her coffin was lowered into the grave to join his waiting dust I had read aloud the chapter on charity in the first letter to the Corinthians, as she had asked me so often to do during her last weeks of purgatory. I remembered how she had said one night, after I had read it to her once more, "This is the answer, there it is, this is the answer. . . ."

As we slowly walked toward the exit, our feet crunching on the gravel, those gentlest words in the Bible sang softly in my thoughts.

Though I speak with the tongues of men and of angels, and have not charity, I am become as sounding brass, or a tinkling cymbal. And though I have the gift of prophecy and understand all mysteries, and all knowledge; and though I have all faith, so that I could remove mountains, and have not charity, I am nothing. And though I bestow all my goods to feed the poor, and though I give my body to be burned, and have not charity, it profiteth me nothing.

If this were indeed the answer, there could be no doubt as to what I should do. . . .

Charity suffereth long, and is kind; charity envieth not; charity vaunteth not itself, is not puffed up, doth not behave itself unseemly, seeketh not her own, is not easily provoked, thinketh no evil. . . . Charity beareth all things, believeth all things, hopeth all things, endureth all things. . . .

Could it really be true? Could this meekness, this passiveness, this serene determination to believe nothing but the best of people really be the answer?

Charity never faileth.

They had been her last intelligible words to me. Maybe the time had come to understand them.

4

MY AGENT came with the contract, an hour before sailing. He now had seventeen European papers and magazines lined up; all that was needed was my signature; the articles I could write later, at my ease. I did not sign.

All during the voyage I doubted the wisdom of my decision. Several times I was about to cable him from mid-ocean, saying I would write those articles after all. It seemed preposterous even to consider that the powers of darkness would give in to nothing. For I just did nothing, except believe the best of them.

I did not send that cable. In New York a letter from Lucille awaited us; the word in the hospital was: never. Nobody seemed to know who, exactly, of the people in control was against admitting the Red Cross, but Mrs. Willoughby seemed to be the front line of the battle, if there was to be a battle, and she was invincible. For, so Lucille had found out, she was paid neither by the city, the county nor the administration; her salary came from a private legacy; consequently, she did not cost the taxpayers a cent and was unremovable. In the meantime, most of the other Quaker volunteers had dropped out temporarily during the summer, for one reason or another; she and Bob Cogswell were the only ones left. To her, there was only one last hope: my articles in Europe. When were they going to be published? When were we coming home?

Marjorie went ahead from New York by plane; I followed with the car and the luggage. She was going to look for another house for us; the one we had lived in had been sold during our absence and our furniture put into storage. This, it seemed, had given the impression we had left Houston for good.

One night, when I telephoned Marjorie from a motel somewhere on the road, she said: "If you could make one wish right now, and it would be fulfilled—what would you wish?"

I know I should have said something gallant, but I could not help myself. "That the Red Cross be admitted to the hospital," I replied.

"All right, dear," she said, "granted. The hospital administration has just informed the Red Cross that they will be happy to have them train and supervise a corps of nurses' aides and orderlies."

"Good Lord! But what . . ."

"There is more," she said. "The administration has, off its own bat, suggested that all voluntary nursing personnel shall from now on be under the Red Cross. That leaves only the administrative volunteers to Mrs. Willoughby. How about that?"

I said, "I can't believe it. . . . What made them do it, in the end?"

She did not know the answer, and maybe that is the secret of nonviolence as a means of persuasion. You are never sure what finally tips the scales—the best in your adversary, ultimately responding to your stubborn appeal to it, or one of the score of political reasons that other people will suggest as having been decisive. Some people suggested it was Marjorie's return to Houston that had convinced the hospital of our intention to remain and made them accept the Red Cross to avoid a sequel to the letter to the *Chronicle* of the previous spring. Lucille was sure it was the result of her judiciously leaked rumor that a series of articles on the charity hospital was about to be published in Europe, soliciting food parcels for the indigent sick of Houston. Others thought there never had been any deliberate resistance to the Red Cross inside the hospital, and blamed the four months' procrastination on mere bureaucratic sloth and the torpidity of the long, hot summer. This, somehow, seemed the saddest explanation of all.

So I cannot truthfully say that I am convinced the powers that ruled the fate of the hospital responded, as individuals, to our mute appeal to the best in them. All I can say is that this explanation alone satisfies the part of me that in the end, beyond the reach of reason, guides my actions, mysterious and elusive as the gentle pull that guides the carrier pigeon home.

CHAPTER 11

To APPROACH THE CITY after that summer
was like climbing back on board a ship after a
long leave ashore.

The distant skyscrapers shimmered golden in the haze,
like the towers of a promised land; so must a traveler in
antiquity have approached the promise of the young Jerusalem when King Uzziah *"built towers in the desert, and
digged many wells: for he had much cattle, both in the
low country, and in the plains."* I had read that chapter in
the Old Testament the night before, in the last motel on
the road; it seemed as if, in those ancient images, the seed
of the future had lain slumbering for three thousand years
without losing its fertility. *"And he made in Jerusalem en-
gines, invented by cunning men, to be on the towers and
upon the bulwarks, to shoot arrows and great stones
withal."*

As I drove into the city, among the noonday flow of
traffic glistening in the sun, the electricity in the air, the excitement of creation was like a physical vibration, a high
sustained whine of energy, like that of a spinning turbine in
a powerhouse. I had forgotten how tremendously exciting
the city was to the newcomer, how suddenly, within its
magic circle, the realization of every dream seemed to

302

move within reach. This was more than just the latest version of Boom Town, U.S.A., this was America as it once had shone across the ocean, star in the darkness. Here in this town, maybe for the last time within the United States, the miraculous process of migration was in operation; once again from all over the world they came, with nothing to call their own but a dream of freedom, to build a city of light that became a beacon to all who lived in darkness. *Home of the Astronauts. Port of Departure to Outer Space.* One and a half million inhabitants; two hundred thousand paupers in slums; sixty thousand illiterates, unable to write the name of the city: Houston.

Marjorie was staying with Debbie and Gus and their two little boys. Our reunion was celebrated with a huge meal of pizzas and California wine. The little boys leaped about in pajamas trying to grab the cat, while a British actor fruitlessly intoned an installment of *Winnie the Pooh* on the record player. In the midst of this, Lucille arrived, impeccably attired for the tropics, with the walk of a heron, the voice of a lute and the language of a Marine. While chewing a piece of pizza that she grimly predicted would play havoc with her hips, we were brought up to date about conditions inside the new hospital.

It was a sobering story. Ben Taub General was becoming exactly like J.D., because of the shortage of personnel and the lack of housekeeping. During the summer months, both the cleanliness of the building and the morale of the staff had deteriorated to an unbelievable degree. The general attitude of the nurses was: "Try to keep them alive until the end of your shift, then go home and try to forget them, for there is nothing else you can do." Miss Lucas had resigned, as had several others who could no longer put up with the misery of neglect. Mrs. Masters had not been in the hospital for two months; rumors were that she was not coming back either. And the general public in Houston knew nothing of all this; everybody assumed, happily, that now the hospital had moved to the new building all problems were solved. The occasional glimpses of the truth that were given them were met with indifference or laughter. To name one instance: a patient had vanished from the Psychiatric Ward, was listed A.W.O.L., and discovered two weeks later in the broom closet on the same floor. They were lucky he was not dead; the newspapers had published the incident as a funny story. But most people had missed the point of the joke: that it had taken Housekeeping two weeks to open that broom closet.

Obviously, there was no hope that things would ever be changed by the people of Houston voting more money for the hospital. Its only hope was volunteers: citizens, prepared to start nursing those patients as if they were their own relatives, and willing to submit themselves to antagonism, ostracism and even open hostility while doing so. Some members of the nursing staff would resent the interference, Mrs. Willoughby was definitely on the warpath, and we should not underestimate the degree to which the summer-long procrastination of the hospital had succeeded in eviscerating the Red Cross program. Mrs. Bannerman had said that, of the long list of people who volunteered early this summer, only sixteen had turned up to be interviewed for the first class, four of them Negroes. The Red Cross was now looking for a chairman for the new corps of volunteers. Well, all Lucille could say was: it had better be someone like General Patton. Anybody gentlemanly or ladylike would be eaten alive.

We had never seen her quite so mad; she must have had a tough time of it, alone in the hospital all through the long, hot summer. When Debbie innocuously mentioned inspiring the new corps with the spirit of the Meeting, Lucille gave her a level look and asked, "You mean the spirit of our saintly, dedicated Quakers?"

Debbie mumbled, apologetically, "I know, we have not been too dependable this summer."

Lucille snorted and said, "Dependable? You people have been more dependable than anyone else. After Bob Cogswell left, I could count on you never to show up! If anybody in this room dares to talk about the Religious Society of Friends in this city, I will personally slam this pizza in his sanctimonious snout." She kicked off her shoes, swung her shapely legs in sheer hose across the arm of her chair and stuffed her mouth with pizza. The little boys watched her chewing with fascination; they had liked her story much better than *Winnie the Pooh*, which the canned British thespian was still ululating in the corner.

Her anger was understandable, but it seemed unfair to the Friends, most of whom, like us, had left the city for summer jobs, leading camps or working for the Service Committee in one of the Indian reservations. But, however valid our reasons, the fact remained that she had been left to defend the Pass of Thermopylae alone. If she had given up, that would have meant the end of the program. She was quite a girl.

2

THE NEXT MORNING, I went to have a look at the hospital myself. I had barely entered the hall to Emergency when I ran into Mrs. Willoughby.

"Well, bless my soul!" she said. "Look who's here. Did you want to see me?"

To my surprise, I realized that I did. I could not help it; I had a weak spot for the woman. Compared to her, fire-breathing Lucille was a fluffy lamb. As I followed her while she strode ahead, I was again reminded of the old tugboat captains of my youth, last survivors of the era of iron men on wooden ships. Lucille, sticking it out one summer all alone, was admirable; this woman had stuck it out for twenty-four years all alone. For almost a quarter of a century she had kept hundreds of Southern ladies at work in the hospital, doing everything except nursing; without her volunteers J.D. could not have remained in operation. She had barracks full of women, making up trays and bandages in sweltering shacks known as Mrs. Willoughby's sweatshops, and somehow she had managed to keep them there, happy and at work. She was impossible to get on with, the way Captain Bakker of the tugboat *Taurus* had been impossible to get on with. As a mate's apprentice in the shadow of his mastodonian moods, I had often lain muttering on my bunk, telling the ceiling that the Old Man was not human but must have been hatched out of an egg on some hot deserted beach, to pop out ready made, a vicious homunculus, complete with cap and a uniform shiny with wear, the captain's rings of gold braid on his sleeves green with oxidation. Oh, how I had hated him! How I had hoped he would crash down the bridge steps and break a leg, or choke in the glass of gin that he tipped so expertly before each meal, after which he smacked his lips and belched like a beast in the barnyard. But when our convoy of six tugboats, pulling that unwieldy dry dock the size of a city block across the Indian Ocean, had been hit by a gale like a planet crashing into the earth, I could have gone down on my knees in front of him in speechless supplication, sick with fear, for we could never hold that dock, floating like a colossal bladder on top of the water, presenting a flank like a full-rigged windjammer to the gale. Undaunted by a hell full of screeching demons, Captain Bakker had coolly commanded that the dock be sunk almost to vanishing point, an order of such audacity that even our mate, long-suffering and eons beyond surprise, had gaped at him, flabbergasted. The order had been carried out, and when the gale was over the dry dock had lain wallowing in the swell, awash like a whale, just below the surface, undamaged, and not a mile off course. It took three days for all our pumps to bring it back up, then we continued our voyage. Never again had I come across another human being quite like Captain Bakker, until the morning when I had sat in front of that desk in the headquarters of the Women-in-Yellow in old J.D., to have my soul frisked by the frosty eyes of the woman now marching me to her lair, like a raider towing a prize.

I sat down in the chair in front of her new desk in the new room, that managed to look exactly the same as the old one. I wondered, vaguely, whether she had managed to recapture the set of shelves Mrs. Kowalski had requisitioned the night we fitted out the Emergency Room. Mrs. Kowalski and she had a lot in common, come to think of it; a scrap with no holds barred between the two of them should be worth watching to us men, from the security of the gallery.

"Well, for goodness' sakes," Mrs. Willoughby said, sitting down in her captain's chair behind her chart table. "What have y'all been doing with yourselves this summer?"

While I told her, I again had my soul searched by the Customs of her frosty eyes. It did not take long; once I had passed muster her expression became again that of a concert goer, stolidly sitting through a piece of atonal music, waiting for Wagner's Valkyries to blast the bilges out of Hindemith. Intimidated by her absent-minded expression, I interrupted my witty description of the ocean crossing to ask, "Well, Mrs. Willoughby, how are things in the hospital?"

"Oh, I've been doing fine," she answered modestly. "Just fine. Let me show you what I've been up to across the hall. That'll give you an idea."

She got up and marched out again, with me following meekly in her wake. She crossed the corridor into a little hall; there she opened one of many doors with a key she selected from a bunch pulled from a pocket in her skirt. Beyond the door lay a small, brightly-painted room deco-

rated with trade posters and smelling strongly of turpen-
tine. Three kitchen chairs painted orange stood in front of
three washbasins, set in a counter against the wall, each
topped by a triple mirror. Against the opposite wall stood
two old hair dryers, looking formidable and a little sinister,
like early versions of the electric chair.

"This is our beauty salon for psychos," she said. "Isn't it
cute? Here is a special instrument for nigger women who
want their hair de-kinked, or whatever the word is."

"It looks very inviting," I said. "The patients must love
it."

"Oh, they're just tickled to death," she answered proudly.
"For the time being, we limit it to psychos, but once we get
more machines, we'll take in patients from the other floors as
well. Looks good, what?"

I looked round the little room, the orange chairs, the gay
posters, one of which showed the Eiffel Tower and asked,
"*Why not Paris on your next vacation?*"

"All done by volunteers?" I asked.

"That's right," she said. "All done by the Women-in-
Yellow. My own fine, fine people. Not some fancy outfit
with airs." And that, it turned out, was all she had to say
about the Red Cross.

Remembering Captain Bakker, I realized she could not
be expected to welcome a second authority on the bridge.
She had run the volunteer program for those twenty-four
years as a one-man operation, master after God of her obe-
dient and doting crew. She was the last person in the world
who could be expected to welcome poaching interlopers in
what she must regard as her sector of the ocean. When I
was a boy, captains of salvage tugs had battled similar interlopers in their sector of the ocean for the possession of a
sinking freighter with all the wiles, subterfuge and fury of
which the human male was capable. The poaching rescue
tug, rushing toward a sinking vessel in a gale from outside
the sector after being alerted by a general S.O.S., would set

308

off decoy flares, and keep radio silence to lull the competition into a false sense of security; savage sea battles had been fought on storm-lashed waves after one of them had cut the other's hawser, violating the inviolate. They slammed at one another with water cannons, line guns and hazardous, ramming lunges of their ice-breaker bows, slithering down the slopes of mountainous swells toward their foe wallowing broadside in the trough; during all this, the sinking freighter went on sending signals of supplication, her captain clutching the rail of his bridge, staring wide-eyed with disbelief in the sleet-streaked night at the monsters of mercy, battling one another like brontosaur bulls in rut.

So I was under no illusion about Mrs. Willoughby's eagerness to welcome the Red Cross. She was going to blast those federal females right out of the hospital, frilly frocks, natty toques, fancy pants and all, until their punch-drunk matron would come reeling into Emergency in her Maidenform bra. Precedent prompted me to put my money on her, in any drawn-out fight; the only trouble was that we were not towing a dry dock to Singapore or salvaging a sinking freighter, but trying to give tender loving care to helpless sick people.

Maybe the secret was her attitude toward the Negro patients. Like Ben Taub, she regarded herself as the protector of a species that was, in actual fact, already extinct: the subservient, laughter-loving darkie of hitching post and minstrel show, who had danced and hand-clapped his merry way into oblivion, together with his massa, his mistress and Miss Prue, so fond of pickaninnies. She had protected him against all outside interference with his state of idyllic innocence. She had defended him against politicians trying to corrupt his ignorance, agitators exploiting his gullibility and firebrands fanning the flames of his explosive passion. But her animosity had outlived her enemy; her great battle, like Mr. Taub's, was not lost or won but past, blown into oblivion with the tumbleweed of history. She and he still sounded their trumpets, but they had become ghosts on a deserted battlefield, commanding ranks of phantoms charging specters, defending a discarded cause for the sake of shadows that had already boarded the ferry for the crossing of the River Styx. To disentangle Mrs. Willoughby from the forest of her generation was impossible. It was a pity she would not relinquish the power she had accumulated, but I realized she might as well be asked to relinquish life itself.

So, whatever way it worked out, I agreed with Lucille: the choice of the first chairman to command the first Red Cross volunteers inside the hospital was a crucial choice. I did not agree that he should be a man like General Patton. He should be a man as undaunted as Ben Taub, as wily as Mrs. Willoughby, as concerned as Dr. Miller, as gentle as Mrs. Judd, as sincerely religious as Miss Lucas. But I agreed as I looked around me that there was no such man in sight. And, high as my regard for the Convoy Commander and his staff in the headquarters of the Red Cross might be, this much I knew: even if such a person were in Houston, which seemed unlikely, they would never be able to find him. Not in a thousand years.

But I underestimated them. They found that unlikely person in the most unexpected of all hiding places. They appointed Marjorie.

3

WHAT DOES a man do when, out of the blue, his wife is appointed General of the Army, a post for which he himself was not a candidate, but for which he might have been drafted, reluctantly, after all others had failed?

Such a man starts, once he has recovered from being hit with a diving board, by congratulating his wife, saying that of course it was the logical choice, and how intelligent of those people to come to this conclusion! Then, artlessly and with sincere concern, he will ask her what exactly makes her think she is suitable? Does she have any experience that she has omitted from her curriculum vitae before they were married? All he remembers, from premarital confessions and lighthearted chitchats while rowing romantically in the moonlight, is that she once was Chief Sprite with the Girl Scouts, and at an earlier date member of a secret organization called *The Ovaltineys* which had for its password *Chuckles.*

Of course, the moment after I had said that I felt sorry. She had told me, ages ago, how she had whispered that secret password to a boy at school, aged nine, who was the hero of her dreams, aged seven. The beast had leaped around the playground triumphantly, yelling, "The password of the Ovaltineys is Chuckles! The password of the Ovaltineys is Chuckles!" This first monstrous betrayal of her life had made her, sobbing, run for shelter into the girls' room; when she first told me the story I had felt like wringing that boy's neck. Now I felt, shamefully, that I was sharing his distinction.

The idea that she was going to lead the new volunteers brought about a fundamental change in my attitude toward the political chicaneries outside and inside the hospital. To contemplate, in an objective, detached manner, the tough time any leader of the Red Cross corps was sure to have was one thing; to realize that your own wife was going to be the target of the fiery darts of the wicked was a different story. I suddenly had a personal stake in the coming combat. If I felt sentimentally affected by the callousness of a boy aged nine, who had betrayed her trust by shouting "Chuckles," how would I feel if experts like Mrs.

Willoughby started roughing her up, with twenty-four years' experience in the meat-packing industry behind them?

And the spiritual wickedness in the air inside the hospital seemed to have grown stronger during the summer. The spirit of kindness that had occasionally brightened the darkness of gloomy old J.D. seemed to have dimmed in Ben Taub. The beds were newer, the wards were lighter, but the floors already as sticky and the Utility Rooms as filthy as they had been in the old place. The relationship between the overworked nurses and the anonymous mass of their patients seemed even more impersonal than before. Miss Lucas, though a head nurse, had used to fuss around her patients all the time, grumbling, telling them off, but by doing so she had created an atmosphere of personal attention; her successor never seemed to leave the nurses' station. I had made inquiries as to why Miss Lucas had left, but, with the short memory of the hospital, only a few people remembered her, and nobody knew the reason for her resignation. Someone in the laundry thought it had been a conflict with one of the doctors; someone in Central Supply asked, "Isn't she the one who threw something in some person's face?" If this was so, I felt sure she had not thrown whatever it was in the face of a person; she must have found herself, at last, face to face with the incarnation of the Spirit of Evil.

It was this place that Marjorie, always assuming the best of people, was about to enter as the chairman of a band of volunteers who, as sure as daylight, would find their road to mercy mined with boobytraps. I was worried, more worried than I had been since I wrote my first letter to the paper. I worried about what they would do to her, but I worried also about what I would do to them in response. Should anyone hurt Marge or make a move to do so, I was afraid I would not turn out to be a very good Quaker. I had to confess to myself, contritely, that I had tried on the armor of God and found it did not fit me, to say nothing of the humble garment of charity; the only thing that seemed to fit me, when I felt protective about Marjorie, was Captain Bakker's jacket with the shiny elbows and the oxydized rings. But in that costume I could hardly be called suitably garbed for turning the other cheek.

Back in Emergency also I was struck by a new toughness in the air that I had not known before. The prevailing attitude toward the patients seemed to have hardened there as well. Outwardly Emergency had improved in several ways, but something was gone, something of which Mrs. Judd had possessed the secret. Mrs. Kowalski, as composed and coolly efficient as ever, minced up and down between the stretchers with the same spell-binding gait of yore. But she ran a tight ship indeed; one of the new Negro orderlies, an articulate, well-read fellow to whom I took an instant liking, summed her up as "The Captain Bligh of the Emergency Room."

Mrs. Judd's little prayer at the opening of the new hospital seemed to have gone unanswered.

4

I WENT BACK on duty in Observation and I soon felt as if I had never been away. Owing to Mrs. Kowalski's ruthless pressure on the Nursing Office, which after Mrs. Masters' departure seemed to have lost some of its power of resistance, Observation was now staffed with a secretary to keep up the records and a motherly, fussily busy LVN, rather like our beloved Mrs. Birdland, called Mrs. Wendell, who did the work of two and also managed to fit in fainting spells because she took slimming pills. She was given to sneaky drafts of double-strength Coca-Cola which she concocted herself out of concentrated syrup and distilled water in the Utility Room, and paid mysterious, lengthy visits to the ex-isolation room, now used for storage. I discovered after a while that she went there because she had hoarded away vast quantities of IV bottles with different fluids, rubber gloves and other articles in common demand, covering up her secret caches with sheets and heaps of gowns, convinced, like a squirrel, that our present summer of abundant supplies would soon be followed by a winter of scarcity. Every Monday morning, when the week's stores were collected from Central Supply, I would drive whole stretcherloads of clanking bottles into Observation; invariably she would send me off on some complicated errand in another part of the building to get me out of the way, so she could bury part of the haul at her ease.

The rest of the time she steamed up and down the aisles like a brisk little tugboat, pushing a sparkling bow wave of chatter and jokes, leaving those patients who still could hear her rocking with laughter in her wash. She sounded gruff and ill-tempered at times, but I saw old men trying to bring down their blood pressures obligingly while she took them, and knew that, seen from a horizontal position, her martial behavior must be endearing nonsense. She and I worked our aisles in virtual isolation; as her orderly, I occasionally peeked around the corner to see if I saw her boots stick over the edge of an empty bed, which meant she was having a giddy spell. In that case I took over the taking of her vital signs as well until she came round again, which rarely took long.

I had just settled down comfortably in this new routine in the midst of the familiar chaos, when disaster struck. In the middle of one morning shift, while patients, doctors, policemen and ambulance drivers were milling about the Treatment section of the Emergency Room as usual, Mrs. Kowalski collapsed. The first I knew of it was when she was rushed into Observation on a stretcher by two nurses followed by a doctor. At first, I had no idea who it was. I saw the stretcher rolled in and noticed the commotion, but I was busy at the other end of the ward. I only realized who it was when Mrs. Wendell came running past, calling, "Mrs. Kowalski! Mrs. Kowalski is sick! Quick, they are going to put her to bed in here!"

I asked, "What is the matter? What happened?" but she did not answer.

They wheeled the stretcher with the still white form past me toward the furthest bed in the women's section. Mrs. Kowalski lay quite still, her eyes closed, her red hair spread out on the narrow mattress, her starched cap awry. She looked, in her unconsciousness, frightened and very young, as if suddenly the truth had been flushed out of its hiding place behind the imperious mask, the lisping voice. Half immersed in the rising water of a nightmare, gasping for air in some ghastly hallucination, lay not Nurse Kowalski but Mopsy, the girl that only her family and her husband knew.

Stunned by the impact of her sudden collapse, everyone acted automatically with coolness and efficiency. The nurses put her to bed, after drawing the curtain around her and her stretcher; the Medical Resident was paged on the intercom. As I stood helplessly outside the tent with its hushed, rustling activity, I was handed her clothes by someone from the inside. I put them on the neighboring bed: her cap, her white uniform, her stockings, and one shoe: a white nurse's shoe, the back of which had been cut open because she always chafed her heels. I stood there, dazed, with that odd shoe in my hand, when the Medical Resident came and vanished inside the tent. He was followed, a minute later, by one of the neurologists.

After a while Mrs. Wendell came out, her eyes wide, her face white. "They think it's meningitis," she said. "They want me to set her up for a spinal tap."

I looked at the shoe in my hand, and suddenly I was overwhelmed by an incoherent grief, a senseless rage. I ran to get the spinal tray; alone in the storeroom, gazing vacantly at Mrs. Wendell's secret array of IV bottles behind the gowns, I thought, "No, no, not her . . . This can't be, this is not possible, not that red-haired terror, not our own, irreplaceable Captain Bligh . . ." I was overcome by a growling, fist-clenching fury against this monstrous place, this Moloch feeding on living people, this insatiable furnace that had consumed Mrs. Judd, Miss Lucas and now, for God's sake, that magnificent creature that all of us had hated with such relish. It was ludicrous, criminal that a hospital should be run like this, that young women barely aware of the fullness of maturity had to waste their life's substance on this machine shop of the human body, this dispensary of merciless charity. Why did girls like the nameless friend of Mrs. Judd, Mrs. Judd herself, Miss Lucas and now Mrs. Kowalski have to pay for a city's heartlessness by giving more than they could be expected to give, more than any decent human being could ask another human being to give? How dare they exploit the compassion of those girls battling hopelessly a city's cynical cruelty to its miserable poor, pleading for mercy in slums, junkyards of discarded humans, each one an Image of our Creator?

But, as I stood there in the Store Room in Observation to find the spinal tray for Mrs. Kowalski, I realized this was merely a middle-aged Walter Mitty's outburst of impotent sorrow at the fall of a sparrow, one anonymous redhead in a metropolis swarming with a glut of youth.

5

FOR THE REST of that day, we moved, all of us, as under a
pall. All of us went as frequently as we could on tiptoe
past the tent in which she lay. She stayed among the sick
and the dying of her Emergency Room until late that
night; then she was taken away. Nobody knew yet whether
it was meningitis or not. Only the next day, the word went
round, "She'll make it, but she'll be gone for a while; she's
just J.D. sick—B.T. sick, I mean."

The moment she was gone, Emergency disintegrated.
She too had, in her own fashion, given it all she had. But,
where Mrs. Judd had given it her tenderness, Mrs. Kowalski had carried the whole works on her back, crawling on
hands and knees in a superhuman feat of indomitable will.
Only as she fell, dropping the lot of us by the wayside, did
we discover that our cosmos had depended for its cohesion
on her whip.

Emergency carried on all right; it always had. Like the
burlesque show in Piccadilly Circus in London during the
Blitz, it was a place that never closed. But it became a
chaos, almost at once. Sheets from the laundry trolley
were flung onto the shelves again by the armful, regardless. Housekeeping boys lolled lazily in doorways, smoking
cigarettes, while doctors and patients tramped through
blood and pus. Dirty instruments piled up on the sink in
the Utility Room. Filthy bandages, blood-soaked sheets,
paper towels, soiled sanitary napkins spilled out of over-
flowing disposal pails. After a few days we pulled ourselves together somewhat, because we had to; we had been
about to grind to a stop in confusion; but the tight ship
became a sloppy one, and strangely enough a callous one
as well. Mrs. Kowalski had rarely said anything particularly gentle or tender to any patient; she had never batted
an eyelid at any sight of sorrow or suffering; yet, by vir-

317

tue of the fierce efficiency with which she ran her Emergency Room, she had created an atmosphere of order and alertness that, somehow, had amounted to almost the same thing. Mrs. Judd, if truth be told, had hidden chronic anarchy under the mantle of her pure, inexhaustible compassion; Mrs. Kowalski, in her chilling role of Nurse Hyde, had magically created mercy out of sheer method. During Mrs. Judd's reign, the changing shifts of young doctors had found their initial quasi-virile aloofness, symptom of the beginners' fear of personal involvement, curbed by that slight, fragile creature's unstinting kindness. The cat-o'-nine tails of Mrs. Kowalski had also managed to cramp their style, why or how was less easy to see. But the moment she was gone, the spiritual wickedness in the air, ever present, alighted in Emergency and made itself at home. Her secret turned out to have been simply that she had cared; after her departure, nobody seemed to care any more.

6

In the meantime, in a long, low-ceilinged attic room in the chapter house of the Red Cross, the first class of volunteer nurses' aides and orderlies was in training. Mrs. Chalmers, ex-director of nurses of a hospital herself and graduate of J.D., was their instructor and future supervisor. She and Mrs. Bannerman together made a girls' wrestling team that I would hate to grapple with, were I Mrs. Willoughby. I had known only one nurse in the class of Mrs. Chalmers, and her name, cross my heart, had been Sister Monster. She had been head nurse on board my hospital ship during the floods, and she was without doubt the most formidable woman I ever transported across the face of the deep. After we arrived in the stricken village where we were to remain as the resident hospital, the Navy landed in small vessels and all the sailors and marines came to our ship to shower. They stood, a long line of hale, naked bodies, waiting their turn in the corridor; every time Sister Monster passed them on her way to the shower to drag laggards out, she caused a rollicking chorus of whistles, cheers and Elizabethan language. But none of the naked males, though especially selected by boards of experts for their courage, dared touch the huge Brünnehild as she strode past their steaming ranks, for she carried a wet towel. After flagellating one hapless prober down the length of the corridor and out onto the deck, where the winds of winter were waiting to turn him, for all practical purposes, into Lot's wife, she could have stormed a battleship singlehanded, as long as she did not forget her towel. The difference between Sister Monster and Mrs. Chalmers on the one hand and Mrs. Masters on the other was that they were not administrative officials; what interested them was the sheer earthy joy of nursing. My estimate was that Mrs. Chalmers would take in her stride anything the hospital might put in her way, as long as they did not try to separate her, or any of her brood of aides, from the patients.

The brood consisted of sixteen people: housewives, schoolteachers, clerks, young girls and a few self-conscious men. For no other reason than that their hearts had been touched, they had joined us from the milling mass of millions that was Houston. To me personally the identity of some of them was a surprise. When I first faced their silent ranks, as they sat at the long refectory table in the classroom, waiting for me to say some words of encouragement, I recognized a few faces that, had I been asked, I would have thought the least likely to be here. There was, for instance, a society hostess in whose home I had once spoken on the subject of the hospital to a roomful of unrelenting ladies chewing petit-fours. I had thought at the time that she hadn't heard a word I said, so preoccupied had she seemed with the tea and the tartlets, while I told her guests about the cockroaches in the drinking water in old J.D. But there she was, distinguished and mundane, smiling enigmatically at the far end of the table. And there was the secretary of the news director at Channel 11, who had sat filing her nails and giving a convincing show of boredom while Nick Gearhart and I had our slanging match. Of all the people I had tried to coax, cajole, convince, trick and threaten into the hospital these were the ones to respond; it seemed another unsettling proof that God, if He did interfere in the minutiae of individual human lives at all, did so with subtle humor. There was no one from River Oaks, not even the young matron who had stood up so bravely and stated she did not want to buy peace of mind but to go into the hospital to work there herself. I remembered how she had said, at the time, that occasionally a chance presented itself to do something and then something else happened and it passed. But there were three Negro girls, and seven of the women whom Marjorie had always known would come to our aid if only we knew how to reach them: the anonymous mothers of Houston, one of them five months pregnant, which did not seem to worry either Marjorie or Mrs. Chalmers unduly. The rather self-conscious, table-drumming males, trying to look superior, were heavily outnumbered; one of them was a scout for the Jaycees, I was delighted to find that they were still interested in the project. All these people were ready to go through untold fears, indignities and dangers of contamination for the sake of those who were sick and alone, not to visit them but to serve them, as the lowest form of human life in the hospital: volunteer orderlies and nurses' aides.

As I sat there, while they waited for me to speak, I realized that I sat facing the real America. Between a meeting of the heads of families, planning to cross the continent in a wagon train, and this meeting there was no essential difference. The wagons, rolling West, had created a nation; these sixteen people were still creating it. As a body has to renew its cells incessantly to remain alive, I thought, so this nation can remain alive only by virtue of people like these, ready to go and find their brother, calling feebly for help in the Valley of Death. I knew that, whether their crossing would succeed or fail, this moment would forever be part of America, as decisive as any battle ever won in the history of this land.

"Friends," I said, "I am sure you must have your apprehensions about what lies ahead. You must be wondering what the reality inside the hospital is like. Maybe I can help you best if you just ask questions."

The questions came. "Would it be possible to work in the Newborn Nursery and not on a floor with really sick people?" "Was it possible to work somewhere where it would not be necessary to deal with bedpans?" "What was the minimum time you had to spend on the floors for your clinical training, and could you choose where you wanted to work afterward?"

All these questions I had once asked myself, so had Marjorie, so had Lucille, who had joined our original training group of Quakers saying, "I'm doing this just for laughs, you know; I can tell you here and now that I'll never go into the wards, for I can't stand blood, I can't stand sick people, and I can't stand bedpans. I'll stick with the babies."

So I told them about the girl who, all by herself, had held the Pass of Thermopylae throughout the summer when all seemed lost, and how afraid she had once been of bedpans. Her story seemed to give them such comfort that I began to suspect the real value of Lucille's lonely stand had been her example to future generations of nurses' aides, giving confidence to the faint-hearted at the beginning of their journey. Life was full of surprises.

After we had talked for a while, I left them to their shepherd, Mrs. Chalmers, while on the periphery of their small gathering, tirelessly, silently, with anxious gentleness, circled the fleeting shadow of their sheepdog Marjorie, watcher on the brink of the great, dark night.

CHAPTER 12

IT STARTED, innocuously enough, with Lucille
going to see Mrs. Willoughby to hand in her resignation from the Women-in-Yellow. Less innocu-
ous was the fact that she wore her new Red Cross uniform to do so.

She wore it, needless to say, as if she were modeling
beachwear designed by Dior; and whereas the mother
hubbard of the Women-in-Yellow had been a reluctant
partner to elegance, the Red Cross uniform really did
something for a girl. It probably was her first tour through
the corridors that gave the new nurses' aide uniform the
nickname of "Interns' Delight." She arrived, flushed with
triumph, in the headquarters of the Women-in-Yellow to
say farewell to her former chief. Something in her attitude,
or the mere fact that she represented a nightmare become real, had the alarming effect of making Mrs. Willoughby, for once, lose her temper. We never quite found
out exactly what happened, but when Lucille came out of
the headquarters of the Women-in-Yellow, several shades
paler, she answered to the question as to how the interview
had gone, "The dull thumping you hear in there is Mrs.
Willoughby, ricocheting off the walls."

After that, things began to happen. In flagrant defiance

of the letter in which the administration had transferred the authority over all nursing volunteers to the Red Cross, Mrs. Willoughby's Women-in-Yellow were sent onto the floors in droves, untrained. The fact that they were dedicated and good-willing was not enough; it never had been. The way untrained volunteers had been allowed to mess with the sick and the wounded was one of the disgraces of the Houston charity hospital; I myself had been an example. No matter how dedicated and highly motivated I had been, I had had no business plunging into highly specialized nursing procedures without a day of training. I had been asked about my experience; when I said I had nursed one patient with terminal cancer and commanded a hospital ship during a disaster, this was considered sufficient to let me loose, without supervision, to play at nurse among people who were, for the most part, in critical condition, and I had been comparatively well screened. I had personally sent high school boys to see the supervisor of nursing services on Saturday nights, after they had come wandering into the Emergency Room, calmly put on scrub suits in the doctors' locker room and started to nurse around at their own discretion. When asked how the hell they had got in here, they shrugged their shoulders and said that they had been told by "a friend" that at Jefferson Davis you could go and be an orderly on Saturday nights.

Unless the Red Cross, with its rigid rules as to training and its meticulous round-the-clock supervision, took all volunteer nursing services firmly in hand, this intolerable situation would never end. There would always be people, even mature and sensible women, who would innocently accept the alternative of "going in there and do some real work at once," rather than submit to the eight weeks of rigorous training the Red Cross aides had to go through before setting foot in the hospital. The Women-in-Yellow, performing an invaluable service in all administrative and productive fields, had no business going in for nursing procedures untrained, unsupervised, and consequently dangerous. In theory, they were to be supervised by the hospital personnel; but in this understaffed, disorganized place, where everyone started to work in a vacuum of his own the moment he arrived on the floor, this was an illusion.

After that first day, when Mrs. Judd had "shown me the ropes," I had been on my own, and so were the Women-in-Yellow, sent into the breach to block the invasion of the Red Cross. They handed out candy bars to patients without checking with the desk whether they were diabetics or on restricted input; they appeared in Observation, asking me casually how one changed IV bottles, without an inkling as to how lethal that could be; the early shift in Pediatrics, that Lucille had covered all summer, was suddenly invaded by resolute emanations of Mrs. Willoughby's iron determination. It was somehow typical, of both the hospital and her, that they went on coming despite the fact that the Chief of Medicine in Pediatrics was said to have stated, with clenched fists, that if ever another of those yellow women set foot on his floor, he would personally throw her out. He could fume and slam his fist on his desk to his heart's content; he was only a mortal, whereas his adversary was one of the last of the demigods that had defended the Alamo and conquered the Comanches.

And this was not all. Even before the new recruits were in the hospital, the fledgling Red Cross corps of nurses' aides was subjected to bizarre discriminations. We were, for instance, no longer allowed to eat in the cafeteria, as were the Women-in-Yellow. Instead of two suites of offices such as they had, we were allocated one tiny, bare room without chairs, where we would have to eat our own sandwiches out of paper bags, standing up. We were not allowed to work during the daylight hours, when most housewives were available for volunteer work and such things as bedbaths and shampoos should normally be given, but restricted to the evening shift and, preferably, the dead of night. We were barred from the Emergency Room, where henceforth only Mrs. Willoughby's women would be allowed to work, regardless of whether they were trained or not. When we asked for a telephone extension in our office, the administration replied that if the volunteers wanted a telephone they could pay for it.

In reassuring contrast to this grotesque attitude of hostility and obstruction, a big Catholic hospital in town, St. Joseph's, applied to the Red Cross for some of its trained volunteer nurses' aides, offering not only to pay for their training, their uniforms and their meals, but promising to provide professional supervisors as well. It cheered us somewhat; at least it proved that, according to normal standards, we provided valuable help. The Red Cross replied that it would be happy to oblige, once the need at Ben Taub General had been fully met.

At first, the spirit of our new volunteers was one of outrage and rebellion; had they been left to their own devices, the program would have been short-lived. For the plan behind these discriminations was not difficult to discern. The hospital had accepted the Red Cross with the utmost reluctance; now the only way to get rid of it was to needle the Red Cross volunteers and their supervisors into protests and complaints to the administration. After a few months of this, a sorrowful letter could be written to the Chapter Manager, stating that the hospital had sincerely tried to accommodate two separate volunteer organizations, but discovered to its regret that this resulted in tensions and complications. So, much as they grieved over this decision, they would have to ask the Red Cross to leave; those volunteers who wished to join the Women-in-Yellow would, of course, be welcome.

If it had not been for our Negro volunteers, the young brigade would have conformed to that plan, for our two supervisors were marvelous nurses but poor politicians. Our Negro fellow volunteers gave us, with some discreet but understandable glee, a short course in how to cope with being discriminated against. Roll with the punches, keep smiling, never let yourself be tricked or bullied into giving up territory already won; if you keep this up long enough you will find that it is the reverse of what you now think it is; it's inspiring.

But, so far, the only one who seemed to be inspired by it was Marjorie. The only outward sign that she had manned battle stations was that she began to refer to the awesome director of the Women-in-Yellow as "Good old Willoughby." It took an intimate knowledge of British history to associate this with the fact that, during the Napoleonic War, the English had referred to their adversary as "Good old Boney." At every new instance of discrimination against the Red Cross volunteers or reports of further encroachment on the floors by the hapless Women-in-Yellow, Marjorie rejoiced cheerfully, "Splendid! First the patients had no volunteers at all to look after them, now they have two brigades competing for the privilege. It is the best thing that could possibly happen to the hospital!"

It was, on condition the Red Cross volunteers equaled her drop-forged, armor-plated cheerfulness, combined with that elusive, faintly mischievous Quaker spirit of nonviolence. The new class was about to go into the hospital for the first time to start their clinical training, and most of them began to suffer from cold feet that had to be warmed with light-hearted banter and constant reassurances that they were doing fine. Marjorie fussed around them with increasing concern, which expressed itself in frequent heart-to-heart chats with each one of them individually. Occasionally I would overhear a phrase. "A year ago? Oh, a year ago I was absolutely certain that I would never be able to give an enema." Or, "Patients with tertiary syphilis? Well, dear, let's cross that bridge when we get to it."

The only time I saw her falter was one Sunday morning, shortly before they were to go in, when she rose to speak during meeting for worship. It was just a year ago, she said, that the Meeting had first made the charity hospital its concern, and fourteen Friends had volunteered to work there. Since that time, many had dropped out of the program for pressing personal reasons; only five were left at work inside the hospital. The need was still as great, the difficulties experienced loomed larger than ever. Now new volunteers were about to join us, it was more than ever necessary that the Meeting remember the Friends at work in that sad place. Not only was physical help necessary, it was imperative that the spirit that had taken us inside in the first place should not desert us. She asked that those who could not help by going in with us, should sustain us with their prayers.

She very rarely spoke at meeting; only a deep and urgent need for help could have made her do so this time. But since those bygone days when we had met for worship in J.D., the older members' concern with the hospital had dissipated somewhat. After worship, one of the weighty elders took her aside and reminded her that matters pertaining to social concerns should be brought up at meeting for business rather than worship. In Quaker language, "she was eldered"; and although the others instantly and indignantly rallied around her, it came as a bitter blow.

The next morning the mail brought a letter from Holland. It contained a postal order from the Amsterdam Meeting for twenty-five dollars, to be spent on small presents for the patients in the hospital, and a little note, *"Our prayers go with you."*

This gentle message of friendship, arriving in her darkest hour, had the effect of Noah's dove. After that letter, she never faltered again.

AFTER BEING FORCED to leave Emergency, because of Mrs. Willoughby's edict, I was transferred to Male Medicine. Only then did I discover why Miss Lucas had left.

Male Medicine was made up of two wards of forty beds, separated by the Utility Rooms and the nurses' station. Most patients were old men, in the terminal stages of cancer and other lingering diseases; only a minority was destined to leave the floor alive. These helpless patients, all of whom needed intensive care, were looked after, in theory, by two RN's, two LVN's, two orderlies, two nurses' aides and a houseboy to do the cleaning. In practice, less than half of these turned up. Absenteeism was rampant, the turnover in the lower-echelon staff such that I never knew, when I came on for my night of duty, whether I would still find the same orderly I had come to know the previous time. The hospital was so critically understaffed that on many nights there was only one RN on duty in the whole of the building: one, for over four hundred patients.

I found that the medical care was very good; it was the nursing care that was the problem.

To start with, there was the lack of cleanliness. I thought I had seen a hospital ward deteriorate after Mrs. Kowalski left Emergency, but I discovered I had seen nothing yet. Bedpans with stools, uncovered, stood on bedside tables next to water pitchers and trays with food. Dirty supplies and equipment were piled high in the Utility Rooms, together with stacks of unemptied bedpans on the frequent occasions that the hoppers broke down. Orderlies and aides, forever at a run, walked across dirty bandages on the floor, around piles of soiled linen. Urine drainage bottles, kicked over, were left where they rolled. Dirty dressings were found in the beds; underneath the beds were dark stains where bloody drainage had run from the ends of chest tubes, dropped on the floor. The trash cans bulged with filth; we heard that tests had been made and that even the buckets on the housekeeping trolleys, carrying the disinfectant solution for mopping the floors, had been found to be staph-infected. Amidst all this, sick people had to be cared for.

They were not, not even to minimal standards. Bedside care was supposed to be given by the orderlies and the aides; RN's and LVN's were so snowed under with ad-ministrative duties that they rarely left the nurses' sta-tion. But the recurrent mechanical chores took up all of the aides' and orderlies' time; the taking of the vital signs was an impersonal ratrace in which they whisked from one bed to the other, breathlessly; I often saw them just estimate pulse and respiration in passing and fill in a "likely" blood pressure on the treatment sheet for those patients who were not critical. Nursing procedures prescribed by doctors were frequently ignored, medications not given, elaborate and delicate machinery like IPP breathing ma-chines, set up at the bedside of dying patients to give them some comfort in their last hours of gasping agony, which had to be operated ten minutes out of every hour to be effective, stood idle during entire shifts or were left on long beyond the prescribed limit of time, thus turning from instruments of mercy into tools of torture.

As a rule, the only people available to give the patients bedside nursing care were their fellows in misfortune. Old men, who could barely stand on their feet, tried to shave their helpless neighbors. Patients in wheelchairs would labor back and forth between the drinking fountains and the bed-side tables, trying to keep the pitchers filled. If someone was in critical need of attention, a call for help would be cried from bed to bed until it reached the nurses' station. One night, when the shift had just come on and the nurses were checking the charts at the desk, there came from the silent ward a feeble cry, "Nurse . . . ! Help . . ." at which someone replied from the desk, "Shut up!" When the voice went on calling, she repeated, "Be quiet!" and was obeyed.

That night, I became convinced of the truth of Miss Lucas's words, when she had warned me never to make the mistake of thinking that the spirit of evil in the hospital was incarnate in one particular individual. "It shifts," she had said. "It takes hold first of this person, then of that person; it's like a moving shadow, an evil spirit. All we can do is put on the armor of God."

She had been right. Every man and woman working inside this hospital was tainted at times with the fleeting curse of callousness. I could feel no animosity toward the nurse who had cried, "Shut up!" Nobody could be held personally responsible for the evil heritage of the Houston charity hospital, ever since it started from a pest camp, fifty years ago: the spirit of Old J.D., the spirit of the human dog pound. It was as senseless to react with anger or indignation toward persons possessed by that spirit as it was to feel anger or indignation toward the malignant cells destroying the patients dying of cancer.

But that night, I thought I knew at last why Miss Lucas had left. She had, maybe on one occasion when she had been all alone in the ward and exhausted after extra duty, come up against that spirit in herself, and the armor of God had not been enough. Maybe she, too, had suddenly heard herself cry, "Shut up!" in answer to a feeble cry for help from the darkness, covered her face with her hands, and fled.

Maybe it was just my imagination. But never before had I realized, to such an extent, the depth of our damnation.

3

FOR THEIR FIRST NIGHT of clinical training inside the hospital, the sixteen new recruits were divided over four floors. Marjorie, Lucille and Priscilla each went with a group of women; I was allotted the four men. Mrs. Chalmers took each group to their station, to introduce them to the nurses.

The hospital was dark and cold; the sixteen apprentices entered a cave of hostility and suspicion. Despite the fact that every floor was understaffed, they were received with chilling reserve. Once I had shown the men the layout of Male Medicine and set them shaving patients for their first assignment, I decided to go and have a quick look at how the others were doing. I wandered from floor to floor, hovering in the shadow, looking, listening, worrying; I did not realize that I had been looking for Marjorie until I finally discovered her, in the bare little office of the Red Cross on the fifth floor. She was talking soothingly to one of the volunteers, a girl who had entered the hospital an hour before saying, "Well, let's see if all this yak about us being needed is for real." The girl, so dapper and challenging when she went in, now stood there wiping her eyes, crying, "I can't understand it! I can't understand how people can *be* like that! How can they *do* such a thing? How can they?"

I asked Marjorie what had happened; she answered, "Nothing serious. It just became a little too much for her."

"Thirty-six hours, for God's sake!" the girl cried. "How can they? For the love of God, how *can* they?"

To my questioning look, Marjorie replied, "She came across a paralyzed woman patient who had been lying on a full bedpan for thirty-six hours. They must have left her out when they were changing the sheets this morning, planning to come back to ner, and forgotten to do so."

"It could have been my mother!" the girl cried. "Imagine your mother lying there like that, for thirty-six hours! And the stench, and the filth, and all these people just lying there with nothing to do but wait, waiting to die! God, I didn't know it was going to be like this!"

I thoughtfully wandered off into the darkness. I knew how she felt; I remembered my first day in old J.D. I remembered Mrs. Judd looking down on the paralyzed man in Observation who had been lying in his own excreta for twenty-four hours, and saying, "There are some things you should never get used to." This girl, like all of us, would have to get over it and yet never get used to it; as long as she realized at each patient that it could have been her mother, she would be all right.

I returned to my orderlies in Male Medicine by the dark back stairs, looking in on each floor in passing. As I looked around Female Medicine, I saw the pregnant volunteer. She was standing by the bedside of an old Negro woman, emaciated to a skeleton, trying to help her drink from a paper cup with a straw. The image suddenly struck me: the young Houston housewife, heavy with child, her arm round that emaciated old woman, was the same eternal image I had glimpsed when I saw Mrs. Judd put her sheltering arm round the dying Mr. Hood. Then the orderly in me noticed that she was at a loss, for the weak old woman did not have enough strength left to drink through the straw. I joined her, glanced at the name sticker glued on the footrail of the bed, said, "Good evening, Mrs. Small," to the patient, and to her, "If Mrs. Small cannot develop enough suction to lift the water in the straw, put her head back on the pillow, like this. . . . Now put your straw in the cup, like this. . . . Seal the top of the straw with your finger. Lift it out of the cup. Carry the water in the straw to her lips, like this. . . .

Put it in her mouth, gently. . . . Now take away your finger from the top of the straw—and so she drinks. See? Try it."

I watched her while she tried it. The old woman, eyes closed, skeleton hands plucking the sheet, smacked her parched lips and drank with little groans of delight. I went back into the shadows.

4

THE NEW ORDERLIES and nurses' aides stayed on the floors until eleven o'clock. Then they gathered in the bare little office on the fifth floor to listen to Mrs. Chalmers' notes and remarks and to put questions. As I watched their faces, I imagined I saw something in all of them that had not been there before. But probably I was being romantic; it could not show yet, not this early, that they would never be the same again as when they had entered this house of pain and death for the first time, a few hours before.

Marjorie and I drove home in silence. She was preoccupied with countless practical details; I was under the spell of a sense of history, of something having happened of much greater importance than that sixteen citizens of Houston had entered their charity hospital as volunteers, to take on the humblest tasks of nursing as an act of brotherly love. Perhaps history had indeed been made tonight; perhaps this first little rivulet running out onto the beach and vanishing in the sand was the beginning of a turning of the tide. Individual kindness and personal concern for the poor, the sick and the lonely seemed never before to have drawn away further from the beach of man's involvement; never before had our neighbor and his feeble cry for help drifted further out to sea, into the cold starless night of charity dispensed by computer. The image of the pregnant young mother, cradling that dying woman with man's oldest gesture of love and protection, seemed to rise in the night over the city like a still, white cloud, touched by the first flush of the dawn.

As this book goes to press, almost two hundred citizens of Houston are on active duty as volunteer nurses' aides and orderlies in Ben Taub General Hospital, and many more are enrolled to be trained. *The Hospital* was written to support this program.

The author's royalties and subsidiary rights have been donated to a trust created for this purpose, named "The Citizens Fund for Voluntary Nursing." Any surplus money will be used to "initiate, encourage and sustain similar groups of volunteer nurses' aides and orderlies in state, county, municipal and other publicly supported hospitals throughout the United States of America."

For information on existing programs, contact your local Red Cross chapter.

For help in starting such a program in your own community, write to THE AMERICAN RED CROSS, Nursing Services, Washington, D.C.

For financial support, write to THE CITIZENS FUND FOR VOLUNTARY NURSING, 285 Madison Avenue, New York, N.Y.

For volunteers, call on any church in America.

Jan de Hartog

Jan de Hartog was born in Haarlem, Holland, in 1914, and ran
off to sea at an early age. In 1940, just after the Germans
occupied Holland, his novel HOLLAND'S GLORY was published, a
rollicking story of the Dutch ocean-going tugboats on which he
had served. Although it mentioned neither the war nor the
Germans, it became a symbol of Dutch defiance and was banned
by the Nazis, but not until 300,000 copies had been sold. The
author escaped to England, by "the long trail": via Belgium,
France and Spain, a journey of six months during which he was
imprisoned five times, crashed with a plane and was wounded by
rifle bullets as he crossed the Spanish border. The journey left
no mark on him, he says, other than that it turned him into a
vegetarian. ("After leading the life of a hunted rabbit for six
months, I just went on recognizing my brother whether roasted,
stewed, fricasséed or smothered with onions.") But in a sense
"the long trail" which started in Amsterdam in April 1943, when
a young man slipped out the back door of an Old Ladies' Home
where he had been in hiding, led to a charity hospital in
Houston, Texas, in September 1962, when a middle-aged
volunteer orderly first entered the Emergency Room.

In the meantime, he sailed many miles and wrote many books
and plays; best known are THE FOURPOSTER, THE SPIRAL ROAD, THE
DISTANT SHORE (movie title THE KEY) and THE INSPECTOR (movie
title LISA).